THE SPLIT-LEVEL TRAP

THE SPLIT-LEVEL TRAP

by

RICHARD E. GORDON, M.D., Ph.D.
KATHERINE K. GORDON
and MAX GUNTHER

PUBLISHED BY
BERNARD GEIS ASSOCIATES
DISTRIBUTED BY RANDOM HOUSE

 Published by Bernard Geis Associates; distributed by Random House, Incorporated, in New York and simultaneously in Canada by Random House of Canada, Limited.

Library of Congress Catalog Number 61-7828

MANUFACTURED IN THE UNITED STATES OF AMERICA

Third Printing

Dedicated to
the People of
Bergen County, New Jersey

Publisher's Note

FIVE YEARS AGO, Dr. Richard E. Gordon, a psychiatrist who practices in Englewood, New Jersey, and his wife Katherino, a graduate student in social psychology, began an intensive scientific study of emotional problems in a typical section of American Suburbia: Bergen County, New Jersey, which is situated on the west bank of the Hudson River, a short distance from metropolitan New York. With the support of Columbia University, the Englewood Hospital and communities in the states of New York and New Jersey, they surveyed thousands of case histories, making creative interpretations and drawing scientific conclusions about suburban mental problems. These conclusions excited attention throughout the medical world. The Gordons' studies are most notable in that they have provided a precise, clear picture of the tremendous emotional stresses that are peculiar to the suburbs. Even more important, they have pointed the way to methods of controlling or preventing these tensions.

The Split-Level Trap is Dr. and Mrs. Gordon's first presentation of their studies to the general public. Most of the material on which the book is based, however, has been published in medical journals. The professional reader, or the serious non-professional, may want to refer to these articles, and they are listed here for his convenience.

Gordon, Richard E., Emotional Disorders of Pregnancy and Childbearing, *Journal of the Medical Society of New Jersey,* 1957, 54:1.

Gordon, Richard E., Sociodynamics and Psychotherapy, *American Medical Association Archives of Neurology and Psychiatry,* 1959, 81.

Gordon, Richard E., Prevention of Postpartum Emotional Disorders, Ph.D. dissertation, Columbia University, 1961.

Gordon, Richard E., Electroencephalographic and Social Psychological Indicators of Nursing Student Performance, *Nursing Research,* 1960, 9:1.

Gordon, Richard E., Psychotherapy by the Family Physician, *Journal of the Medical Society of New Jersey,* 1960, 57:6.

Gordon, Richard E., Scholarship Programs for Adult Citizens, Letter to Representative Frank Osmers, *Congressional Record*–Appendix, 1958, A 4071.

Gordon, Richard E. and Gordon, Katherine K., Some Social Psychiatric Aspects of Pregnancy, *Journal of the Medical Society of New Jersey,* 1957, 54:12.

Gordon, Richard E. and Gordon, Katherine K., Community Mobility and Emotional Disorder, *Journal of the Medical Society of New Jersey,* 1959, 56:2.

Gordon, Richard E. and Gordon, Katherine K., Psychiatric Problems of a Rapidly Growing Suburb, *American Medical Association Archives of Neurology and Psychiatry,* 1958, 79.

Gordon, Richard E. and Gordon, Katherine K., Emotional Disorders of Children in a Rapidly Growing Suburb, *International Journal of Social Psychiatry,* 1958, 4:2.

Gordon, Richard E. and Gordon, Katherine K., Psychosomatic Problems in a Rapidly Growing Suburb, *Journal of the American Medical Association,* 1959, 170:15.

Gordon, Richard E. and Gordon, Katherine K., Social Factors in the Prediction and Treatment of Emotional Disorders of Pregnancy, *American Journal of Obstetrics and Gynecology,* 1959, 77:5.

Gordon, Richard E. and Gordon, Katherine K., Social Psychiatry in a Mobile Suburb, *International Journal of Social Psychiatry,* 1960, 6:1, 2.

Gordon, Richard E. and Gordon, Katherine K., Social Factors in Prevention of Postpartum Emotional Problems, *Obstetrics and Gynecology,* 1960, 15:4.

Gordon, Richard E., McWhorter, J. E., Singer, M. G. and Gordon, Katherine K., Coronary Artery Disease in a Rapidly Growing Suburb, *Journal of the Medical Society of New Jersey,* 1960, 57:12.

Acknowledgments

We wish to express our appreciation to Dr. Henry A. Davidson, superintendent of Essex-Overbrook Hospital and former president of the New Jersey Neuropsychiatric Association, for his constructive comments on the manuscript and, in particular, for his helpful suggestions regarding the statistical presentation of psychiatric problems. We acknowledge, also, the assistance of Dr. Thomas De Cecio, former president of the Bergen County Medical Society, who reviewed the sections dealing with medical and psychosomatic disorders and clarified many important points. Finally, we are grateful for the generous help we received from Dr. Adella Clark Youtz of Teachers College, Columbia University; her recommendations were especially valuable in the sections dealing with children's problems.

The Authors

Contents

THE SPLIT-LEVEL TRAP

PROLOGUE

Signs of Stress

IF THE DAY is clear and if you climb high enough, you can look over treetops and see the city. Distance stills its frantic motion and silences its huge noise. Lonely and remote, it might be the ghost of a city that rose and fell here centuries ago. Its presence within view of this pretty green town seems incongruous and illogical.

Only when you climb down from your hilltop and shut the city from view, do you feel, again, its closeness. In this age, distance is not real. It is a malfunction of the eye, a vestigial thing left over from another age when twenty or thirty miles meant a day's travel. Today, twenty or thirty miles are a mere commute. You are not far from the city, here in this town. Except politically, you are not even outside its boundaries.

This town is Suburbia. The far yet close city could be any city, or it could be a big industrial plant or complex of plants, or it could be any other large magnet that draws men in search of jobs. Without it, the town would not exist.

The residents of this town like to think of it as a peaceful country community. Even to the casual observer, however, it is different. There is a restless, dynamic quality in the air. Everywhere new buildings are going up: housing developments, schools, shopping centers. The town is sweating to make room for more people, and more and ever more. Those who already live here, in turn, seem anxious to move somewhere else. Many of the houses have FOR SALE signs staked into their front lawns. Moving vans are a familiar sight. The town has an unsettled look, a feeling of rootlessness and constant motion.

Many of the town's people, too, have a pins-and-needles quality; they seem uncomfortable sitting still. Many of the husbands who leave for the city in the morning seem to be in a hurry. Some are cheerful and confident, but some wear a haggard look, as though the night's sleep has done them little good. Some of the wives' faces are serene, but some look tense and anxious. Some of the children on their way to school look bright and happy; some are loud, pushy, ready to squabble at the smallest provocation, and some are shy and timid.

Some are worse off. One of the young husbands who went to work in the morning is feeling ill. His stomach hurts. He doesn't feel like eating lunch. Early in the afternoon he suddenly starts to vomit blood. He is rushed to the hospital with a hemorrhaging ulcer.

In one of the split-level houses, a young mother is crying. She is crouching in a dark closet. Voices in the walls are telling her she is worthless.

In a house in an older section of town, a middle-aged woman is also weeping. For several hours she has been lying across her bed without moving. Finally she gets up, takes a bottle of sleeping pills from the bathroom cabinet, empties the pills into her hand and swallows them. She goes back to her bed and lies down to die.

As night falls, three teen-age boys visit the home of a girl in one of the town's more expensive sections. The girl's parents are out for the evening. She lets the boys in. The boys take turns with her on the living-room couch.

In the darkness between two houses, a young man creeps up to a window and looks in. He is disappointed, for the housewife he sees is fully clothed. He disappears into the darkness to look for another window.

Down at the police station it has been a fairly quiet night. A few juvenile delinquents have been hauled in, as usual. A drunken commuter is sleeping in a chair; the police have taken his car keys and are waiting for his wife to come and drive him home. Suddenly the door of the station house bursts open and a wild-eyed young mother comes in. She begs to be locked up. She talks incoherently of performing sexual perversions with her husband and stabbing her new baby.

Another young mother sits in her house alone. Her husband is not there; nor will he ever be again. He has told her very bluntly that he does not want to live with her any more. She is trying to think how and where her marriage went wrong.

The night's last train from the city pulls in. A prosperous-looking middle-aged man gets off. He has spent the evening with his mistress. He walks away from the train hurriedly, for he wants to be as far from it as possible when it starts. He is afraid that something in him wants death, and he thinks this suicidal demon will one day hurl him beneath a train's wheels.

What has been happening to these people? What is missing, what is so terribly wrong, in this pretty green community?

Cast of Case Histories

EIGHT FAMILY CASE histories are used in this book for purposes of illustration. No case was drawn entirely from any one family or person, but each represents some of the situations, problems and personality-types most commonly handled in a suburban psychiatric practice. If any characteristic in these cases reminds the reader of any traits in himself, the coincidence is of course intentional.

These are the cases:

Alice and Carl Hager are company transferees who buy a split-level house in a new suburban development. They have two sons in grade school. Alice is a shy, unassertive Southern girl who has great difficulty adjusting herself to the suburban community.

Gina and John Conning are another young suburban couple. Their story illustrates some of the emotional stresses that may attack a mother with a new baby in the suburbs. It also shows how problems can arise in a cultural intermarriage (Gina is an Italian-American Catholic; John is a descendant of long-line American Protestant ancestry). Gina's and John's problems are complicated by sexual difficulties and by a conflict with the older generation (John's parents).

Eve and Fred Bright are a third typical young couple, with two teen-age daughters and a son. Their problems stem particularly from their driving ambition to climb socially and financially.

Diane and Link Weber are a couple whose marriage is torn apart by social forces working in and around the suburban community.

Alec Green is a suburban teen-age delinquent. His story shows how well-meaning parents in a society of abundance can raise children who go alarmingly wrong.

Tom Krazinkow is a young single man of European parentage who has seldom succeeded at anything in his life and has given up trying. He is lonely, miserable and defeated: an example of the driftwood our society casts out and leaves behind in its struggle for personal advancement.

Martha and George Kohler are a defeated middle-aged couple. George cannot keep up with the competition in his job as an appliance-store manager. Martha finds that the world has moved on and left her behind. Her children are gone; there is no job for her to do in the suburban society.

Audrey and Harley Tragg are a middle-aged couple who have achieved the economic success that suburbanites dream of. But they aren't happy, and they can't understand the reasons for their unhappiness.

Part One

MOTION AND EMOTION

CHAPTER 1

The Movers

Our Mid-Century Americans

This country has always been a country of movers. It has nurtured them; they it. It was built, and is still being built, by brave, self-reliant people who have been willing to cast themselves off from old places and old family ties, to move out in search of a better life in a new, unknown land. The national nucleus, the Thirteen Colonies, came into being because pioneers from Europe moved to the New World in the hope of finding here something that their old homelands had not supplied.

Today we are a nation of movers on a vastly greater scale. It is not only the hardy few who uproot themselves to seek better things, but the many, the great mass of us. We move in many ways. Like the pioneers, we move geographically: one out of every five Americans will probably be living in a different home this time next year. Probably to a greater extent than the pioneers, we also move economically and socially. We are concerned with getting ahead. We are chronically dissatisfied. We want bigger jobs, higher incomes. We want to move across class lines and up to higher social strata. We want to move from low-status to high-status neighborhoods. We want newer and shinier cars, richer houses, better schools for our youngsters. We are constantly seeking a better life.

One kind of motion goes hand in hand with another. A family whose income is rising will generally move geographically—into a bigger house or a higher-priced neighborhood. A low-income family that wishes to move upward socially must usually begin by moving economically—by boosting its income. A family that wishes to earn more money must often move geographically in the hunt for a better job. Today the majority of Americans are, one way or another, on the move.

Industrialization and prosperity—particularly our incredible sustained boom since the Second World War—have made this mobility possible. There are relatively few opportunities for motion in less prosperous nations. A family is more or less confined to its ancestral village. The family does not fret constantly about being stuck in a particular geographic, economic and social niche, for there is nowhere else to go. The family has always been here; so have its neighbors. The desire to climb is kindled by the opportunity to climb. In America, the siren Opportunity sings from all sides.

This huge panorama of mobility, this great economic upgrading of people since the 1940's, has created a tremendous and apparently insatiable demand for houses and for more spacious, more costly apartment developments. The most satisfactory answer to this need has been found in the mass-produced housing of the suburbs; and it is the suburban town that most often becomes the mover's home. The suburbanite, in fact, can probably be said to be the most typical mover.

There are movers elsewhere, certainly: in the cities and, to a lesser extent, in rural areas. But the dominant phenomenon of American population movement since the Second World War has been a massive flow into, and shuttling back and forth among, the suburbs. The percentage of the total United States population in the cities and rural areas has been dwindling. Suburbs have grown explosively. Of the entire United States population increase from 1940 to 1950, almost half showed up in the suburbs of the nation's 168 metropolitan areas. In the next decade the suburbs grew even faster. Between 1950 and 1959, nearly two-thirds of the nation's increase appeared in the suburbs. The central cities of the 168 metropolitan areas increased in population by about one and one-half per cent during those years; the suburbs increased forty-four per cent. And the moving vans that lumber along suburban streets carry not only furniture, but family ambitions.

It has become fashionable in recent times to speak somewhat disparagingly of people thus in upward motion. The phrase "status seekers," introduced into the language by Vance Packard in his book of that name, has a faintly nasty ring. Packard himself did not intend that such a stigma be attached to it, but the phrase is used in some circles to describe newcomers and upstarts who are threatening established social bastions. It is thought wrong, in some obscure sense, to seek status. The phrase "keeping up with the Joneses" has a distinctly mocking quality.

We feel guilty when we demonstrate a liking for material luxuries. We harbor a notion that we would be purer and happier if we were poorer—if we sat on hard benches and contemplated the Infinite instead of our wealthy neighbor's house and Cadillac. The overworked, debt-hounded suburban commuter is the hang-dog hero of cartoons and the subject of satirical books. His accomplishments in making a better life for himself and his family are belittled. He speaks disparagingly of himself and his life, not proudly.

Yet it is the mover—the restless, never-satisfied, status-seeking, job-hopping, climbing middle-class consumer—who has been the backbone of American growth. His mobility is not only a result of national wealth, but a basic cause of it. His fierce desire for self-betterment has created a market for business and fertilized a prosperity that would have sounded utterly fantastic twenty years ago. By fighting for more money and more houses and more social standing, by keeping up with the Joneses, by migrating in mass from the lower to the middle classes, from farm to city to suburb, the movers have built themselves an opportunity for good living that is absolutely unparalleled in world history. Whatever the evils of our nation's much-chastised materialistic philosophy, it is hard to think of many evils more unendurable than poverty. With increasing wealth come security and the opportunity for a richer, more satisfying, more interesting life—for travel, cultural enjoyment, recreation.

Why do we needle the typical American about his shiny mass-produced house and car, his manners and mores? Possibly because he represents the great sad joke of our time. Having amassed a wealth that used to be the subject of fairy tales, he often finds that he isn't happy after all. Somewhere, something is missing. He has created an opportunity for a richly rewarding life, but somehow he finds it hard to take advantage of the opportunity. He is torn by anxieties and tensions, hounded by ulcers, menaced by heart disease. He gropes for tranquillity and finds it only fleetingly in pill bottles and a cocktail glass.

To poke fun at him—at ourselves—may help a little. But not much. It would be much more useful to understand him. For the suburban mover is the archetypical twentieth-century American. Indeed, it may turn out by the century's end that he is typical of half the world. Many nations—including Britain, West Germany and Soviet Russia—are experiencing a new prosperity. In these nations as in ours, incomes are rising; poverty is dwindling; people are moving, climbing, demanding apartments and houses, pouring into newly developed communities. The world, like America, is growing ever more mobile, and the dynamic, chaotic suburb is mobility in a nutshell. Like rural Winesburg and industrial Middletown in another era, the mobile suburban town represents the thoughts and feelings of the majority of Americans. Here, concentrated and magnified and stark, you can see all the good and all the hurt of the modern American—the man on the move.

Gauges of Tension

The increased tenseness of life in modern America, particularly in the cities and suburbs, is a phenomenon that has been widely noticed. Businessmen joke sadly about ulcers. Magazine articles tell us how to relax. We are urged to seek peace in religion. Europeans scoff at us for the hurry and worry in our lives (not realizing that they are traveling the same road themselves, a short way behind us). We hear repeatedly that we are among the world's top nations in per-capita smoking, drinking, divorce, crime and juvenile delinquency. From the pulpit, the TV stage, the floor of Congress, it is observed gloomily that, between our painful stresses and our materialistic striving, the nation's moral fabric is shredding.

The suburbanite is not unconscious of an increased tension. He often thinks he'd like to chuck it all and buy a farm. He dreams of a quiet little rural town, far from the rush and roar of world affairs. He speaks of the "good old days." He is certain that, somewhere, there is to be found a more peaceful, more relaxed kind of living than the kind he now lives.

Is this sensed tension real? Or is it more a manifestation of that universal trait, the nostalgic yearning for days of childhood when one didn't have to work for a living? All kinds of human progress, from simple individual growing up to the expansion of nations and the enrichment of cultures, are inevitably soured somewhat by a feeling that the earlier era was, in some respects, better. Undoubtedly when man first discovered fire, there were many who grumbled that life had been more livable without sparks flying about and ashes underfoot; and undoubtedly there were old men who sat sullenly out in the cold, sneered at the soft younger generation huddled about the embers and predicted the quick extinction of the human race. Does our sense of increased tension come from the same frothy mix of nostalgia and imagination?

No. This stress is real. It can be shown to be real through statistics.

In the northeast corner of New Jersey, there is a county that can provide statistical evidence. Bergen is its name. It is typical of get-ahead communities everywhere. It lies across a river from a vast magnet that draws men in search of jobs: New York City. It is part of an immense three-state, twenty-one-county commuter anthill spread around the city. Like other suburban areas in the United States, it has grown tremendously in population during the past twenty years, and particularly since 1950. Between 1950 and 1958, the population of its seventy towns grew by an estimated twenty-seven per cent. As towns in general go, this is rapid growth. As suburban towns go it is about average. (Some suburban communities more than doubled their population in the 1950's.)

Thus, loosely speaking, Bergen County can be regarded as a fairly typical cluster of mover towns, with social problems similar to those of mobile urban and suburban communities throughout the nation and the world. Bergen County can be used as a sample suburban area.

The problem is to find out whether life in modern suburban America is truly more stressful than the small-town life of the nation fifty or a hundred years ago. One way to do this is to compare two groups of communities: some that are typical of modern America (the towns of mobile Bergen County) and some that are typical of the vanishing good old days.

The census has shown that Americans are now typically suburbanites rather than city-dwellers. Largely for this reason, it seemed useful to study Suburbia rather than the city as an example of modern America. Morever, cities are far more complex. The city contains many neighborhoods, little towns in themselves, isolated by cultural, racial, language and other barriers. Each neighborhood is a study in itself; it isn't necessarily typical of modern America. Mobile, suburban Bergen County seemed better to represent a changing America in a nutshell.

How does Bergen County compare with less mobile old-time communities? Happily there are still many such communities left, though their share of the national population is diminishing rapidly. They, too, feel the effects of mobility and change, but to a lesser extent. One quite typical cluster of such towns is a rural county called Cattaraugus, in western New York State. Cattaraugus County is much like Bergen County in climate, topography, flora and fauna. It is vastly different in most other respects, however; and the single basic reason for this difference is that Cattaraugus is not situated near a metropolis or any other large job-magnet. Cattaraugus' people are not primarily movers. The more restless among them have left to work in places like New York City and live in places like Bergen.

In which of the two counties, if either, is life more stressful? One excellent way to find out is to go to hospitals in the two and compare their respective percentages of psychosomatic illness. A psychosomatic illness is a physical disorder with emotional roots—an illness associated with or precipitated by emotional disturbance. High blood pressure is such an illness. So are peptic ulcers. In coronary thrombosis (heart attack), emotional factors may also play a part. If one hospital turns out to have a significantly higher percentage of psychosomatic patients, this will be a fairly reliable indication that more emotional tension exists in that hospital's community.

Here are statistics covering a two-year period at Olean General Hospital, Cattaraugus, and Englewood Hospital, Bergen:

Of all patients admitted to rural Olean General during the

period, 2.4 per cent were hospitalized for heart attack. At suburban Englewood, the figure was 11.7 per cent.

At Olean General, 6.7 per cent of the patients were under treatment for high blood pressure. Englewood: 14.3 per cent.

At Olean General, 2.8 per cent were in for duodenal ulcers. Englewood: 9.6 per cent.

The inference is plain: something is troubling people in Bergen—something whose effects are not nearly so intense or so widespread in rural Cattaraugus.

There are other ways to see and touch the stresses of suburbanites. Instead of comparing mobile and non-mobile counties, for instance, you can compare mobile and non-mobile people. If mobility is the key to the greater amount of emotional stress in Bergen County, you'd logically expect to find more movers in a group of suburban psychiatric patients than in a random group of non-patients.

The hypothesis holds up. In a random group of Bergen County people who hadn't visited psychiatrists, thirty-three per cent were found to be mobile socio-economically—some falling, but the great majority rising. But in a group of two hundred and fifty-five married men and women who had sought psychiatric help, the proportion of movers was much higher. Among the men patients, forty-nine per cent were mobile. Among the women: fifty-one per cent.

To get at the same disturbing fact in yet another way, look at the children. The general emotional health of a community can be judged to some extent by the severity of the community's juvenile delinquency problem. This doesn't provide a complete diagnosis, of course, but it can provide a possible indication. If there are many delinquents in a community, obviously something is wrong; something is disturbing the youngsters.

These are the delinquency rates (number of court-recorded delinquents per one thousand youths aged five to twenty) in Bergen and Cattaraugus for the year 1956:

	Bergen	*Cattaraugus*
Boys	40	8
Girls	5	2

The picture is distressing and even frightening. Bergen's delinquency rates look like those of a city—where life is perceivably more stressful than in the country. The movers who have contributed so much to the building of America, who are its backbone and its future, have apparently created for themselves a way of life that is dangerous to them. It is important to find exactly where and how this disturbed modern community—this archetype of the mobile world, this Disturbia—has gone wrong.

CHAPTER 2

The Young Wives

The Main Complaint

Who suffers most in Disturbia? In popular literature and folklore, it is the young husband fighting to get ahead. He is portrayed as a man running up a down escalator. He cannot stop running, for as soon as he does, he is carried back to where he started from. Only by uninterrupted exertion can he maintain his position, let alone advance. We see him rushing for his morning train with breakfast half-eaten and undigested, fighting to hold his place in a jungle-like world of business, working and studying and worrying far into the night, relaxing too little, hounded by ulcers and finally struck down by heart disease.

Except in a few women's magazines, his wife is shown as living a considerably easier life. In humorous short stories and television skits that grope for a laugh by exaggerating what are felt to be universal truths, we see the wife scurrying home from a neighborhood coffee circle ten minutes before her husband is due. She melts a frozen dinner. Her husband staggers in at the door, tired but determined not to complain. He romps with the kids, swallows his meal, mows the lawn, settles down to do several hours of paperwork he has brought home from the office. His wife has long since settled comfortably in front of the TV set. "I'm tired," she says.

How true a picture is this? Superficially it may have truth in it. It often gets its hoped-for laugh, and this indicates perhaps that the situation it exaggerates is recognizable to readers and listeners. Perhaps the suburban husband does, indeed, work harder and longer than his wife. But this fact alone doesn't argue that her life is therefore more serene. Work is only one of many things that can upset tranquillity.

There is a quick way to get a rough estimate of who in Disturbia feels the most pain: by finding out who visits psychiatrists in Bergen County most often. This finding will not, of course, be scrupulously accurate, for there could be many reasons why one man or woman visits a psychiatrist while another doesn't. Money or the lack of it, time or the lack of it, all kinds of factors can affect the picture. Some are more accepting of psychiatrists, others of priests. Men may visit doctors in the city rather than near home. But on the whole, when you are dealing with large groups of people, these side issues tend to balance themselves out. It can be fairly safely assumed that, if one group visits psychiatrists more often than the other, the first group is feeling more need of psychiatrists' help.

This table shows which group loomed largest among 746 adult psychiatric patients in Bergen County during the years 1953-57:

	Age	*Women*	*Men*
Married	44 and under	36%*	22%*
	45-59	10	7
	60 and over	3	2
Single	All ages	10	10
		59	41 (100%)

* These figures indicate percentages of the total male and female patients.

A stark picture. Of all the people in the sample, thirty-six per cent—more than a third—are young married women. The number of disturbed suburban young wives is more than half again as big as the number of young husbands, and more than three times as big as any other group. (Other surveys of both private and public psychiatric patients in the suburbs have turned up similar findings.) There is a strong indication here that things are troubling the young wives more often, or more severely, than anybody else.

But the picture is not yet complete. Perhaps young married women everywhere, mobile or not, are more prone to emotional difficulty than other people. To see whether this is the case, compare Bergen County again with a calmer, quieter place—this time with slow-growing, mostly rural Ulster County, New York. Ulster is much like rural Cattaraugus in most respects. Its population is growing a little faster than Cattaraugus', and this must mean that there are somewhat more movers coming and going through its towns. But Ulster is nothing like Bergen. Its growth rate is less than one-half that of the suburban county. It has movers, but its social atmosphere is not shaped and dominated by them.

Once more, psychosomatic illness comes in handy as a gauge of emotional upset. If there is a difference in serenity between the mobile suburban county's young wives and the rural county's, the difference is likely to show up in hospital records of psychosomatic patients. Englewood Hospital can serve again as the sampling place for Bergen; Kingston Hospital can serve for Ulster. If young women bulk significantly larger among psychosomatic patients in one hospital than in the other, the logical conclusion will be that more anxiety exists in the young women of that hospital's county.

The table on page 37 shows a count of young women patients, aged eighteen to forty-four, who were treated for two psychosomatic disorders in the two hospitals over a two-year period.

Disorder	SUBURBAN *Englewood Hospital*	RURAL *Kingston Hospital*
High blood pressure	8% of all patients were young women	1.5% of all patients were young women
Duodenal ulcer	12.5% of all patients were young women	7% of all patients were young women

Obviously something is troubling Disturbia's young women. What is it? The stress of mobility?

It looks likely, but the case isn't yet proven. For there may be important differences between Bergen and Ulster other than mobility. Perhaps, for example, the reason for Bergen wives' greater tension lies somehow in the simple fact that more of their husbands are long-distance commuters. Or perhaps the vastly greater amount of automobile travel in suburban Bergen, and the consequently greater concentration of exhaust fumes in the air, may in some way contribute to high blood pressure or gastric ulcers in young women.

To check out such possibilities as these, compare Bergen with another suburban county instead of a rural one—but a suburban county less mobile than Bergen, one whose growth is slower, whose communities are more integrated, whose neighborhoods more typically have a stable core of long-time residents and common backgrounds. Such a county is nearby Essex, New Jersey. Essex' population increase from 1950 to 1958 is estimated at ten per cent (against Bergen's twenty-seven per cent). Unlike Bergen, Essex has not experienced a tremendous flood of newcomers during the 1950's, for not enough new houses have been built in the county to invite such a flood.

Aside from the mobility of its people and the degree of integration in its communities, Essex is very similar to Bergen. Both are suburban. From both, husbands log heroic mileage in their daily pilgrimage to New York City. In both, the air is generously spiced with auto exhaust fumes. If there is a difference in their emotional climate, the difference could hardly spring from any other source than Bergen's greater mobility.

And there is a difference, a startling one. It shows up in the records of psychiatric in-patients—people hospitalized for severe mental or emotional disorders. Of all in-patients in Essex County during a two-year period, ten per cent were young married women. In Bergen: twenty-two per cent.

It looks quite definitely as though life in our increasingly mobile world is dangerous emotionally for young wives—more for them than for anyone else. There is one more comparison that can be made to illustrate this fact starkly. Instead of comparing Bergen with another county, compare today with yesterday—Bergen now with Bergen at a time when it was less mobile.

The current big rush into this county started around 1950. Here are samplings of adult psychiatric patients in Bergen County at three intervals during the decade, showing the proportions of young wives and husbands in each period:

	1950-52	1953-54	1956-58
Young wives (18-44)	25%	30%	34%
Young husbands	25	21	14.5
All others	50	49	51.5
	100%	100%	100%

(The proportion of wives and husbands in the county's total population did not change during the decade.)

The trend is sharply clear. As the county grew more crowded during the decade, as its communities disintegrated under the torrent of mobile newcomers, the proportion of emotionally troubled young husbands went down. This does not indicate that mobility has a calming effect on men. What it does indicate is that the number of troubled wives increased so tremendously (along with certain other groups such as single men and the middle-aged) that the percentage of the young husbands shrank.

Or try another probe through time, using psychosomatic illness again as the indicator. At the beginning of the decade, of all patients at Englewood Hospital suffering from duodenal ulcers, seven per cent were women aged eighteen to forty-four. By 1956-58, the figure was up to twelve and a half per cent.

None of these statistics indicates necessarily that mobile women are under greater emotional strain than men. What is more likely to be true is that women are *succumbing* to strain in larger numbers. Men are taught from boyhood to be stoic, to disregard pain. Women in our society generally lead more sheltered lives, and when something hurts, they are more likely than men to go to doctors quickly.

Nonetheless it is obvious that unpleasant things are happening to the young wives who come, so full of hope, into the apartments and housing developments of Disturbia. The case history that follows, the story of Alice Hager, illustrates some of the principal problems of disturbed suburban women.

The Split-Level Trap

In a corner of a dark bedroom closet, in a three-year-old split-level house, a young housewife crouched like a small, frightened animal. Her husband pleaded with her to tell him what was troubling her, but she would not speak. She stared out at him fearfully. Every time he reached down to touch her, she shrank away.

She was terrified. "People" were staring at her, laughing at her, reading her mind. Voices from the walls were talking to her in angry tones. The "authorities" were looking for her. They were going to take her away somewhere and lock her up for her bad thoughts and for failing her husband and children.

The pathetic story of Alice Hager (as we will call her) illustrates some of the emotional stresses that bear on young married women in a mobile society. Alice Hager's case is bizarre, but by studying the bizarre you can often see things exaggerated and highlighted that might not otherwise be apparent. The great majority of women, subjected to the same stresses as Alice, merely become blue, nervous, vaguely dissatisfied with life but not sure why; they develop insomnia or headaches or indigestion; they take pills but don't consider seeking psychiatric help. Alice developed more severe symptoms because she was more sensitive—her adjustments were in more delicate balance.

She had been made sensitive by traumatic experiences in her childhood. She came from a moderately wealthy family in a small, stable Southern town of old American heritage. The family fortunes had been dwindling since the Civil War, partly because of unwise investments by her grandfather and father. Like many declining families that once knew wealth and power, Alice's family had little left to sustain its morale but pride in the past.

Alice's mother, Sarah, was a socially ambitious woman. She fought a losing battle to maintain the family's aristocratic position and privileges. It was a losing battle because there was no economic power to back it up. As Alice grew from infancy into a small-boned, blue-eyed little girl, there were more and more arguments between her parents about money. Sarah would bewail the family's mounting debts, cry that the creditors might come any day and take away the house. These arguments frightened Alice.

Her father began to drink. He was a weak, kind man. Alice was very fond of him. Often he would sit Alice on his knee and read to her, but there were more and more nights when he would come home late and drunk. He and Sarah separated when Alice was ten. He became ill with cirrhosis of the liver. Finally, destitute and malnourished, he had to be sent to a local hospital, from which he was transferred to a mental institution. He died there at an early age of chronic alcoholism combined with physical and mental deterioration.

Most people who go through such nightmares learn, over the years, to live with the resulting emotional wounds. Alice did. She emerged as a delicately pretty girl, shy, retiring, but with a sunny disposition that endeared her to her classmates in school. There wasn't enough money to send her to college, as her mother would have liked, so she went instead to a six-month secretarial school. She landed a job as a secretary in the Southern regional plant of a national chemicals corporation.

Here she met Carl Hager. Carl was a tall, spare, ascetic-looking young engineer who liked to talk of theoretical and ethical aspects of science and enjoyed listening to chamber music. Though Alice shared none of these interests, she was fascinated by them and admired them. Her mother, too, was attracted to Carl. Sarah felt that a new aristocracy of intellect was arising in the South to replace that of inherited wealth. She felt that the family would gain status by attaching itself, through Alice, to a man of Carl's intellectual air.

Carl was an upwardly mobile young man. His father had come to this country from Germany and had worked fourteen hours a day to build up a small contracting business in Philadelphia. Only the old man's massive drive kept the business alive, and when he died it died with him. By that time Carl was in high school. His father hadn't left much money, but he'd left something else equally important in launching Carl's career: a burning urge to get ahead. Carl won a college scholarship, took courses at night while working during the day, earned his bachelor of science degree and signed on as an engineer in the large company that was later to hire Alice. His income started where his father's had left off.

In due course he was assigned to the Southern plant. He and Alice were married six months later. Alice thus hitched her wagon to a rising star.

Promotions came rapidly for Carl. He and Alice rented an old house in a slow-growing town not far from the small town of Alice's birth. They had two sons. Alice's mother came frequently to see the young family, to help and baby-sit. Carl and Alice had a wide circle of friends in the area, many of them Alice's old schoolmates. Life was pleasant.

Then Carl was offered a big promotion and a transfer to New York headquarters. Naturally he accepted. The job itself was good, and the New York area had many fine universities. He,

Alice and their two boys trekked north that autumn and settled in a new home in a mobile Bergen County suburb.

A transfer does not usually affect the husband as much as the wife and children. The husband, though he changes his domicile and his working location, remains in the same social organization: the company. In its plant or offices, he is among people who speak his language. All are consciously working toward the same twin goals: the financial success of each and of the company. The transferee thus has much in common with his new colleagues, and he may quickly make friends among them. If he wants it, help is available to him in adjusting to his new job and location. His colleagues show him where to find the water cooler and coffee wagon, brief him on the local office or plant regulations, answer questions he may ask about his job, take him to the restaurants they have found most satisfactory for lunch. Indeed, this orientation for newcomers may be provided in a more formal way by the company itself.

The wife is not so lucky. She is not naturally thrown together with her new neighbors, and she may be too shy to make the effort of introducing herself to them. In any case she may have little in common with them, little to talk about. No orientation, formal or informal, may be provided. She finds herself alone in a house, surrounded by a sea of strangers in an alien world.

Thus it was with Alice. To her, the new neighbors didn't seem to be at all like the gracious, charming folk of her Southern girlhood. They were people of so many different kinds, so many national origins and cultural backgrounds and religions and ways of talking, that they bewildered her. She couldn't understand them. Some impressed her as being loud, aggressive people, the kind that she thought of as "pushy." Others seemed incredibly busy, always rushing somewhere, hurrying too fast to stop and chat. Some seemed withdrawn, as though on guard against something. No one appeared to care much who Alice was; in fact, few people seemed to have noticed that a new family had dropped into their midst. No one knocked on her door to welcome her to town as she and her Southern friends would have done for a new neighbor; no one brought her a cake or invited her over for a cup of tea; no one offered to help her unpack or look after her children.

Sometimes, at the supermarket or at the railroad station, waiting for Carl, Alice saw women whom she judged to be the kind she could befriend. But she didn't know how to meet them. She was a shy girl. Throughout her life she had waited for other people to make overtures to her; and in the easygoing society of her younger days, this had happened often enough. There had been natural occasions for it to happen: in school classes, at dances, at church activities, in the corporation's offices. Now there were no such occasions. She was alone in the house all day. Around the house the mobile society swirled, too busy, too full of its own problems, too alien to understand or—even if it did understand—to help.

Carl was also too busy. He worked hard all day, often came home late at night and dead tired. Sometimes he brought home a briefcase full of work to do on a weekend. Anxious to make a good life for himself, his wife and his sons, he was fighting hard for further promotions. He was attending a university three nights a week, seeking his master's degree. He seldom took Alice out at night, and even on weekends when he brought home no office work, he was too busy around the house to spend much time with his family.

The demands of home-ownership were hard on him. Being city-bred, he was not skilled in home repairs or handy with tools. The jobs took him a long time, often turned out unsuccessfully and usually left him frustrated and irritable. Sometimes, reluctant to try a small repair by himself, he called in a local craftsman, fretted over the long wait before the craftsman could tackle the job and then fretted over the bill.

Thus Carl was too tired, too heavily burdened with his own problems, to be of much help to Alice. A frequent subject of magazine cartoons is the mythical suburban wife, dressed to go out, trying to haul her weary husband from his armchair. In real life it is not very funny. He needs to rest just as badly as she needs to get away from the four walls that are closing in on her.

Alice thought she might find companionship if she joined a club of some kind. But she knew of few in the community that interested her. She was not diverse in her interests, had no hobbies or special enjoyments such as Carl's love of chamber music. She had once played tennis, but the town had no tennis club and there was always a crowd of teen-agers at the public courts. In any case, daytime activities seemed out of the question because Alice had no one to take care of her children.

There was a women's club in town, and Alice timidly inquired one day about the chances of joining. But the club had a long waiting list and couldn't tell when it would be able to accept any more newcomers as members. One of the older residents in the community told Alice that some of the members intended to keep the new "riff-raff" out. Alice wondered if this meant her.

Alice did not recognize that, had her old home town been inundated by newcomers, many with alien ways, she and some of her old friends might not have welcomed the outsiders. Sometimes, when people's economic and social positions are threatened by rising newcomers, a phenomenon occurs that resembles prejudice and snobbishness. Those who feel threatened or crowded, those who have had difficulty adjusting to changes in society, will cling to positions of strength by trying to hold down the newcomers. The club that Alice tried to join contained many women whose husbands were feeling keen competition in their jobs and businesses from the climbers who were struggling up from lower classes and pouring into the suburbs. Most old-timers in a community, or on an economic or social stratum, adjust to the rise of newcomers and work out means of cooperative progress with them. But when pushed too strongly to share a hard-earned position of security, they may build barriers in the way of the newcomers' climb. Negroes, Jews, Italians and other racial and cultural groups, and even newcomers of old American Protestant ancestry, are encountering these barriers as they rise in our society.

Newcomers in Alice's town were not only competing with the clubwomen's husbands; they were starting to take over the town at the voting booth. Their housing developments were eating into beautiful woodland. Their cars were turning once-peaceful Main Street into a nightmare. They were demanding the time of tradesmen, who used to serve old customers quickly and deferentially but now made these old-timers wait in line with the newcomers. The newcomers were temporarily overcrowding the town's resources. The women's club was resisting being overwhelmed, and was trying to preserve its graciousness.

Alice did not understand all this clearly. She took her rejection by the club as a personal affront. She was angered by her belief that the club was categorizing her as riffraff along with her neighbors, against whom she herself felt prejudice. She began to wish that Carl had never been promoted and transferred to this bleak, unfriendly place.

Meanwhile her sons were growing progressively harder for her to manage. Carl, laden with work, left their upbringing almost entirely to Alice. A boy needs firm handling such as a man can give, and Alice did not know how to fill the role of a man. She didn't know how to guide her sons, teach them the things boys need to know. She didn't know how to throw a baseball, nor how to counsel a boy who has been bullied. Nor did she know how to discipline a boy, how to train him to have a sense of responsibility, consideration of others, an awareness that the world will expect him to work for his living. A man usually has had more experience in laying down the law firmly, providing plenty of reward for useful behavior but cracking down when the occasion demands. Alice couldn't be this firm; she was too unassertive, both by nature and training. She avoided showdowns with her sons. She didn't insist that they study hard in school, nor that they carry out their chores and responsibilities.

She put away their toys instead of making them do it themselves. When they misbehaved she looked the other way, or nagged and sighed futilely. They saw that she could be pushed around and took advantage of the fact. In her exasperation, she began to scream at them. This went against her upbringing and was greatly demoralizing to her. The boys grew steadily more unruly, fought constantly between themselves and with other youngsters, did poorly in school. One of them, in a temper tantrum, hit her on the cheek, leaving a great red bruise. When she told Carl he seemed more angry at her than at the boy. He felt that raising children was her responsibility.

Like many other wives in Disturbia, Alice was being asked to fill the role of both woman and man in the family. She was willing to try, for she was as eager as Carl to get ahead. She took on his burden in order to free him as much as possible for his battle to win promotions. But she was expecting too much of herself. She was a woman. She had been trained to be feminine, to shun aggressiveness, to leave firmness to the men. She could not learn overnight to be a man.

The mobile town, which she had at first felt to be coldly indifferent, began to seem hostile. People were trampling on her.

At the supermarket, women shoved ahead of her in the check-out lines. On the roads they swerved ahead of her, missing her fender by inches and not seeming at all apologetic. Tradesmen seemed eager to cheat her. Even her own family seemed hostile. Her sons were rude, openly disobedient. Carl, weary and irritable, wanted only to be left alone with his high-fidelity set and chamber music at night, barked at her when she asked him to take her out or discipline the boys, frequently remarked about her ineffectiveness as a mother.

•

Alice was up against facts of mobility. Many of her neighbors seemed loud and pushy to her, for she had grown up in an environment where women are protected, where they are expected to be unaggressive and quiet. A few of her neighbors probably were pushy, though not as much so as she thought. If they want to climb, people of minority religions, racial and national groups particularly may have to be aggressive. Unavoidably this aggressiveness becomes a way of life for them. This assertiveness need not be offensive, but in her unhappiness and confusion, Alice noticed only the more unpleasant aggressiveness around her.

The retailers and other businessmen of a mobile community are also influenced by this boiling environment. Back in Alice's home town the butcher on Main Street always gave her a fine, lean cut of meat. He hardly dared do otherwise. He knew most of his customers by sight and many by name. His clientele didn't change much from month to month. He ran his business on a highly personal basis. A single dissatisfied customer could badly hurt his reputation.

Here in Disturbia, the hurried young man at the supermarket counter passed out his packages of meat mechanically and impersonally. He gave the best cuts to the women who demanded them. The quiet, passive women simply took their chances. The supermarket management didn't want to alienate customers; yet it realized that old ones departed and new ones arrived every week.

Alice let the mobile community walk all over her. She couldn't make herself argue when a tradesman gave her inferior merchandise. When one of her sons broke a neighbor boy's bike, and the boy's mother stormed across the street to demand that Alice pay for repairs, Alice meekly paid. When another neighbor's children trampled through her flower beds and destroyed some carefully cultivated seedlings, Alice said nothing. When she was called to the school for a conference about her sons' bad behavior and poor work, she humbly admitted that it was probably all her fault. She began to wonder whether people were purposely picking on her.

She was lonely and unhappy. Her house was an island in a sea of hostility. She desperately wanted people to be her friends. Human beings can't function well alone—and this was especially true of Alice. Ever since her father had left the family many years before, her need for human affection, praise and encouragement had been intense, her tolerance of their absence small. The town was not providing for this need. She longed to be in a social group of some kind—a glee club, perhaps—but none seemed to exist that would admit her. At least, none had come forward and invited her to join. She didn't realize that, in this seething society, you don't get far by waiting for invitations. The aphorism, "all things come to him who waits," was written for a stable society in which people knew each other.

With too little encouragement, too few others to tell her that she was doing a good job or to help her do it, Alice began to dwell on the thought that—as Carl suggested often—she was a failure as wife and mother. Her sons were becoming school and neighborhood problems. Carl was away from home more and more often, and when he did come home he was gruff and touchy. She realized that she was nagging and sighing more than she once had, and she recognized that a whining note had crept into her voice. Were these things making her less attractive to Carl?

Winter came, and with it the winter blues. Alice felt really trapped in the house now; she couldn't even chat very often with the few neighbors she liked. Her head throbbed with the clunk-clunk of the washing machine, the yowl of the vacuum cleaner and the shrill voices of children. She realized, with bitterness, that her high school and secretarial school education were not serving her. In her present role, she felt, she need hardly have gone beyond the sixth grade. She desperately needed stimulation, challenge.

The Christmas blues were still worse. This was the season when everyone was supposed to be happy, yet Alice couldn't get into the spirit of the time. Her unhappiness was sharpened by the feeling that it was unnatural amid all the festive Yuletide decorations. Carl, too, was grumpy and critical. The cellar was leaking, and he hadn't been able to get anyone to fix it. The builder of the house, who had guaranteed a dry cellar for one year after the purchase date, had collapsed his corporation and gone to Florida.

Carl was also worried about his job. He was in a semi-executive position, in charge of certain aspects of chemical research. He enjoyed working in the laboratory, but the administrative side of his job frustrated and angered him. He was not good at handling people, had ruffled some feathers and brought criticism down on himself. He seethed with impotent rage at the way in which personalities and emotions interfered with his ideal of an unfettered forward march of science. He had brought this anger home with him over the Christmas holiday, and it boiled up strongly as he looked at the flooded cellar and listened to Alice's complaints.

Alice yearned to go back to the warm, friendly town of her girlhood. As spring approached, she asked Carl several times whether there was a chance he might be transferred back to the South. The first few times he shook his head irritably. Later he became obviously impatient at the question, asked angrily if she didn't want him to succeed. He was getting ahead in the company and in his education; the New York area was where he wanted to be. Perhaps, Alice thought, he saw her now as a block to his progress. He wanted to move ahead; she wanted to go back. She wondered whether she should take her weight from his shoulders.

One afternoon, in a fit of weeping, she began to pack a suitcase, intent on fleeing to the South and her mother. As she was finishing, the phone rang. It was the school; one of her sons was throwing an unmanageable temper tantrum in the principal's office, to which he had been dragged for kicking a teacher. Would she come and get him right away? Confused, tense and worried, she dashed from the house and drove to the school. When she entered the principal's office she found that she was carrying the suitcase. People were looking at it, and at her, questioningly. She thought: "Am I going out of my mind?"

She had other reasons to think that she was, indeed, going mad. Lately she had been having strange, sudden dizzy spells. Sometimes her heart pounded as though she had been running. There was a frequent, alarming sensation of tightening in her stomach and throat. A few days after the suitcase incident she went to a doctor, but he found no physical causes for these things. "They're all in your head, Mrs. Hager," he told her. "You must get hold of yourself."

She misinterpreted what he said. Now she felt sure she was a mental case. The fear of insanity grew in her and joined all her other problems. She felt sure she was about to follow her father into a barred-window mental institution. Her symptoms themselves became causes of disturbance; the more she worried about them, the worse they grew.

The doctor had not fully explained to her the nature of her symptoms. They were not in her head. They were real. Her heart really did pound. Her stomach and throat muscles really did contract. Blood vessels in her abdomen dilated, drawing blood from her head and causing real, physical dizziness. She was reacting in a perfectly natural way, with reflexes present in all of us, to an environment that made her afraid. Her symptoms were the ordinary symptoms of simple fear.

Steadily her emotional turmoil grew worse, feeding on itself. She had two acute anxiety attacks in the supermarket—fits of dizziness that came on when women accidentally bumped into her. She took their acts to be deliberate, hostile; and the fear symptoms followed automatically. After the dizziness subsided, she noticed that people were—naturally—staring at her, whispering to each other about her. She became afraid now to step out of her house. Out was where you got pushed around. She was afraid, too, that she might have another embarrassing attack in public; and this made her cling to the house still more fearfully. In the turmoil she was unable to think clearly, and this gave her one more reason to believe she was going insane. Once she found herself driving down a strange road in her car, with no idea of where she was going or why. She turned around and fled home, sobbing hysterically.

Her behavior grew almost babyish. She complained often, begged Carl to take her South again, wept at small frustrations. His patience with her grew ever shorter, and his criticism of her apparent weakness and ineffectiveness grew ever more bitter. His own burdens were heavy; he could not carry hers also. He angrily told her that she was an inept mother and a worthless wife.

Then the last blow hit her. Her mother died.

She felt completely alone, abandoned on an inimical shore. There was nowhere left to run. The whole town, even her husband and sons, were against her. She didn't have a friend left in the world.

The thought of going to the supermarket now became almost intolerable. She forced herself to go, feeling that if she didn't prepare the family's meals she would lose the last tenuous hold she had on Carl and the boys.

One day, driving home, she accidentally went through a traffic light as it was turning red. She didn't notice the light until she was halfway across the intersection, for her mind was on other things. Horns blared at her. She was frightened, felt that the police would chase her, began to race homeward. Her mind was in such turmoil that, by the time she was halfway home, she was no longer sure why the police were after her. She was sure only that they were. Every auto horn that sounded seemed directed at her. Every pedestrian seemed to stare at her.

The authorities were coming to punish her for failing her family, just as her mother had threatened they would punish her father. She was going to be locked up like her father. She was going to lose her home and family. Panic-stricken, she drove the car into her driveway, jumped out and ran upstairs to the bedroom. She crawled into a closet and hid in the darkness, shivering with terror, waiting for them to come and get her. A fire or ambulance siren sounded in the distance. She was sure they were coming.

Fearful hallucinations can easily develop in anyone who is in so highly agitated a state. Alice was concentrating so hard on her own fears and anxieties that the outer world became less real to her. Her attention was drawn into herself, and the things she noticed there were, for her, starkly real. It isn't hard to understand why she began to hear a voice telling her she was no good. The voice sounded like her mother's.

This is what happened to one woman who came, ill-prepared, into the mobile society. Unlike the stable society, it did not support her in her role as housewife and mother. It expected her to support herself. She needed to be firm, tough and self-reliant. She needed to make friends by herself, work out her own means of bringing workaday companionship and encouragement into her life, stand up for her rights against those who might trample her in the surge of daily events, lay down the law squarely to her sons and insist firmly that her husband help. She was not equipped to do any of these things, for they were not necessary in the stable society of her girlhood. Lacking the right equipment, she collapsed.

Most mobile women do not collapse, for few are as highly sensitized by earlier experiences and constitution as Alice. But for many, the same stresses that bore on Alice are real and painful. The mobile life is a more difficult thing to handle than most of us realized when we embarked on it.

Alice eventually found her way back to happiness. (Her long, hard road to recovery will be explored in Part Two.) But her story was tragic nonetheless. It was tragic because all the pain, all the struggle were unnecessary. Alice could have avoided unhappiness if she had recognized that life in the mobile suburbs would be different from that in the quiet, stable town of her girlhood, and if she had prepared herself for that difference.

Disintegrated People

If Alice's troubles could be summed up in a few words, they would be these: she lived in a socially disintegrated town. Social disintegration, in all its many manifestations all over the world, has been the ugly sister of industrialization, urbanization, prosperity and mobility. It is the key fact of the modern disturbed suburb.

To understand what has happened to people in Disturbia, compare this place with an idealized rural community or industrial-town neighborhood—the community that was once typical of America. That was a more integrated community. It was held together by a powerful social fabric in which each individual had status and from which each could draw the satisfactions he needed.

People didn't move in and out of this community much, for there weren't many places to go or convenient ways to get there. Job opportunities were pretty much limited to the community itself. There were few mass-communication media to penetrate its horizons, and a trip even to the next state was a major problem in travel. People tended to stay put. The number of movers, arriving and departing and climbing within the community society itself, was relatively small. People knew their places in the society and generally drew satisfaction from this knowledge. It was a cozy, stable, predictable world. Since the community was not dominated by restless, hard-driving climbers, families felt no great pressure on them to advance economically or socially. Each was content to move slowly, if at all, for that was the speed of the neighbors.

The people in this town knew each other well. The majority were old residents; many had been born and brought up here. Families were together: grandparents, parents, children, uncles, cousins, all living within the community. Having been near each other so long, and having shared the same general experiences, these people had similar tastes and values and understandings.

They spoke the same language, played the same games. They helped each other with life's chores and crises.

The town in which they lived was their town. They had deep roots here. Not being caught in a frantic battle to get ahead, they had time to give to the town. They had time and energy to organize clubs, hobby groups, social events, sports events, parades. The town, too, had time. Its growth was slow. Its schools weren't overcrowded; nor were its clubs and other organizations. Newcomers such as Alice Hager could be assimilated without strain. There was room for everybody, wherever he wanted or needed to be.

In this town, people had status based on things other than income and material possessions. A housewife, for example, contributed a beautiful voice to the church choir, or won prizes at the summer flower show, or—and in those days this was enough—raised a batch of healthy youngsters. From these things she gained the self-importance that every human being needs. She was able to do so because her neighbors had lived near her long enough to know her attributes. They had had time enough to notice her. Almost every individual in the community had a place, a status, that was uniquely his and universally recognized.

The typical man in this town did not commute far, nor did he wear himself out fighting to get ahead. Unlike Carl Hager, he came home with time and energy to give his family. Nor did home maintenance demand inordinately much of him. He didn't feel compelled to make his house look like a magazine advertisement. He had other ways of earning status in the community than beautifying his home. He had sports, clubs, community activities. Like his wife's, his standing in the town was based on his being known by the townspeople. He may have worked longer than forty hours, but when he put down his tools or his pen he tended to forget business. He wanted to earn more money, but this wasn't a driving obsession. The pace of life for him was leisurely.

The wife also, typically, had a full and easy-going life. Nearby were her mother, aunts and grandmothers, old ladies with time on their hands and a need to be useful. The older women eagerly helped with the new baby, gave counsel on the problems of womanhood and motherhood, baby-sat so that the young wife could get out of the house. The wife had many friends, many activities, all developed over long, slow years. She lived in a less mobile society where a girl normally stayed with her mother until married. Typically she hadn't gone to college, nor worked as a secretary in the city, nor seen glamorous moneyed worlds outside her home community. To her, homemaking was not drudgery. It was one of the prime reasons for her existence. It was a satisfying life, for it was carried on in the right kind of human environment: plenty of help, plenty of companionship, a feeling of usefulness and importance.

The mobile suburb is a different world. It is a town of eternal coming and going. Whole neighborhoods, whole vast subdivisions, are made up of newcomers. The typical family in this town is a climber family, restless, anxious to move on and up. Any family that stands still seems, by comparison, to be slipping backward. There is a sharp, unrelenting competition to get ahead.

These are people of many national, religious and cultural backgrounds; many codes of values, ways of thinking and acting and talking. Many find it hard to befriend their neighbors. Some don't care to.

The melting pot once associated mainly with the city has overflowed into the suburbs. City living, with its high disease, crime, delinquency and divorce rates, has long been recognized as stressful. Now, in the suburbs, still more ingredients are being added to the melting-pot stresses: the pressures of commuting, home and car ownership, pulling crabgrass.

Few families have roots in the suburban town; most assume they'll move somewhere else one day. There is a lack of real, loving interest in the town, and as a result there is a lack of social machinery by which people can get to know one another easily. There may be too few clubs, sport and hobby groups, dances and other social events. Nobody has been interested enough, or has had time or energy or baby-sitters enough, to start them. Or not enough people of like interests have chanced to drift together. Those facilities that do exist are likely to be—like the schools—overcrowded. Newcomers may have a hard time breaking in.

There often is a hard core of mostly longer-term residents who are caught in a frantic whirl of children's and adults' civic, social and charitable activities. Though these people aren't lonesome or left out as Alice was, they often resent their heavy load of responsibilities. These overloaded people, especially the better educated, are often bored with the repetitive, unrewarding nature of fund-raising, bridge, bandage-wrapping and envelope-stuffing. They would welcome help from newcomers, but because of the community's disorganization, the necessary contacts aren't made often enough.

Lacking permanence and homogeneity in its population, the town has not had a chance to build a solid social structure. Each family, not being known in the town at large and lacking other ways of gaining status, vies with other families in conspicuous consumption. Each tries to have the most attractive home and the costliest car.

Actually the town is populated not by families, but by the spun-off nuclei of families. Husband, wife and children have come here to live by themselves, leaving their relatives behind. Upon the two parents falls the whole burden of raising children, making a living, battling sickness and money problems and all the other large and small crises of human existence. The spun-off family faces life alone. There is no natural source of help and counsel. There is no natural substitute for the larger families that have been left behind, little built-in social machinery by which people who might help and advise each other can be brought together. Each family races about its business of getting ahead. Its own problems make such heavy demands on its energies that there is little left over for the problems of its neighbors.

This is the disturbed suburban town, epitome of the mobile world. It is a world of people in restless motion. They have come like pioneers into a new land, from other places, other economic and social stations. With a brave independence of spirit, they have deliberately broken from old family ties, old neighborhoods and old cultural groups. They have ventured out on their own, seeking higher goals.

What they have done is in keeping with the American tradition. The immigrant's son lifting himself by his own bootstraps, the girl leaving home and family to follow her husband into the unknown, the family from a minority cultural group fighting to win acceptance in higher social strata: these people are typical of the national spirit.

But it is important to recognize the consequences of moving too fast. It is essential to see that one can take too large a bite of independence.

CHAPTER 3

Childbearing

Four Walls and Baby

The stresses that attack mobile people can be thought of as falling into three main groups:

First there are the sensitizers—intensely upsetting experiences such as the bitterness and separation of Alice Hager's parents and her father's death in a mental institution. These sensitizers make a man or woman more than normally thin-skinned emotionally, easily upset, easily hurt. They often occur in childhood, for children are far less able than adults to fend for themselves and can be badly hurt by events that an adult might find merely irritating. However, sensitizers may occur at any time in life. Loss of a husband or wife, loss of a job, prolonged illness—any such intensely unhappy experience might act to thin the emotional defenses.

Second: the pressurizers. These are the continuous or repeated stresses of life—stresses that are particularly numerous in the mobile world. In Alice's case some of the pressurizers were drudgery without reward, lack of friendship and stimulation, lack of understanding and companionship from Carl, responsibilities of managing home and children in a competitive community without help or guidance. Probably no single one of these hurt as sharply as Alice's childhood experience; but all of them, gnawing at her constantly, kept her tense, unhappy and afraid. They kept her in an emotionally unstable condition—a precarious balance which any new, hard shock might upset.

Third: the precipitators. A precipitator might be thought of as the final shock or series of shocks that brings on an emotional collapse. In Alice's case some of the main precipitators were Carl's angry criticisms of her inadequacies and fears, her son's hitting her and her mother's sudden death.

Not all emotional disturbances have precisely this background, of course. You can't point to the sensitizers, pressurizers and precipitators in every case. People and the doings of people are often hard to fit into neat, preconceived patterns. Nonetheless this three-part categorizing of stresses is a convenient way of looking at emotional problems in the aggregate.

While the sensitizers are usually related to an individual's past life, the pressurizers and precipitators are more often related to his present social environment. They are more affected by mobility; they are more likely to spring from the special social problems of the modern Disturbia. Thus the social psychiatry of mobility is more concerned with them than with sensitizers from childhood or other past periods.

The three-part categorizing of stresses is particularly useful in studying emotional problems of pregnancy, childbirth and new motherhood. Women who have reached this stage in life are going through an experience that severely tests their physical and emotional fitness. Whether they find the experience a happy one depends largely on these two interrelated kinds of health. Women who have been subjected to a large number of stresses—sensitizers and pressurizers—may break down emotionally under the heavy new stress of childbearing. The maternity experience, in other words, becomes a precipitator.

Emotional breakdowns in childbearing occur vastly more often in the mobile suburbs than in integrated communities. Among

746 psychiatric patients in Bergen County—men and women, all ages—fully nine per cent were young wives with maternity problems. In a comparable group of people visiting a rural psychiatric clinic, only two per cent were maternity cases.

Most suburban mothers are familiar with the "baby blues" in one form or another, either from personal experience or from listening to other women in the maternity ward or the neighborhood. In its mildest form it is a day or two of gloom during the first month after birth. The world looks dark, the future black. Tears flow uncontrollably. Small irritations balloon to outrageous size. Happily the pall of gloom usually lifts after a day or a week, and the world is made new. But not always. For some new mothers, the baby blues deepen into a disturbance so severe, so seemingly complex and intractable, that they need help to make the sun shine again.

Childbearing is traditionally thought of as a gloriously satisfying experience, the pinnacle and indeed the prime function of woman's existence. That it is not felt to be so by increasing numbers of mothers is a sad fact of our mobile society. It is a fact that deserves study.

The case of Gina and John Conning is a study of the baby blues in deep indigo. It shows how such a disturbance develops and where it may lead if unchecked.

Collapse of a Bridge

This is the story of a mobile young couple who started out with a wide cultural gap between them. They tried to bridge it, but things didn't work out and the bridge collapsed. Out of this fact and others related to mobility, there grew an intricate web of emotional disturbance.

Gina and John Conning came into Bergen County during the mid-1950's, full of hope for a bright future. Two months after her first baby was born, in the small dark hours of a snowy morning, Gina appeared at the local police station in a state of acute terror. She was hatless, had bedroom slippers on her feet. She was shivering violently. At first the police could get nothing out of her but the plea, "Help me!" They sat her down and gave her a cup of coffee. She calmed down a little, but her story was still almost unintelligible. All the police could understand was that she was being influenced from afar by some mysterious, sinister agency that wanted her to perform sexual perversions and stab her husband and two-month-old baby boy. Sobbing, she begged to be locked up.

The police, puzzled and apprehensive, telephoned John, who left the baby with a neighbor and hurried down to the station. Both he and the police frankly admitted to each other that the affair scared them. Here was a woman whose mind was gone. Here was a really weird case; here was lunacy.

Actually Gina's mind was not "gone" at all. As a mechanism it was functioning soundly. It was simply misinterpreting things that were happening around and within the body it served. There was nothing weird about the case. Complicated, yes. Deep and mysterious, no. Nothing had happened in Gina's mind that could not be simply explained.

Gina had been born in New York City of Italian Catholic parents. Her parents both died when she was ten, and she and her sixteen-year-old sister went to live with relatives. The loss of her parents was a severe shock, but Gina adjusted to it. The Italian city neighborhood in which she grew up was a village within a city, a warm, cozy world, almost an integrated community. In this world and in the city's excellent schools, Gina ripened into an intelligent, extraordinarily attractive girl with many friends of both sexes. She became interested in art and creative writing. Now her home neighborhood could no longer hold her. Like young people the nation over, she sought broader horizons in the larger cultural world of the great city.

Gina's sister, Gloria, had accepted it as her responsibility to watch over Gina as the younger girl grew up. The relatives with whom the two were living had little money. To relieve them of some of the financial burden Gloria went to work as soon as she left high school, contributed to the apartment rent and grocery bill. The loss of her parents and the responsibility of caring for Gina put Gloria under great stress, and sometimes she showed this stress in violent outbursts of temper. It was not unusual for her to throw things, strike Gina, even brandish a knife. Occasionally too, she had emotional problems over the men she dated. She would come weeping to Gina, confide that she had slept with a man and sob broken-heartedly that she was sinful and worthless.

Gina eventually graduated from high school, got a stenographer's job and moved into an apartment of her own. It was small and cheap; but she kept it scrupulously neat and decorated it with her own paintings and sculptured figures. She enrolled in a series of university courses in art and advertising copywriting, hoping that she might someday find a career in one of these fields.

She met John Conning at a coffee shop near the university. He was a sandy-haired, genial, easygoing young man. He had just been discharged from the army and was taking night courses in business administration and accounting. He was nursing big dreams. He had just started to work for his father, who owned a small sheet-metal business. The business was a sound one but wasn't growing. It could be made to grow, John was convinced, by applying modern automation principles, both in the production shop and in the office. His father had been unwilling to make the necessary investments, however; he had almost gone bankrupt during the Depression and now wanted only to pile up cash in the bank, however slowly. John's dream was to convince the old man that a carefully planned investment would not be a gamble, that such an investment was necessary to keep the aging business from sinking out of sight amid the young, vigorous competition that was springing up on all sides. John hoped to pilot Conning Sheet Metal, Inc. to new heights of success.

Gina admired his dream. She, too, had a dream, and she saw

in John an opportunity to realize it. Her dream was to break away from the old, warm, too-comfortable city neighborhood, to move up and away from the past and into a bigger and brighter—even though colder—world. By marrying John, a middle-class man, she would automatically raise herself. Together, if John's dream came true, they might rise still higher.

Gina did not think these things out in so many words. But the thought of climbing was decidedly in her mind when she accepted his proposal of marriage. The fact that he was not a Catholic did not trouble her. They had many other things in common. John was interested in art and eager to learn more about it from Gina. Gina, in turn, picked up from him his contagious excitement over modern economic theory and business practices, and his urge to sell his ideas to his father.

They moved into an apartment in Bergen County, within moderate commuting distance of the plant. Right from the start, Gina failed to please John's parents. They were third-generation Americans who had struggled hard to get where they were, and now they feared and resented other, newer climbers who were struggling upward and competing with them.

In a world where there is plenty of room for everyone—a tropical island, for instance, where there are more fish in the sea and fruit on the trees than the population can eat—prejudice does not arise so readily. There is usually room for one more newcomer. But in a competitive world, where the demand for jobs and other good things is always hot on the heels of the supply, people will try to protect their domain from threatening newcomers.

Racial, religious and national prejudice were not much in evidence in the American West of pioneers days. There was plenty of room for everybody then. About the only lively prejudice that existed was that between settlers and Indians, who each wanted the land and who each, as a result, propagated the feeling that the other was racially unqualified to have it. Today the nation is more crowded. Less educated, socially or economically declining people like John's parents may show prejudice against people who are different. John's parents saw Gina and people of her national, religious and economic background as intruders from below (while, at the same time, hoping that John would climb and intrude somewhere above).

John's plan to revolutionize his father's company did not go as well as John had hoped. The old man was afraid to spend the money, and in any case he saw no reason why he should let this young whippersnapper tell him how to run his business. For twenty years the company had got along fine without the newfangled automatic equipment that John was talking about, and for twenty years the accounting and billing and record-keeping had been handled without any help from electronic machines. The old way was good enough.

John's father was failing to adjust to a changing world. All around him his competitors—many of them men of Gina's background—were investing in new equipment. They were holding their costs down; his were soaring. His profit margins shrank. When he was forced to raise his prices, old customers took their business elsewhere.

To hold the business together, he drove both himself and his son six days a week. John often came home late at night, so tired that he could only watch television for an hour and fall into bed. Gina still had her job in New York. It did not demand much of her, and she was usually much less tired than he. She kept up her friendships and artistic interests in the city, sometimes visiting the city alone when John was too tired to go with her. John's mother, who phoned the apartment often to talk to her son, was indignant over Gina's absences. A wife's place was with her husband.

Gina had always been meticulous in her housekeeping and about her person. On the infrequent occasions when John's parents visited the apartment she doubled her efforts. She swept and scrubbed and polished until everything shone. But John's mother was always able to find fault with something. She frequently made remarks about Gina's mode of dress. John's mother thought women should dress modestly, but Gina dressed to please John and to show off her considerable physical charms. John, embarrassed and irritated by the controversy, suggested to Gina several times that she try to please his mother more. The first few times he said this she became furiously angry. But finally she gave in. She bought clothes that, to her, were unattractive and dowdy. She did not feel like herself in them. Anger seethed inside her at the thought that other people were controlling her life, trying to change her personality.

While this tension was building up in Gina, another kind of trouble began to develop. The use of artificial birth-control devices, forbidden by her religion but not by John's, made her feel so guilty that she often was not able to respond to him as affectionately as she wanted to. Partly because of this, and partly because John was so often exhausted, sexual intercourse between them became less and less frequent. Gina wondered whether his love for her was simmering down. She thought perhaps his mother was turning him against her. She was hurt and angry.

Despite John's precautions she became pregnant three years after their wedding. The apartment was too small for a child, and both John and Gina were anxious to improve their physical comforts and social status. They decided to buy a house. John's parents thought the idea was foolishly extravagant; they themselves had lived in apartments for the first twenty years of their married life. They made plain their guess that it was Gina, not John, who wanted the house; that Gina in her greed for the better life had wheedled and nagged John into an unwise decision.

John and Gina insisted on a house, however. To pacify John's parents they bowed to the older couple's strong suggestion that the house be an old, inexpensive one in one of the county's slowly declining old neighborhoods, and that it be in the northern part of the county where real estate was relatively cheap. This was a peace-making compromise on John's and Gina's part; the house they bought was far from ideal. It meant a long commute for John, and he came home later and tireder than ever. For Gina it meant quitting her job and living in a neighborhood of older people. There were few wives of her own age with whom she could make friends and have fun. When her baby grew, there would be no other children close by to play with.

Most older people have adjusted well to the mobile society, but those who haven't—like the elder Connings—frequently make trouble for the younger adult generation. Because his father failed to see how the company must adjust to a changing world, John had to work until exhausted. Because the older couple failed to understand the needs of young people in a modern suburb, John and Gina had to live in a house that was wrong for them and would be wrong for their child or children. The elder Connings demanded too much of the younger couple and gave little of value in return.

In the integrated society of the past, it was easier for older men and women to be helpful to young adults. The elders were counselors: a lifetime of experience had given them wisdom on which the younger drew gratefully. The modern mobile society has changed so rapidly in the past few decades that older people's experience is not always so useful. Those who lived the early half of their lives in a more stable world may still think in terms of that world. They may still live by its rules and values, and thus may counsel younger people accordingly.

Thus young adults today often find themselves ambushed—caught between the demands of the mobile society (which are not easy to fulfill in any case) and the conflicting demands, the inflexible attitudes and values, of change-resisting older people. This ambushed generation sometimes tends to follow the suggestions and demands of older people automatically, out of reverence. Down through human history, elders have had real wisdom to contribute, and it has paid to listen to them. But in today's fast-changing world it is often wiser to season reverence with the salt of independent thought.

Gina became dissatisfied with her new home even before her nine months of pregnancy wound to a close. She became less and less able to visit her old friends and pursue her literary and artistic interests in the city. In her new home community, she found, there were few outlets for these interests. The library was small, carelessly run. There was little demand in the town for a lively cultural program.

Gina also found that, suddenly, she was without friends. The families in her immediate neighborhood were all older people. Most were pleasant and friendly, but their interests were different from Gina's. There was no other young wife nearby with whom Gina could swap experiences, with whom she could talk about pregnancy and motherhood in the modern world.

The baby came, and Gina's visits to the city stopped almost entirely. She was trapped at home with a strange, frightening small being whose demands kept her on the brink of exhaustion. There was no one to show her the ropes of motherhood. She had to learn the hard way, do it by herself.

She was confused by all the conflicting advice she read in magazines and heard from neighbors. Feed water for colic; don't feed water. Take the baby out every day; keep him in when it's cold. Feed on schedule; demand-feed. All of her advisors seemed to speak with equal authority. She was a perfectionist; she wasn't the kind of mother who can nonchalantly let things take their course. She wanted to do everything exactly right. Yet she did not know what was right.

In an integrated community, such problems would not normally arise. Not only does a new mother have her mother, sisters, cousins and aunts to help and advise; the advice is likely to be homogeneous. These are people who have lived near one another for generations. This community has a set of rules to fit every occasion—rules that have proved workable over many years and can be observed with confidence. Feed water for colic; keep indoors in cold weather or when the wind is from the north; feed on schedule. These are the rules such a society lives by successfully. While the individual may disregard them if he pleases, they are comforting to fall back upon when there is no other basis for decision. In another culture a different set of rules may be equally acceptable and comforting. In the mobile society no such universal, all-occasion rulebook exists. The people are of too many different backgrounds, heading in too many different directions.

Being a perfectionist, Gina not only became extremely confused and worried about her baby; she also became badly overworked. To care for a new baby alone is hard work enough, but Gina also tried to keep her house spotless. Every day, compulsively, she cleaned the rooms, washed and ironed for the baby. John was seldom able to help, for he worked hard also. Gina handled the baby's care entirely by herself, from changing diapers to night feeding. She expected too much of herself. Her body never had a chance to recover after the physical stresses of pregnancy and labor. She ended each day more and more exhausted.

Gina saw suddenly that she was in a trap. Her life, once so vital and stimulating, had degenerated into a treadmill of confusing baby-care and household chores. She yearned to do something in which she could use her brain, her literary and artistic abilities. She desperately needed reassurance that she was doing a good job. She needed fun away from home, stimulation and challenge—occasional rewards.

But the mobile society rewards success in business, not in the home. The climber husband, rough though his life is, has this very great consolation: he is patted on the back for a job well done; he has a chance to earn promotions; he may secretly enjoy his neighbors' envy when he brings home money enough to buy a new car or a costly set of lawn furniture. He is a knight in shining armor. While his armor may be dented and his body bruised, the world's applause can make it seem worthwhile.

His wife gets little reward or recognition for her work in the home. Nobody hands out medals for successful child-raising. From the position of housewife there are few, if any, promotions.

Gina's tensions mounted. She had severe headaches, was unable to sleep. She was afraid she might be handling the baby wrong. She was angry about John's parents, about John's apparently diminishing interest in her, about the endless drudgery of her days. She wondered what had happened to her life. All the fun, all the people, had gone out of it.

Still more worry was added to her load. John's father's business was beginning to have serious trouble. Its competitors were gaining—and its customers were leaving. Its sales and profit margins were dropping alarmingly. John couldn't persuade his father to make the necessary modernization. Instead, the older man drove John harder than ever. It seemed likely that John's pay, never high, would have to be cut temporarily while the sick business tried to regain its strength. John was frustrated, worried about bills, scared of the future. He seemed to grow more tense, more irritable, every day.

One evening, weak with fatigue, Gina changed the baby's diapers before putting him to bed. The baby was fretful; he squirmed and cried shrilly. Anger boiled up in Gina, and suddenly she had an urge to stick the safety pin into the baby. The urge frightened her. Could she really do such a thing?

She began to have nightmares in which she stabbed John or the baby. In one of the dreams, her sister Gloria handed her a knife, and an unseen power forced Gina to throw it at John. Gina woke from these nightmares screaming in panic. She did not understand what was putting these ghastly notions in her head.

She grew afraid to go to sleep, and this contributed to her worsening insomnia. Insomnia is usually simply explained. It is basically an inability to relax. As you gnaw on an aching tooth though you know this won't stop the aching, so the insomniac's mind gnaws at problems and dwells on powerful emotions—fear, anger. The problems and the emotions are too large, too insistent to be left alone. Thus the insomniac lies staring into the dark as the small quiet hours tick by, unable to put aside his worries and relax into the restorative coma of sleep.

Like many other emotional symptoms, insomnia is a self-feeding thing. Without sufficient sleep, the body builds up toxins that cause measurable physical changes. They interfere with normal body processes, cause miscellaneous aches, pains and discomforts. And, of course, they increase the general feeling of fatigue; they increase irritability, and they reduce the tolerance of every-day annoyances and frustrations. As the body's distress signals grow louder, the mind has more to worry about—it is progressively less able to lapse into the sleep for which the whole being cries. When people are deprived of sleep for long periods of time they may hallucinate. Their inner distress becomes so great that the outer world—the world of real sights and sounds—fades into unreality. The mind concentrates so hard on inner misery that its attention to outer things weakens. It begins to hear voices that are not really there.

Gina lost sleep not only as a result of insomnia, but also through the nightly demands of her baby. She was not carried to the point of hallucinating, as Alice Hager was. But she became progressively more fatigued, more irritable, more angry. Small problems ballooned.

Like Alice Hager's, Gina's mind now began to misinterpret the data streaming into it. Where Alice had misinterpreted things happening on the outside, Gina misinterpreted those on the inside. She did not clearly understand where her mounting anger was coming from. She was bewildered and frightened by it.

It was a terrifying situation. Gina had heard that wifehood and motherhood was a delightful, fulfilling experience. She was finding it to be something entirely different: a trap, a weary labor, a monumental disappointment. She had heard that a mother instinctively and always loves her baby. Why did she, Gina, not always love hers? Was there something missing in her? Was she somehow unnatural, insane perhaps? How could a normal mother have such angry feelings toward her own infant son? How could she dream of stabbing her husband?

Gina was battling an emotion she had never learned to handle. She had never experienced such overwhelming anger, and she had no idea how to control it. Like Alice Hager and thousands of other girls, she had been trained in a pattern of behavior designed for another, more stable culture. She did not know how to push back when pushed, how to say no when the mobile society demanded too much of her. She allowed anger to simmer inside her. It was an alien thing, a mysterious devil of unknown origin and intent. She grew afraid that, one day, it might get totally out of control.

The fear of uncontrolled anger, of hurting or killing loved ones, is a common problem in new mothers who live in Disturbia. Sometimes women actually do lose control of such anger; they actually do fly into spasms of rage in which the baby or husband is injured or, rarely, murdered. But this is uncommon. Cases like that occur almost always among economically indigent women of an unusually violent, aggressive nature—not the typical woman of our society. And almost always, these women have enormous provocation, far more than Gina had experienced. It is the fear, not the act, of uncontrolled anger that crops up most often. Sometimes the fear is of suicide. Almost always there is a sense of being in the grip of mysterious, frightening, uncontrollable emotions.

When Gina's baby was about six weeks old something happened that complicated her problems. She visited her obstetrician for a postpartum physical examination. During the course of the examination, Gina suddenly found herself aroused, in the grip of wild sexual excitement.

That this should have happened was understandable. Gina's sexual relationship with her husband had been unsatisfactory for a long time, and ever since the seventh month of pregnancy, Gina and John had abstained from intercourse entirely. Thus, Gina was in need of sexual gratification. In addition, glandular changes had taken place during pregnancy and lactation which in her, as in many women, had the effect of increasing sexual desires. She was in a condition in which any small reminder, such as the physical examination, could raise her desires to a high pitch.

The problem was intensified by the fact that she lived in a modern mobile society which has made women more knowledgeable about sex. In the old-time American communities, people didn't talk about sex much, nor did they have mass-communication media in which sex was continually thrown at them. Indeed, there were many wives in those towns who went through life without ever knowing that it was possible for them to enjoy sexual experience—they saw intercourse simply as a duty to their husbands. Women today are more informed. And this has created problems. Knowing that it is possible for her to achieve sexual enjoyment, hearing other women talk about it, seeing it portrayed in realistic (and often surrealistic) detail on the movie and TV screen, the modern wife may fret more when deprived of it than did the wife of fifty years ago.

In Gina's case, there was an additional complication in that she had been introduced to the facts of sex through the adventures of her sister Gloria. This was a dramatic and impressive introduction, not what most girls get. It had the effect of making Gina more interested in sex than most girls. Yet, because free indulgence is not countenanced in girls by our society or by Gina's religion, she had always kept her interest under firm control.

Gina did not understand the background of her seizure of desire in the doctor's office. She was bewildered by it. She thought the doctor might have aroused her on purpose, perhaps as part of some obscure postpartum treatment. When she got home and the arousal persisted, the thought persisted that it was the doctor's doing. He was controlling her.

It is not hard to see how this thought may have arisen in Gina. She was not yet fully recovered from childbirth, she was further weakened by lack of sleep, and she was under severe emotional stress from other causes. She was thus unable to think clearly and reasonably. Presented with a baffling circumstance, the mind will seek an explanation, an interpretation. It can seek only in the realm of the individual's own knowledge and experience, and if the knowledge is incomplete the experience may assume greater importance. Gina had not studied psychology, sociology or medicine, and didn't know exactly what was going on around her and inside her. Her recent experience, however, had been suggestive of the idea of control. Other people had made her wear clothes she didn't like. Some mysterious force had made her want to hurt John and the baby. It seemed logical to suppose that this sudden sexual arousal was also dictated by others. She was a puppet; others worked the strings.

During the following weeks she made wild demands on John. She had never felt so aroused sexually before. She wanted to experiment with new techniques and positions she had heard and read of, some of which were unusual and most of which she had been taught to think of as perversions.

John was horrified and frightened. He had been brought up in a cultural group which, considerably more than Gina's, frowned on free expression of emotions and desires. He enjoyed a man-to-man joke about sex acts that he considered perverted—just as he enjoyed a TV murder thriller—but to be asked to participate was something else again. He recoiled from Gina. He began sleeping in the guest room, telling Gina that he would return to her side when she calmed down.

This increased Gina's anger, and also her sexual frustration. She began to masturbate for the first time in her life. She was filled with feelings of immense guilt. It was wrong for a woman's thoughts to dwell so much on unusual sex acts. Why couldn't she put them out of her mind? Why was the doctor doing this to her?

Her insomnia grew worse. Her anger mounted. Thoughts of hurting John and the baby came more frequently. The idea grew that these thoughts, too, were put in her mind by the doctor or by someone in league with him.

Her angry thoughts at first had included stabbing or cutting with all sharp objects—safety pins, hatpins, pieces of glass. Gradually they centered on knives, a natural result of Gina's having seen knives brandished in her sister's hand. Gina grew terrified that, one day, she would kill John or the baby with a knife. Every time the baby cried, every time John spoke an angry word, the terror seized her powerfully.

One day, when the baby was fretful and she was exhausted from house-cleaning for an impending visit by her parents-in-law, she became so frightened that she gathered all the knives in the house and threw them into the trash can. When John came home that night, he asked why there was no knife with which to butter his bread. She burst into tears and told him of her fear.

Once again mobility hurt Gina. If John had been a man of her own lower-middle-class European cultural group, he would probably have reacted differently. He would have been used to violent emotional outbursts. The idea of a woman waving a knife or throwing a dish would have been nothing new to him. He would have reacted with anger of his own, or else told Gina to lie down and sleep it off. He would have understood, and in his understanding the storm would eventually have blown itself out. But in her mobility Gina had married away from her own cultural group. John reacted—again—with horror and fright. In his culture, women did not express anger by screaming and waving knives. They tended to seethe in quiet bitterness. (A woman of middle-class American Protestant ancestry, caught in Gina's kind of situation, might more typically have been afraid of poisoning or suffocating loved ones than of stabbing them.) John could not understand Gina's fear of hurting with a knife. It was alien to him. His reaction increased Gina's feeling that she was full of unnatural thoughts.

That night she lay tossing in bed until long past midnight. John was in the guest room. Her mind skittered restlessly from one problem to another. Her legs and back ached with fatigue. Finally, utterly exhausted, she fell into a fitful doze. Then the baby began to cry.

Her anger welled up intolerably. She tried to comfort the baby but he continued to cry, probably sensing that he was not being handled gently or lovingly. For a while, Gina stood over the baby's crib, holding her head in her hands. She was going to kill him, she was certain.

She ran downstairs, threw on a coat and fled to the police.

Like Alice Hager, Gina eventually struggled back to a normal and a happy life—as we shall see later. But Gina's story (like Alice's story) was doubly sad because it could have been avoided. Nothing happened to Gina that could not have been prevented.

Mathematics and Tranquillity

The case of Gina and John Conning illustrates a key fact about emotional disturbance. It shows that emotional stresses are cumulative. The sensitizers, pressurizers and precipitators pile up on an individual like weights on a string, until finally there are too many and the string snaps. It is the number of stresses and the speed with which they pile up—the sheer weight and shock of them—that determine whether there will be emotional trouble for the individual who isn't prepared to cope with them.

The nature of the disturbance—the array of symptoms—depends on many things: on the nature of the stresses, on the individual's constitution and experiences early and late in life. Gina's symptoms involved knives and sex, for she had been impressed by these things as a girl. Other women, up against the same stresses of mobility and childbearing, might have reacted in a different way, with other kinds of disturbance—depression, for example, or a fear that the baby would die.

It is often hard to explain the nature of a disturbance, to discover precisely why one troubled man or woman fears knives while another has bizarre hallucinations. Symptoms are many and varied; they grow from the vast complexity of human experience. But the fact that there is a disturbance, the simple fact of its existence, is not hard to explain. It is a matter of mathematics: the individual has been overwhelmed by too many stresses.

Stresses might be thought of as falling into two categories: active and passive. An active stress is an unpleasant circumstance acting directly on the individual, such as the exhausting and confusing demands of her baby on Gina. A passive stress is a lack of reward or pleasure, such as Gina's being cut off from her artistic interests and friends. Both kinds of stress weighed heavily on Gina, for she was living the mobile life, the life in which stresses lurk around every other corner, waiting to land on the unwary and ill-prepared. Eventually the weight of stress grew too great for her to bear. She gave way.

This mathematical approach to emotional problems was demonstrated between 1957 and 1959 with groups of expectant mothers in a Bergen County hospital. This approach can be used with other groups—men and women, married and single, young and old—and with other stressful life events such as going away to college, entering military service, divorce and retirement.

One phase of the study was designed to test the proposition that stresses can be thought of in mathematical terms—to find out whether people carrying more stresses really do have more emotional trouble. Since there are thousands of possible varieties of stress, the first task was to group childbearing stresses into broad types and find out which of these types were potentially the most damaging in the lives of new mothers. Each expectant mother was interviewed, and each one filled out a questionnaire on the stresses in her past and present life. A few months after giving birth, she was checked again to see how she had weathered the experience emotionally.

It turned out that fifteen types (or stress factors) were significant. Each of these fifteen factors showed up often in the lives of mothers who became disturbed during the maternity experience. The normal mothers, those who came through birth and new motherhood happily, were much less likely to have experienced these factors. The table below lists the fifteen stress factors and shows how often each of them showed up in the lives of normal and disturbed mothers:

STRESS FACTORS	*Percentage of normal women experiencing factor*	*Percentage of disturbed women experiencing factor*
I *From Past History*		
1. Wife's mother died before wife was 21	5%	17%
2. Husband's father is dead	27	47
3. Wife was previously divorced	1.5	5
II *General Stress*		
4. Wife has illness apart from pregnancy	15	25

III ***Factors Indicating Mobility Stresses***		
5. Husband's occupation higher than his father's*	12	35
6. Husband's occupation higher than his wife's father's	11	37
7. Husband's education higher than his parents'	21	41
8. Wife's education higher than her parents'	19	37
9. Wife's education is incomplete	16	33
10. Husband often works at night	6	18
IV ***Stresses Related to Childbearing***		
11. Wife has had no experience with babies	4	20
12. This is wife's first child	19	54
13. Wife has no mother or sister in county	43	66
14. Wife has, or has had, physical complications of pregnancy	27	50
15. Physical complications of pregnancy in wife's family, previously	9	18

* Higher in status or income, as measured on a standard socioeconomic scale.

Plainly these fifteen factors are strongly associated with emotional problems in maternity. The dynamics behind most of the factors are plain. Factor one, for example, the early death of the wife's mother, could mean that the wife has had too little advice or help with her new baby and is not used to seeking counsel from older women. This could lead to overwork and confusion, as it did with Gina. Factors five through nine are not actually stresses in themselves, but they indicate that the new mother is mobile and thus might be suffering from any of the many stresses that attacked Gina and Alice Hager. Other factors may not be so readily understandable, but will be made plain in later sections of the book.

Now the key question can be asked: If a new mother has many of these stress factors at work on her, is she more likely to have emotional trouble than a wife with fewer factors? In other words, is the mathematical approach valid?

To determine this, stress factors were counted in the lives of new groups of expectant mothers, and each mother was assigned a score indicating the number of stress factors she carried. The mothers were divided into five groups according to their scores, ranging from those with two or fewer stress factors to those with eleven or more. The table below shows what percentage of mothers in each group became emotionally disturbed during the maternity experience:

Stress-Factor score	Percentage disturbed
0-2	12%
3-4	15
5-6	63
7-10	78
11 plus	100

The proposition holds: the more stresses, the greater the likelihood of emotional trouble. It turned out, too, that the mothers with the most stresses were likely to have the most severe disorders.

Gina Conning's disturbance is an illustration of the way in which these stress factors pile up. There were eight stress factors in Gina's case. Her mother had died before Gina was twenty-one. Gina had had no previous experience with babies. This was her first child. John's occupation was higher in status than Gina's father's had been (indicating that Gina was mobile). Her education was higher than her parents' (again, mobility). John's education was higher than his parents' (which led to a clash of views on business policies). Gina had no mother or sister in the county. And John often worked late at night. Gina thus fell into the group with a 7-10 stress-factor score. In this group seventy-eight per cent have trouble.

COMPARABLE STRESS FACTORS AMONG OTHER GROUPS

Stress Factor	Percentage of normal people experiencing factor	Percentage of psychiatric patients experiencing factor					
	Men and Women	Young Married Men	Young Married Women	Young Single Men	Young Single Women	Middle Aged and Older Men	Middle Aged and Older Women
I From Past History							
1. Mother died before person was 21	8%	11%	13%	4%	3%	14%	6%
2. Father died before person was 21	12	14	12	13	10	14	13
3. Parents separated or divorced	8	14	20	7	10	9	4
4. Person was previously divorced	2	5	9	—	—	12	8
II General Stress							
5. Physical illness of person	38	76	70	65	48	70	44
6. Physical illness in his family	—	70	64	32	39	72	54
7. Emotional illness of person	4	33	19	37	34	32	19
8. Emotional illness in his family	13	39	40	17	31	35	29
III Factors Indicating Mobility Stresses							
9. Education incomplete	20	59	38	52	43	—	—
10. Business or financial trouble	—	71	—	39	11	49	—

This same mathematical approach to people's problems is useful in studying other groups than childbearing women. The table on the preceding page lists some of the stress factors found in the lives of these other groups. In the same way as with the new mothers, it shows how often each of the factors showed up in the lives of normal and disturbed people.

One fact that shows up clearly in this table is the stressful nature of physical and emotional illness in an individual's own life and in his family history. Illness is also important in the lives of children. Among child psychiatric patients, fifty-three per cent had had serious physical disorders, as compared with only sixteen per cent of normal children of the same ages. Separation or divorce of one's parents also turns out to be a significant stress factor—more important than parental death, particularly among younger women.

As with the childbearing women, stress-factor scores were calculated for these other groups of people. The average score for psychiatric patients was over four. For normal people, the average score was less than a third as high: 1.3.

Thus it is scientifically accurate to think of emotional stresses in terms of numbers. The more stresses you carry, the greater is your danger of emotional disturbance. It now becomes easier to answer the question: why are suburban people today more tense, more troubled than small-town people used to be? The answer is simply that the mobile life has created more stresses.

CHAPTER 4

The Young Husbands

The Speculative Way of Life

Consider now the young mover husband. His life, like his wife's, is shaped by prosperity. He has (he doesn't actually own; the bank owns, but he has) a quarter-acre of America in which he may do more or less as he pleases. On that quarter-acre stands a house: six, seven or even eight rooms; furniture in every room; every closet and cabinet overflowing; a new car in the garage. All this is his.

There are only a few other nations on earth in which the general population may even wish for such wealth. In America, to many young men as they leave high school or college, it is more than simply a wish. It is a plan, a downright expectation. If they do not win it, they will feel they have failed.

The mobile husband lives in a society that seemingly compels him to improve his income regularly, to drive on and never sit back satisfied. Success is defined as upward movement. Failure is defined not as poverty, not as losing one's shirt, but as lack of movement. The young husband runs an endless race. He often feels guilty when he isn't overworking. He *must* get a raise this year. He *must* be promoted. If he finds himself on that darkest of all dark streets, the dead-end job, he must fight his way out immediately. His primary purpose in life is to get ahead. Before that purpose, others pale. He will willingly sacrifice peace and comfort for it; he will move away from his oldest and dearest friends; he will abandon a house on which he has labored with pride and love. He will neglect his wife and children for this goal of his—perhaps reluctantly and perhaps unhappily, but nonetheless with the conviction that he is doing what is best. In *The Organization Man,* William H. Whyte, Jr., quotes a young executive as saying that he'll be glad when his children grow up—for then he'll be less conscience-stricken about neglecting them. The young executive is typical. He seems resigned to the probability that he will continue to neglect the youngsters. The possibility that he might instead neglect his job apparently does not cross his mind. The job is more important.

The young husband is driven not only by the desire for success, but also by the fear of failure—failure, that is, as the mobile world defines it. To stand still while one's competitors forge ahead, to watch one's friends move away to bigger houses and more gracious living, to be abandoned in a dismal economic backwater, to see reproach in the eyes of one's wife and children —none of this can be pleasant under any cirumstances. It is doubly unpleasant in the disturbed suburban town, for the young husband may know of no other means than economic success for gaining applause, recognition, satisfaction, status in the community. No other arena of success may seem open to him. He succeeds at this one thing, or he plunges to the pit of despair.

Some mobile men are also goaded by a fear of falling *back* economically. Some have memories of the Great Depression, in which their fathers or fathers' friends lost businesses, jobs, savings and hope. Some recall economic tragedies that ended in suicide, alcoholism, commitment to a mental institution. Many others remember more recent recessions, retrenchments and cutbacks in which they themselves, or friends or neighbors, faced hardship as a result of layoffs or pay cuts. Some fear they'll lose their jobs as a result of automation. A man with such memories and fears may strive with an added degree of anxiety, almost desperation. He is haunted by nightmares of returning to the laboring class of his forebears.

Goaded thus from behind, tantalized from in front, the young husband keeps racing. Eventually, if he is not careful, he may fall into a typical trap set by the mobile world. He may fall into the speculative way of life.

He begins to overreach himself, betting everything on his ability to catch up. He takes a higher-paying, more responsible job without being sure he can handle it. He may kid himself and his employer about his experience and preparation. The job scares him but he grabs for it, hoping he can train himself before it beats him. Job precariously in hand, he buys a bigger house to keep up with his friends and competitors and to impress his business guests. The house is one step ahead of the job: he can't really afford it, and the monthly payments scare him as the job did. But he bets on salary raises to pull him out. Similarly, seeking recognition, he signs up for other monthly payments on furniture, a car, perhaps a country-club membership. He hopes that the recognition, the status thus gained, will help him get ahead in business. After all, he argues to himself, he needs a nice place in which to entertain his boss, his colleagues who may be future bosses, his clients, customers, prospects.

Thus everything he has is built on speculation. He is locked into time payments that he isn't sure he can support, but which he hopes to support through future successes in a job that he isn't even sure he can keep. He has a job that frightens him, but which he hopes to succeed in partly by virtue of possessions he isn't certain he can pay for. It is a house of cards, a juggling act. Let one thing slip out of place, and it may collapse about his head. Caught in the speculative way of life, a mover husband lives with fear.

It is small wonder that mobile Americans talk often about security. Security is the mobile family's dream. A house paid for, a job nailed down, a future bound in iron—this is suburban heaven. The mover husband reaches for security with all his might, but—like Tantalus' water—it always seems to be just beyond his reach. He could be secure if he were willing to climb one step at a time, but he is driven to taking giant steps. His house is out ahead of his job; his job is out ahead of his training and experience; his desires are out ahead of everything. Though he yearns for security with all his heart and soul, he tends in his hurry to fight for the trappings of security—big job, big house, big car (Vance Packard's "status seeking")—rather than for security itself. He builds around himself a façade of affluence, for this can be built quickly. He is in too great a hurry to build real security slowly.

Working too hard, worried about his family, hounded by fear, unable to relax, the suburban fast-climber husband is not as happy a man as he might be. If there are many stresses on him, or if there have been traumatizing events in his earlier life that have left him more than normally sensitive, he is in danger of emotional upset. He contributes heavily to the fact that the proportion of coronary thrombosis patients at the Englewood Hospital is almost five times as large as at rural Olean General, and the proportion of duodenal ulcer patients more than three times as great.

Telltale Hearts

What kinds of men are most likely to become disturbed in the mobile community? As with women—as with anybody—the answer can begin with a simple mathematical statement: Those who have been subjected to the greatest number of stresses are in the greatest danger of emotional trouble. A man who went through severe traumatic experiences as a boy will often be bowled over by only a few stresses in his present-day life. A man who had a happy childhood and early manhood can usually withstand more stresses in his present life—but if there are enough of them, if they accumulate to his particular breaking point, he too will have trouble.

This, then, is the general picture: men under greater accumulated stress have trouble more often. But who are these men? Are there certain kinds, certain groups, that appear to run into greater stresses than others?

Once again, the statistics of people in large numbers can supply answers. Distinct patterns are discernible.

One indicator of emotional stress, many authorities believe, is coronary artery disease. This disease has roots in heredity, diet, body chemistry and body mechanics, but more and more evidence is pointing to the importance of chronic emotional stress. A susceptible man who works too hard, hurries too much, relaxes too little and sleeps badly, who is chronically tense and fearful and who often goes through periods of acute worry, can experience glandular and other changes in his body that may affect the arteries nourishing the heart. Like the stomach or duodenal ulcer, heart disease is principally an ailment of men, though women—particularly women executives—are catching up as the world grows more mobile.

Some striking facts emerge from a study of heart-disease patients from 1954 to 1958. One is that, in general, men of higher income groups tend to succumb to this disease at an earlier age than men of less wealth. The table below shows how men heart patients in two age groups were distributed among four income classes:

Income Group	*Patients Under 50* (*Per Cent of total*)	*Patients 50-65* (*Per Cent of total*)
Upper middle	24%	10%
Mid-middle	43	34
Lower middle	26	42
Lower	7	14
	(100%)	(100%)

In the younger group of men, fully two-thirds came from the two higher income classes. In the older group, the two lower classes were much more heavily represented. To put it another way, a man is statistically more likely to have a heart attack early in life if he has won economic success. He is more likely to have an attack in late middle age if he has had only limited success. (Men over sixty-five are not included in this study; in the older ages so many organic factors are involved in heart disease that they cloud the picture of emotional stress.)

It is not hard to see reasons behind these figures. In a mobile community, young men who have reached the mid-middle or upper-middle income classes have often done so through fierce, hard climbing. Not all have had to climb, of course; many were born on these levels of wealth. But many were born in the lower or lower-middle income groups, and for these men life has been a struggle. In climbing so far so fast, they have exposed themselves to a great variety of stresses. These are the men who may have early heart trouble. The farther the faster, the sicker the quicker.

These high climbers continue to have trouble in late middle age, fifty to sixty-five. But now the lower income groups begin to feel life's effects more strongly. A man who lives in a climber society without climbing may begin to feel, as retirement age approaches, that he has failed. Many of the men he knew when he was younger are now far away and high up. He is physically comfortable; he has a pleasant home and plenty to eat—but in the mobile world this is not always satisfactory. The non-climber may feel left behind, washed up. He may have tried to compete with other more aggressive men and lost. He may still be trying to compete, without success. He may be worried about retirement income, about ill health. Life has given him too little reward and too much punishment. His painful tensions may lead to a heart attack.

Whose situation is worse? Who has the best chance of pulling through his heart ailment and going on about his life? The table below tells the story of 190 men who were hospitalized with coronary artery disease in Bergen County. It shows the percentage of men in each income group who lived six months or more after admission to the hospital:

Income Group	*All Ages to 65*
Upper middle	50% lived
Mid-middle	35% lived
Lower middle	27% lived
Lower	16% lived

The men in the upper groups stand far better chances of survival.

The principal reason is plain: the higher-income men are, on the whole, economically more secure. They can stay in the hospital without fretting so much about how they will pay the doctor. When the doctor advises them to slow down, to stop working so hard, they are in a better position to do so. The men in the lower income groups are not so fortunate. Many are in no position to slow down. They have been competing not to get ahead, but to hold their own, to avoid sinking. To stop competing, for many of them, is to face the tragedy of downward motion in an upward world.

High-Stress Jobs

Heart disease statistics can also show much about the degrees of emotional stress in various occupations. There are ten occupation categories that show up repeatedly in Englewood Hospital's coronary disease records. These Stressful Ten are listed in the table on page 90, along with the mortality statistics for a group of 244 men who were taken off these jobs by heart attacks.

EXECUTIVES, PROFESSIONALS & OWNERS	*Per Cent Who Lived (All Ages to 65)*
Low Mortality	
1. Bankers, brokers, large-firm executives	77%
2. Merchants, retail store owners	100
3. Sales, insurance and real estate	58
High Mortality	
4. Small business owner-managers	30
5. Small business hired managers	7
6. Construction: owners, independent craftsmen	20
7. Accountants and lawyers	25
EMPLOYEES AND LABORERS	
Low Mortality	
8. Laborers, vehicle and machine operators	39
High Mortality	
9. Bookkeepers, secretaries, clerks	8
10. Foremen, supervisors, inspectors, etc.	7

Looking over this table, you can see that many of the high-mortality jobs share certain characteristics that don't appear, or don't combine in the same painful ways, in the low-mortality jobs. There seem to be four principal job characteristics which can not only produce severe stress but also block efforts to alleviate that stress. These four characteristics are:

1. Financial insecurity. Executives of large companies are frequent victims of heart disease, but their companies usually support them while they are laid up, and these men can often find ways to slow down when they get back on their feet. Thus their mortality is low. Lawyers, accountants and independent craftsmen are not always so lucky. Nor are those small businessmen who operate their own shops, which must close down or can continue only at a limp in their absence. Bookkeepers and clerks are

often troubled by their low salaries. They worry about doctor's bills and are fearful of losing their jobs. (Unlike laborers, they are usually not protected by a union.) For many men in these high-mortality jobs, the hospital stay becomes a new stressful factor in itself; they lie in bed tense and worried instead of enjoying a healing relaxation.

2. Supervisory responsibility. Men who must manage other men, who daily become involved in interpersonal tensions and who carry a burden of responsibility for business successes and failures, often have a good deal of stress in their lives. Thus industrial foremen have higher mortality rates than the workers under them. Small business owners and managers are worse off than salesmen, real estate men. (Salesmen, in turn, have a higher rate than bankers and executives. Possibly this is because many salesmen work on commission; they face financial insecurity when hospitalized.)

3. Direct personal involvement in the business. Lawyers, accountants, men in the construction trades often personally serve their clients and customers. They cannot easily hire proxies to serve in their absence. Merchants and retail-store owners often can.

4. Economic decline of a business. Small businesses have a more precarious hold on life than large corporations. They feel economic recessions and market shifts much more keenly, can be wiped out by a single mistake. Economic decline is a hazard of small-business owners and managers more than of big-business executives. A man whose business is sinking can feel tense and hopeless. To be whisked away to a hospital during so crucial a time may only increase his tensions.

Two very mobile occupations, vehicle driving and sales, show up with striking frequency in almost all rosters of emotionally troubled men. Each job has some special features that apparently put men under more stress than most other jobs.

Drivers of trucks, buses and taxicabs must daily make hundreds of split-second, life-or-death decisions. They must stay keyed to a high pitch of alertness all the time they are on the road. A moment's letdown can cost them their lives or their jobs. This alone is stressful enough. In addition they may often be deadlined, required to reach a destination by a certain time. Obstacles constantly frustrate their efforts to make their deadlines: traffic lights, traffic jams, rush-hour crowds. All this adds up to a good deal of tension. Statistically:

In a random sampling of normal people	2% were drivers
In a group of peptic ulcer patients	13% were drivers
In a group of coronary disease patients	9% were drivers
In a group of private psychiatric patients	5.3% were drivers or from drivers' families

Salesmen do a good deal of driving, hence are subjected to stresses from this source. Moreover, many of them spend much time in distant travel. This may lead to problems at home. In their jobs, too, they fight competition perhaps more directly and more steadily than almost anyone else. Competition is with them every day, not merely lurking around the corner but in plain view, teeth bared. All this puts the typical salesman under stress.

In a random sampling of normal men	6% were salesmen
In a group of heart-disease survivors	24% were salesmen
In a group of married male psychiatric patients	16% were salesmen
In a group of disturbed boys	10% were salesmen's sons
Among couples with marital difficulties	18% included a salesman husband

It would be a mistake to draw from this the conclusion that all vehicle drivers and all salesmen are tense. Many are not. It depends on the individual man, his adjustment to the mobile world, the sum total of stresses he is carrying and other factors perhaps not related to his job. Conversely, it would be a wild goose chase to search for an occupation in which no stress exists.

Much as men dream of it, there is in the mobile world no niche with built-in tranquillity.

There are, however, tranquil men. And there are some companies in which life is calmer than in others. How is this happy state achieved? Certainly not by the mere fact of having selected a certain occupation or a certain field of business.

The story of Fred Bright, which follows, is a study of a tense man in a tense company. It examines some of the more common ways in which mobile men may be frustrated in their search for peace.

Tension, Inc.

The case of Fred Bright illustrates one of the most common and most joked-about phenomena of the mobile world—the psychosocial process by which a man may get a peptic ulcer.

Fred came from the Midwest. His father, a small-town lumber dealer, had contracted an ulcer as a middle-aged man. Nonetheless he tried to put his three sons through college during the Depression. It was a heavy financial sacrifice for him, but he passionately wanted his boys to go out into the world and make a name for themselves. When Fred was starting his sophomore year at the state college, his father died of a heart attack. Fred, youngest of the brothers, had to leave college at the end of that year, without graduating.

Fred went to work as a salesman. He had some thoughts of returning to his interrupted education after a year or so, but he gave up the idea when he began to enjoy quick success in selling. It seemed to him that he could make his way in the world, achieve all his ambitions, without the preparation that is symbolized by a college degree. He changed jobs often, each time for the better.

When he was twenty-two he visited the state college for the graduation exercises of his former classmates, and at a sorority party he met a pretty blonde sophomore named Eve. Eve came from the lower middle class. Her parents had worked hard to send her to the college. Her father was a foreman in an automobile plant, and her mother had worked as a maid for wealthy families to supplement his income and add to the funds set aside for Eve's education. Their motives were not entirely concerned with education, however. Eve's parents were only passingly interested in her college grades, but they were greatly interested in her progress in acquiring social graces and meeting upper-middle-class young men. Eve's values were the same. She was a charming girl of sweet disposition, but misguided. She was not interested in acquiring an education that would help her to be a useful, productive member of society. The focal point of the college for her was not the classroom, but the sorority.

She was attracted by Fred's glittering new car and by Fred himself. Here was a young man who was already on his way to success. His classmates were only now stepping wide-eyed into the world, but he was already established in it. He was also tall and handsome, with the look and confident air of a man who would one day be an executive.

Eve left college to marry Fred, and they set up housekeeping in an apartment outside Cleveland, Ohio. Two daughters arrived quickly. Fred continued to progress, and by the time he was drafted at the beginning of the Second World War, he had a lucrative selling job with a medium-sized plastics company.

He returned to the same company after his discharge and picked up quickly where he had left off. Eve presented him with a son. They moved to a larger, more expensive apartment and filled it with furniture bought on credit.

Then misfortune struck. Fred's company merged with a larger one. In the merger, Fred's job vanished. He was offered a choice: quit, or take another job at lower pay in the parent company's New York sales office.

It was really not a choice. Like many young couples, Fred and Eve were neck-high in installment debt. Eager for material well-being, they had borrowed from the future to surround themselves with belongings. They had no savings. They could not afford a hiatus in income while Fred hunted for another job. Fred morosely agreed to be transferred to New York.

Fred thus learned at first-hand what it is like to be economically insecure. In the nights when he and Eve mulled over this choice that was not a choice, he saw with terrible clarity what might happen to him if he were ever deprived of income. His drive to succeed had always been strong, nurtured by his father's ambitions, insecurities, illness and sudden death. Now Fred began to run in earnest.

The New York transfer was a difficult adjustment for Fred, but in the end he made it pay. He pushed his income back up to its former level and beyond. Working long hours, traveling extensively, driving himself hard, he became one of the company's star salesmen. Finally he was offered a minor executive job in the sales department.

Fred was not really ready for such a job. He was a little too young, too inexperienced in handling men as subordinates. He sensed this; and so, possibly, did the company. But the company, like the American economy as a whole, was in a hurry. To keep abreast of the boom, to expand into the areas of opportunity that were opening on all sides, it was necessary to push young men into jobs before they had accumulated quite enough wisdom through experience and training. Fred could not refuse the job. To refuse promotion in the rush of modern industry often means to be shelved. In any case, Fred badly needed the extra salary. He and Eve by this time had bought a house in the suburbs, a new load of furniture and appliances, a new car. They both had felt that Fred needed these things to maintain his status as a rising young man in the company. After all, a star salesman can't entertain his boss in a small apartment or take customers out in a five-year-old car—not if he hopes to get ahead. Other young men in the company had new houses and new cars, and it was necessary, Fred reasoned, to surround himself with the same symbols. Thus he had bought beyond his income, gambling on the hope that the fact of possession would help him to increase that income—or would, at least, help make it secure. Beyond this was the simple fact that he and Eve were impatient to reach the better, richer life for which they, as mobile people, were striving. In typical mobile fashion they were overreaching their income. They still had no savings.

Thus Fred took the job for which he was not yet prepared. Having speculated in his buying of material things, he was forced now to speculate in his acceptance of a job. He was forced to gamble on his ability to learn the job fast enough. There was much to win but also much to lose. He could, conceivably, fail to learn the job and be fired or demoted.

If Fred's father had still been living, Fred might have been more in the habit of asking help and counsel from experienced men. But the idea of asking help on his new job was foreign to Fred. He felt that it might somehow hurt his reputation and chances of success. To ask for help was to admit inadequacy. Fred felt that he must maintain an air of dynamic confidence, such as is portrayed in executives you see on the covers of business magazines. To improve his success in this area, he took a course in developing a magnetic personality, one of many such courses offered in the city. Thus he strove for the quickly-acquired façade of confidence rather than for the real confidence that would have come, more slowly, from learning his job carefully. It was part of a whole façade syndrome that has crept into our mobile society because people are in so great a hurry. Fred's façade of confidence was created for the same reasons as the façade of affluence that he and Eve were building around themselves in their suburban home community. The façade gave them quick status, instant recognition. But it was a precarious kind of status. They could be toppled from it easily.

Wearing confidence like a mask, Fred plunged into his new job. He tried to learn it by trial and error. He made many mistakes, which caused him a good deal of worry. Each decision that backfired made him more anxious about the next one. He grew tense and nervous.

The speculative spiral did not stop with Fred's accepting the new job. It now seemed necessary for him to buy a larger house and a more costly car. Fred himself would rather have waited a little while before making these purchases, but Eve wanted them right away. He at least had the status of his job and the applause that went with it: she had no status in the suburban community beyond that which she gained through the family's façade of affluence. She wanted to impress people. She wanted to move into the higher social circles of the community—the country-club set—and she did not see how this was to be done without making a show of wealth.

Fred was not hard to persuade, for he, too, wanted to be known in town as a big man with a big job. In buying a bigger house with a bigger mortgage he gambled on his ability to hold the job which previous speculation had forced him to accept. He also bet on continued rises in income, for—as before—he contracted to pay a little more than his present income could cover.

Eve now wanted to join the country club. She was charming, sociable and energetic, but she had been having difficulty in making friends in the community. In her ambition to make a high place for herself and her family, she had antagonized many women in the social strata to which she aspired. They thought her overaggressive, pushy. Had she really been of service to the community she would, in time, have won the acceptance she wanted. Human liking, friendship, is based on mutual usefulness. People in the old-time integrated towns liked each other because they served each other. A man had status when he had something useful to contribute. Eve did not understand, for her parents had not taught her, that society rewards those who are prepared to produce something for it in return.

She wanted acceptance instantaneously, and she strove for it by making a show of wealth. She gave expensive cocktail parties, complete with maids hired for the occasion. The people she was trying to impress came to these parties and drank the liquor, but it was obvious to them that they were there to be impressed. Eve was not giving them a useful service. She wanted their companionship but they didn't need hers. She was asking them for something without offering anything useful in return. If she had given cocktail parties for shy newcomers such as Alice Hager, the outcome would have been different. But the upper-middle-class people Eve was trying to woo failed to respond. They themselves aspired to higher planes. Why should they trouble with a petitioner from below who had nothing to contribute?

Eve felt that membership in the country club might help the family in its climb. She wanted her two daughters, as they grew up, to be with the "best" children of the town. She pointed out, too, that through the club Fred could cement friendships and make new contacts that might be valuable to him in his career.

They could not easily afford the country-club dues. Fred planned to pay for them out of the increases in income to which his membership in the club would, he hoped, contribute.

Fred Bright was living the speculative way of life—the typical life of many mobile Americans. He was always fighting to catch up; he never reached a plateau on which he could rest. He never built up a really effective cushion of savings or other sound investments. He and Eve never waited for reality to catch up with their dreams. The skilled mountain climber avoids releasing an old handhold or foothold until he has thoroughly tested and firmly grasped the new one. He is content to move up slowly because only thus is he safe. Fred and Eve were impatient. They wanted to climb fast. They went from hold to hold by leaping into space and hoping. They were eternally in danger. Fear skulked ever outside their door.

It seemed to Fred that he was always just one or two thousand dollars short of real security. If he could somehow get hold of two thousand—if he could win it in a contest, or have it willed to him by a rich relative—if he could just get hold of that much money in a lump, he could solve all his problems. He could pay all his bills, retire all debts but his home mortgage, lie down blissfully on the golden plateau that was always, maddeningly, just out of reach. The trick, he thought, was to get such a sum of money in a single wad, to get it suddenly, before future spending plans could start eating it up.

A chance to do so arrived. One of Fred's office friends came to him with a hot tip on some uranium mining stock. It could be bought for a dollar a share, his friend said, and there was a good chance it would rise to at least two dollars within the following few months. Once again, Fred speculated. He borrowed two thousand dollars on his life insurance policies to buy the stock on margin. When it sank to sixty cents, a margin call forced him to sell out. Now he was saddled with yet another debt. Once again he had made the mistake of doing things by trial and error, without seeking counsel. Once again he had been in too much of a hurry. He had tried to make a killing overnight instead of being content with more sure, more slow-building, investments.

Luckily for him, his speculation on his job was turning out a little better. He was making the grade, but only barely and at the cost of hard work, hard worry and constant tension. The corps of salesmen and sales-office managers under his command had not easily accepted his leadership. Some were older men than he. Some of them and some of his superiors were Ivy League men to whom he considered himself socially inferior. Tense and anxious about his job, Fred pushed his subordinates as hard as he pushed himself, earning resentment from many. Their sales record, for which he was held accountable by the higher executive echelons, was merely passable. He had never been shown how to be firm, yet considerate and encouraging. Not having had much guidance in his own life, he didn't know how to guide others. He didn't know how to get the best out of people.

There are many corporations that consider it a moral duty and business necessity to make men feel easy in their jobs—to encourage and praise, to let every man know exactly where he stands. There are also many that don't. Fred's company was in the latter category. In the great shining office tower to which he reported for work each morning, economic fear was used as a goad. Fred did not know where he stood. He did not know whether his job performance was satisfactory. There were legends that lived in the building, some true and some probably exaggerated, telling of men who had thought they were performing well and who had suddenly been fired; men who had been promised raises and had never seen them; men who had returned from vacations to find others sitting at their desks. The atmosphere in the building was electric with tension. Every man looked for small indications that might reveal his standing and his future, and small things waxed unrealistically large. It was a good sign if your boss looked into your office to say good morning; it was a bad sign if he didn't. It was dangerous not to invite the boss home for dinner at least once a year; it was a knell of doom if, invited, he turned you down. If, riding down in the elevator with you at five o'clock, your boss invited you to stop in the bar for a drink, it was necessary to accept no matter what calamity might result at home.

While fighting with such anxieties at the office, Fred was also subjected to mounting stress at home. Eve was still having only limited success in breaking into the country-club set. Every week there were real or imagined rebuffs. Every weekend there were parties to which she and Fred or their children were not invited. Troubled by tensions of her own, she was growing irritable, critical and suspicious. Her once sweet disposition was crumbling away. She began to make remarks suggesting that Fred's late nights and frequent trips away from home were not all connected with business. She was especially acid when he came home bearing the telltale signs of a drink at the bar with his boss, a colleague or customer. He was never able to explain adequately to her why the noontime and five o'clock drink were, in his view, necessary to his position in the company. The bar on the ground floor of the office building served some of the same purposes for Fred as the country club: it was a place in which to firm friendships, mend fences, clinch arguments and pick up useful gossip. It was one of the few pipelines Fred had to the top executive offices. Eve was not able to understand why such business could not be transacted during office hours. To her, Fred's increasing absence from home represented a decreasing desire in him to spend time with her.

Fred was also troubled by his son, a thin, moody boy, now age nine. Fred Jr. appeared to be developing into a more or less general failure. He was doing poorly in his schoolwork—not failing, but barely getting by. He was a sissy—had no interest in either sports or hobbies, was continually picked on by other more aggressive boys who knew he would never strike back. He spent his time hanging around home, preferring to be in the same room with his mother.

Fred sensed that he should spend more time with the boy. He remembered happy days spent with his own father and older brothers fishing, camping, hunting. He realized, dimly, that

Fred Jr. was failing to become a man because there was no one to teach him how. But it seemed to Fred that the situation had no remedy. His primary duty to his family, as he saw it (and the creed of the mobile backed him up), was to be a good provider. He was pouring his energies into the fight to get ahead and pay off the ever-mounting bills. There were also the house and grounds—part of the façade of affluence—to maintain. Life could not fairly demand more of him—he was already giving all he had.

Sometimes he made a grim effort to be a pal to Fred Jr. But all the time he and the boy were out in the backyard throwing a ball, Fred was tense and fidgety, thinking of the screen door that had to be repaired, the office work that had to be done, the long hard Monday ahead. He played with the boy not because he wanted to, but because he felt he ought to. Magazine articles, his wife and his conscience had told him he should. A game played under such compulsion is not fun: it is in itself tension-producing. Fred Jr.'s rather girlish awkwardness added to Fred's irritation. Thus their brief hours together, and the occasional family outings through thick, crowded, ill-tempered traffic, were seldom pleasant for either man or boy. There was a lack of honest companionship between them.

Fred could not relax. The drive to get ahead had come to dominate him, and anything that did not contribute to that goal was an irritation. A day's adventure with a boy, a quiet afternoon in the shade of a tree, a good book, a symphony: these things lose their magic when the mind is too strongly preoccupied with material striving. To those living the speculative way of life, an idle hour is a wasted hour.

You can't easily relax merely by willing it. Relaxation comes in well-practiced activities that are not associated with danger, punishment, fear or strain. Fred had given up all such activities long ago. He played golf with a bet on each hole; cards for high stakes; catch with his son out of a sense of obligation. He relaxed only after two or three drinks.

Now a new burden deposited itself on Fred's shoulders. Eve's father died, and her mother asked if she could come and live with the Brights temporarily. Both Fred and Eve were good-hearted people, and Fred particularly was in the habit of taking on burdens without first considering his ability to carry them. He wanted to be a good Joe. He didn't want to admit that there was anything he couldn't or wouldn't do. The older woman moved in.

Eve's mother, who had worked in the homes of wealthy people, admired the pomp and ostentation of wealth. She admired its façade without having any conception of the productiveness, the usefulness to society, that must usually lie behind wealth. She wanted to build the façade by itself, quickly. As soon as she was settled in Fred's home, she began suggesting purchases. It suddenly seemed necessary to buy new wall-to-wall carpeting. You couldn't be high-class with a faded rug. New draperies, too. Those old ones weren't modern enough. Eve had pushed Fred before, but there had always been a point at which she had stopped. Now, with mother and daughter cooperating, Fred was pushed harder than ever. Bills mounted alarmingly.

Eve's mother was not making herself a useful member of the community or the family. She did not encourage Fred's son and daughters to apply themselves to their schoolwork, but instead encouraged Eve's efforts to push the girls into young pre-debutante society. She encouraged the girls' attention to clothes, to social graces, to the façade, but not to things that would one day make them self-reliant, productive members of society. She did little to help Eve around the house. She felt that, as an older woman, she was entitled automatically to veneration and economic support.

Fred and Eve Bright thus were ambushed as John and Gina Conning were. The older generation in their home was making demands of them but giving nothing in return.

As Fred's daughters grew toward their teens they became a new source of worry for him. Eve was anxious for them to become "popular"—meaning attractive to boys—as she had been. As she saw it, a girl's best chance of success lay in studying and practicing popularity. Eve would have been indignant to hear it said in so many words, but she was teaching her girls to concentrate on the use of sex to make their way in the world. Instead of learning to be useful to their family, society and their future husbands, they were learning to cultivate a magnetic façade by means of which they, like their mother, could one day attach themselves parasite-like to climbing men.

Eve didn't make the girls do much work around the house. Often when she asked them to dry the dishes or clean their rooms, they complained that the "crowd" was expecting them and they had to hurry away. Eve let them go, on the theory that time spent with the crowd was the most important part of the girls' education. Who dried the dishes? Fred. Similarly, Eve didn't make the girls do their homework when some allegedly pressing social engagement called them out of the house. She bought them new clothes whenever they claimed it was necessary for popularity, running up charge accounts that added to Fred's month-end burdens. She let them bring the crowd home with them and take over the living room at any and all times. When Fred complained that he sometimes liked to rest in the living room and might feel less tense if the house weren't thundering with loud voices and loud music, Eve told him that parents must make certain sacrifices for their children.

Perhaps they must. But not to the extent that they are turned out of their own living rooms. Children can justly be expected to give their parents something in return. They can be made to help around the house, to be considerate of their parents' needs. Many mobile people have adopted the notion that you must eternally give to children; otherwise you are not a loving parent. It is seen as old-fashioned and unenlightened to discipline kids firmly, no matter how understandingly, to deny them some of their wishes, make them respect the wishes of adults. Such mobile parents have relinquished control. They have dropped the ball; the kids have picked it up and are running away with it.

Fred and Eve were ambushed from both sides: older and younger generations were squeezing them. But it wasn't only his daughters' lack of discipline, their laziness and selfishness, that made home stressful to Fred. To make things worse, he began to worry about his daughters' sexual conduct.

The older girl, Fran, aged fourteen, was an eager student of her mother's teachings. Fran saw that a popular girl could have all kinds of fun. Such a girl could go to all the big dances, see all the movies without paying, be in on all the good times. As Fran's breasts filled out and her hips rounded, she studied the use of her charms to gain her ends, with her mother's and grandmother's encouragement. Now the parties in Fred's living room occasionally became ominously quiet. When Fred came downstairs he would find all the lights out. He'd switch them on, find the kids sitting two to a chair, the boys' mouths smudged with lipstick. Fred remembered that, in his own youth, he'd felt sheepish and embarrassed when an adult caught him petting. These boys and girls in his living room, however, merely grinned at him arrogantly or giggled. As soon as he went back upstairs they switched the lights back off.

Fran scornfully told Fred he was hopelessly old-fashioned. Eve often sided with her daughter. After all, said Eve, you can't expect a girl to be a hermit. A time came, however, when Eve switched on the living-room lights and saw an older boy hastily pull his hand out from under fourteen-year-old Fran's skirt. Then Eve had angry words with her daughter. Eve didn't realize that she herself had laid the groundwork for this event. In her worship of the cult of popularity, she had pushed Fran into early dating, dancing and other heterosexual contacts. It was almost inevitable that Fran would begin early to experiment with more adult forms of sexual stimulation.

The Brights' younger daughter, Ginny, twelve, began to ape her sister as she passed into adolescence. Now Fred worried every time his daughters were out of the house. He sometimes suggested that the kids be chaperoned in some of their activities, but his daughters, his wife and many of the other mothers in their social set laughed at the idea. This, they said, was not Victorian England. Kids must be free to find themselves without adult interference. They must not be repressed, or all kinds of neurotic trouble might result.

But Fred was worried about a more likely kind of trouble. He wondered what would happen if Fran or Ginny, experimenting with sex without having the knowledge or experience to control it, became pregnant.

By the time he reached his early forties, Fred was a very tense young man. He hurried wherever he went, even when there was no real reason to do so, for he had in him the constant sense of too much to do and too little time. He drove his car fast and recklessly to save a few minutes' commuting time. He was a table-tapper, a pacer back and forth. He had the wrinkly brow that shows chronic tension of the scalp muscles—and the frequent headaches that often result from such tension.

He was also beginning to have pains in his stomach and chest. The chest pains were sometimes accompanied by an alarming palpitation of the heart, and they worried him seriously. He remembered that his father had died of a heart attack. People who have experienced illness in the family, particularly when young, are usually more anxious about similar problems of their own. Could he be heading for the same end as his father? Actually he wasn't in danger of a heart attack—not necessarily, although he might have had an inherited predisposition and should have been taking particularly good care of his health as he grew older. The chest pains resulted from the simple fact that the muscles in his chest were chronically tense; the pain was the ordinary ache of muscular fatigue. The heart palpitation was the result of fear: the fear of economic disaster that was always with him. Every time something threatening happened at the office, every time a higher executive criticized him or somebody failed to invite him to an executive conference, his heart pounded and his chest hurt. It was exactly the same physical reaction that would arise in a man who rounds a corner and comes face-to-face with a tiger. But its cause was less obvious. Fred did not understand it, and thus the symptom became a new worry.

The stomach pains were in reality more serious. They were the beginnings of an ulcer.

When a man is gripped by anger or fear, his body automatically makes ready for violent physical action—for fighting, running, climbing a tree. An extra supply of hormones is shot into the bloodstream. This keys the body up for supernormal effort. The heart begins to beat faster, increasing the supply of oxygen to the muscles. The muscles become tight—not only the skeletal muscles, but also certain internal muscles such as those of the stomach and intestines. Glands become overactive, including those that secrete some of the digestive juices.

It is a marvelous mechanism. But it has no provision to accommodate itself to the needs of a man under chronic stress—a man such as Fred Bright. When the key-up mechanism is evoked too often or for too long, it may begin to harm the body which it was designed to help. Changes may take place in the stomach or intestinal walls, and the result may be that the stomach begins to digest itself. The digestive juices eat their way into the stomach or duodenal wall. This is a peptic ulcer.

A little exercise, relaxing play, would have helped Fred get rid of some of this excess energy and its chemical counterpart in his blood. But even when Fred did exercise—playing golf for money, playing with his son out of duty—he only increased his tensions and maintained the harmful processes that were going on in his body.

Like many men, Fred tried to disregard the warning signals of his body's barometers. He had been trained since boyhood to grit his teeth at the pain that indicates body tissues may be undergoing damage. As in his job, he scorned to ask for help. Eve was much like him in this respect. Both of them felt that it was immature to be anything but independent. They felt that they must stand up to life without help, that they must grin and bear their stresses. This was their definition of maturity. They thought of it as immature and "neurotic" to admit that their perfectly real stresses were bothering them. In stoic fashion they tried to hide their pains and tensions, or to dismiss them as imaginary or temporary. Thus they failed to take the simple steps that could have helped them find a calmer, happier life.

Fred's pains eventually grew so bad that he went to see a doctor. The doctor told him that he had developed an ulcer, prescribed a rigorous diet and advised him to slow down. This was easy to advise. But Fred was not in a position to slow down. His speculations were still driving him; his golden plateau was still out of reach. He had his mortgage, his car payments, his life insurance loan, his country-club dues, his other miscellaneous debts to pay off. He wanted to send his kids to college. He wanted to hire a maid for Eve. He did not feel secure enough in his job to cut his work load even a little. He had to work late at night; he had to travel; he had to visit the bar; he had to push and worry. Otherwise—who knew what might happen to him?

Finally, one day, Fred began to vomit blood. He was rushed to a hospital, hemorrhaging internally. The ulcer had eroded a large blood vessel. Bleeding heavily and in shock, Fred was a critically ill man.

Thus the speculative way of life, nurtured in Disturbia, brought a hard-working young man to death's door. There are hundreds of thousands, possibly millions, of Freds in the nation's suburbs. In boom times, they are pushed into jobs without adequate preparation. They try to learn through trial and error rather than by seeking counsel of wiser, more experienced heads. Eventually their speculative structure begins to crumble. They make costly mistakes on the job. It becomes harder for them to meet their mounting debts. The structure falls apart.

This, perhaps as much as anything else, may contribute to the periodic business recessions with which free economies are plagued. Boom times are speculative times. When the speculators start having to pay for overreaching themselves, the boom ends.

CHAPTER 5

Marriage and Divorce

The Fraying Knot

It is a sad but inescapable fact that America, the most prosperous country in the world, has one of the highest divorce rates in the world. Our wealthy, mobile society is as rough on marriage as it is on individuals.

Back in 1900, the United States marriage rate (number of marriages per 1,000 population) was 9.3. The divorce rate was 0.7. In 1955, the marriage rate was the same: 9.3. But the divorce rate had more than tripled, to 2.3.

Divorce rates alone do not tell a reliable story, for they are partly a function of law. They reflect not only the desire of married people to cut the knot, but also the degree to which these people succeed in convincing the courts that divorce is necessary —and, further, their ability to stand the considerable expense. Since 1946, when the United States divorce rate shot up to a fantastic 4.3, many states have toughened their laws and instituted reconciliation procedures. Thus our present divorce rate might be considerably higher (though probably not as high as

4.3; that was partly a postwar phenomenon) if we were still operating under the laws of the 1940's.

A somewhat more reliable gauge of marital success or failure is that of separation. In general, it is easier and cheaper to separate, remaining married but living apart, than to divorce. Several times as many marriages end in separation as in divorce.

Hence, in comparing the marital statistics of mobile and stable communities, it will be useful to look at both divorce and separation records. The table below compares Bergen County with slower-growing, more stable Essex County. It shows the change in number of divorces and separate-maintenance arrangements in both counties from 1950 to 1956. During this period, New Jersey's laws were changed to hold marriages together more firmly. It worked in Essex. It didn't work in Bergen.

	Divorce	*Separation*	*Population*
	Change 1950-56	Change 1950-56	Change 1950-58
Essex	−17%	−2%	+10%
Bergen	+26%	+100%	+27%

Apparently married couples are having an increasingly rough time in Bergen, but not in Essex. As the lawmakers intended, the number of divorces and separations dropped in Essex, even though the county's population grew slowly. But in Bergen, the number of divorces increased at roughly the same rate as population, and the separations went wild.

What is happening to marriage in our mobile society? There are several powerful forces at work.

The Suburban Schism

One of the most striking facts about marriage today is that the husband and wife, having formally joined themselves together, go on to live much of their lives asunder. The man goes to work;

the woman stays home. They live in different worlds. Neither may know much about the other's daily affairs. They may lose, or never develop, the habit of talking to one another; for there may be little of common interest to talk about. At suburban parties the husbands gather at one end of the room, the wives at the other. The husbands discuss business, home repairs, sports. The wives discuss babies, cooking, clothes. Indeed, the husband and wife may have two entirely different circles of friends, circles that overlap only at an edge. The husband has his friends in the city world of business; the wife, hers in the suburban home community.

In time this rift may widen and deepen until the apartness is completed by divorce. Living in different environments, meeting different people, subjected to different influences, a man and woman who once matched neatly will change until they are badly mismatched. Most commonly, the man will grow—in education, social skills, earning power—while his wife stands still (as is illustrated in the case of Link and Diane Weber, which follows). The man, out in the world of business, continues his formal and worldly education, meets women who are new and fascinating to him. His wife is isolated at home, her life a dreary treadmill of household chores. A time comes when they are so far apart, so different, that their once close union must be dissolved. This is probably the most common kind of marital difficulty among mobile people.

Much less frequently, the wife outgrows the husband. This happens most often when the husband is declining or standing still amid the great upward surge of society around him or when the wife is independently wealthy, very attractive to other men, or a career woman—when she does not have to depend on her marriage for economic security. She grows tired of him and leaves, especially if she has a suitor on tap. Only a minority of wives enjoy this economic freedom. Most, deprived of their husbands by divorce, would face severe money trouble and perhaps disaster. Their earning power is less than their husbands'. For this reason, and because men's role in society allows them more growth, the more usual picture is that of the husband walking out on the wife.

Consider how all this differs from life in the stable communities of the past. In these communities there lived a kind of family that was vastly unlike the mobile suburban household: the farm family. This was a close-knit unit. It wasn't split down the middle with the man and the business of earning a living on one side, the woman and children and home on the other. In the farm family, home and business were one. True, husband and wife each had their special roles, but they overlapped one another. The wife, though her principal duty was in the home, nonetheless helped her husband with chores around the farm—feeding the chickens, harvesting the crops. The man, in turn, carried water and cut firewood for the home. He also played a big part in the education and bringing-up of his children—particularly his sons, whom he trained by example for the day when they could take over the farm's management. Man and wife knew much about each other's business. They shared the same experiences. There was small chance that one could grow without the other.

Economic need was a basis of marriage. A farmer sought a wife not only to satisfy his sex urge but also because he needed a woman and children to help him run the farm, to help make it grow. Today many marriages, particularly very young marriages such as that of Fred and Eve Bright, are formed on the basis of romantic love. Romantic love is so formless, so elusive a thing that novelists have spent millions of words trying to define it and analyze it, and still haven't arrived at any universal conclusions. Not only is it ephemeral, not guaranteed to stay alive, but it is often a weak bond in any case. The farmer continued to need his wife even when the "romance," if any, was dead. If she left him he faced severe problems in keeping the farm going. The modern mobile husband does not usually need his wife economically. She needs him, but he continues to work at his job and draw his salary whether she stays or goes.

Even the non-farm families in these old-time towns, even the families whose men left home each morning to work somewhere else, had a closeness with each other and their lifelong friends and neighbors that the mobile family often lacks. The husband, not caught in a desperate struggle to get ahead, shared his wife's deep interest in the community that was their home. He and she often enjoyed the same activities together. They knew the same people. They were likely to be together more, to have the habit of talking with each other.

The wife, too, was likely to know more about her husband's job than does the modern suburban wife. This was not only because he had more time to talk to her about it, but also because the job was typically easier to understand. The world today has grown so complex, technologically and economically, that jobs have had to be divided and re-divided into increasingly narrow specialties. A hundred years ago it was possible for one man to know all there was to know about the company where he worked. Fifty years ago a man could know the whole of any one area in the company: production, or sales, or accounting. Today he may be in a still narrower compartment. He is hard put to explain to his wife exactly how his work contributes to the corporation's profits, or just what it is that he does. She may feel far removed from his daily struggle; she may not see how she can help him with it or counsel him on it. Instead of providing a bond between them, the business of earning a living keeps them apart.

Religion and the Pants-and-Apron Question

The factor of religious intermarriage has been mentioned often as another reason behind the rising divorce rates in our mobile society. How important a reason is it?

There is no question that the number of religious intermarriages has increased as the mobility of Americans has increased. More and more each decade, young people have gone beyond the boundaries of their home towns to seek fortunes and find mates. The old, stable communities were often one-religion towns; this was their nature; this is one reason why they are referred to as integrated. But America, the industrialized, urbanized America into which young single men and women venture, is an all-religions society. In a vast swirl of cultural mobility, Protestants and Catholics and Jews jostle one another. Sometimes the jostling is bad-tempered, sometimes amicable. Sometimes a spark strikes. A marriage takes place. With each stir of mobility's spoon, the likelihood grows that people of different faiths will meet and marry.

Observations in Bergen County show that such marriages are more likely to run into trouble than one-faith marriages. John and Gina Conning, for example, had a good deal of trouble. A late-1950's sampling of normal married people in the county, people whose marriages were at least moderately happy, showed that twenty-four per cent were intermarried. But among young divorcees, thirty-nine per cent had been married to men of different faiths. And among couples seeking psychiatric help for marital problems, forty-two per cent were intermarried.

Yet there is an unanswered question here. Was it the religious difference itself, the failure to see eye-to-eye about church, that caused these divorces and brought these couples to psychiatrists?

In the majority of cases, no. Only in the minority of intermarriages is the quarrel about religion the most important rift. Other quarrels usually bulk larger. For when two culturally mobile people of different faiths marry, they often bring together far more than opposing religious views. They may bring together dissimilar cultural backgrounds, opposing ideas on the roles of man and wife in the home, divergent feelings toward parents and children and sex. These things usually cause far more trouble than religious controversy. The difference in faiths is usually more a sign of other, more hurtful differences than it is itself a cause of strife.

For example, in many countries the man of a family is traditionally and undisputedly the boss. His responsibility is to earn the family living, period. His wife cooks his meals and mends his clothes, cares for children and home, and would no more think of asking him to help with the dishes than she would put her head in a lion's mouth. She is happy in this position, for the community supports her. She is recognized as having an important role, gets plenty of help and companionship from the other women, has small desire to be doing anything else. Happy and securely protected, she may have no desire to know about finances and business matters and may be glad to avoid the competitive world.

The family may happen to be Catholic, for this religion predominates in some of these countries. The religion may have little to do with the cultural acceptance of authoritarianism in the man; the two facts simply exist side by side. When the family migrates to America, the two facts tag along. A son, who has observed the old man in action and absorbed his ways of looking at things, goes out into the mobile society and marries a Protestant girl.

The fact that she attends a Protestant church, again, has little to do with the case. It is largely a side issue. What is important is that she has been raised in a different culture. She comes, perhaps, from a family that has had several generations to absorb American ideas about the equality of men and women. She has lived in a society where women have helped to pioneer in harsh lands, fight off Indians, turn wilderness to farm—in a society where women have fought for their rights at the voting booth and elsewhere. Her mother took no bullying from her father. Her brothers treated her as more or less an equal. When she left high school, she went on to college or out to work as they did. She was expected to stand on her own feet. At home, she and her mother had the men's help with household chores. When there were discussions of important matters around the dinner table, all were invited to contribute ideas. The women were not expected to stay home, tied to purely domestic duties, but to work at paying jobs or in community activities.

It is easy to imagine how such an intermarriage might end in discord. Even if the two meet each other halfway, each might still be unhappy. The wife might feel a loss of freedom and independence, an insult to her intelligence. The husband might sense himself to be surrendering his position of dignity, knuckling under to a woman-dominated culture, losing his masculinity.

Even a woman who accepts authoritarianism in the man, who has the same cultural background as her husband, may have trouble in Disturbia. For the modern mobile society does not support the woman whose duties are exclusively domestic. Alice Hager discovered this. The housewife in the less mobile male-authoritarian culture is usually comfortable in her job. She is protected by the men and helped by other women in the family, not asked to be self-reliant or face problems by herself. Equally important, her role is respected by the community: she draws applause and other satisfactions from it. Even if tragedy should occur, as in wartime, and she should lose her husband, she and her children usually would receive much material and emotional support from their families and old friends. This is much less likely to occur in the modern mobile community, where families are independent and may never get to know one another well enough.

In Disturbia the housewife's job, considerably harder than in an integrated society, earns less respect. One reason for this is the decline of the housewife's economic value since the time when most Americans lived on farms. The husband doesn't need the wife so greatly. Another reason is the increasingly high level of American women's education. In an industrial society where more and more women are taking on challenging jobs in business, domestic chores seem increasingly dull and menial by comparison. The heroine of the suburban culture is not the wife and mother, but the career girl.

Thus even a woman who comes from a family where father was boss may rebel when she marries and settles in the disturbed suburban community. Her husband, following the example of his father, does not trouble her pretty head with financial matters, gives her a household spending allowance, seeks intellectual stimulation with other men instead of with her, won't change a diaper or dry a dish, and fails to understand why she should want to get out of the house. His mother was happy with this arrangement—why not his wife?

Decliners

A third fount of marital discord in our mobile society is economic decline. In an upward-moving society that lays great stress on material gain, it hurts badly to stand still or to sink. Downward motion, real or apparent, is attended by ugly footmen: fear, guilt, blame, feelings of failure and uselessness. Immersed in such a cauldron of seething emotion, husband and wife are more than normally sensitive. Small differences of opinion flare up into spiteful quarrels or subside into sullen, hate-charged silences.

It is hard to tackle emotional problems from a position of economic decline. The husband must fight to hold his head above water. Though his tensions have given him an ulcer or high blood pressure or a damaged heart, he finds it hard or impossible to slow down. The wife has economic insecurity and an irritable husband added to her other problems. She may feel trapped in a hostile—or, at best, uncaring—world. Neither can easily calm down until the economic situation is improved. Eventually the pressures become too great—the marriage explodes.

Gather any group of mobile people who are having or have had marriage trouble, and the chances are you will find decline in the backgrounds of many. In a sampling of contented married people in Bergen County, only eight per cent were sinking economically. Among couples who sought psychiatric help, nineteen per cent were declining. Among divorced and separated men patients, twenty-five per cent were going down.

When a marriage does start to crumble, from this or any other cause, it often crumbles with accelerating speed. A man and woman who have been punishing each other will, in time, become conditioned to react with anger to each other's presence. When the conditioning has been going on for a long enough time, even innocent words or gestures by one may provoke an angry response from the other. This anger provokes answering anger, and the vicious cycle of conditioning continues. When a marriage has reached this state, the mutual angry response may continue even when the basic problems that started the rift have been solved. Thus a new problem has arisen: how to extinguish the conditioning.

The Lost Controls

The end of many a marriage comes when one partner or the other, abandoning the effort to find solutions to problems at home, begins seeking the things he or she needs—love, praise, usefulness, sexual or intellectual stimulation—through extramarital relationships. Once this happens, the hope of straightening out the marriage dims markedly. With the delinquent partner no longer striving to solve them, existing problems loom larger. New problems arise; jealousy, bitterness and anger swamp the family. The point of no return may now have been reached.

This fatal step into extramarital companionship is much easier to take in our mobile world than it was in the typical old-time community. In that town there were social controls which worked to prevent such a step. This was a town in which you and your business were known by many people. The moment you did anything that was in any way out of the ordinary, news of it spread through the community. There were eyes everywhere. Unless you were prepared to face some quite harsh music—social and even economic ostracism—you did not dare conduct an extramarital affair in any but the most difficult circumstances of secrecy and fear. It was almost impossible to conduct a casual affair. It had to be dead serious (and hence worth all the trouble of keeping hidden) or not at all. If you did unwisely begin a casual flirtation, your family or your spouse's or both landed on you. In this closely controlled situation, it was hard for married people to step out on each other.

The mobile husband and wife are not under any such control. Typically their families are far away, geographically or in spirit. The community around them does not know, and indeed does not much care, what they are doing. A casual flirtation can begin easily—particularly for the husband, who leaves home each morning to spend the day in a different world. He can take a woman to dinner in the city, or call at her apartment, with virtually no fear of being seen by anybody who knows him or who would report to his wife. Gradually and easily, the casual flirtation becomes more than casual and more than a flirtation. Another mobile marriage begins to come apart.

The case study that follows, the story of Link and Diane Weber, illustrates some of these problems of marriage in Disturbia. In particular it illustrates the problem of a man's growing while his wife stands still, and the problem of a double standard in attitudes toward sex.

The Widening Gap

Diane's parents were easygoing, comfortable, fifth-generation Americans of the mid-middle class. They had settled in Bergen County when Diane was a baby, and had stayed in the same roomy old house ever since. She led a happy childhood in which there were no notable problems, no sensitizers. She had a circle of good friends and a moderate number of casual weekend dates as she reached her teens. In school her work was a little above average. Her parents didn't demand much of her, and she enjoyed basking in the warmth of home with them and with her brothers and sister. She was unassertive, somewhat shy, and a little spoiled. She was, in many respects, an American type: the girl-next-door. She was cheerful, serene, pleasant, and confident that one day a nice young man would come along and take care of her as her parents always had.

R. Lincoln Weber came up from laboring class origins. His grandparents had come to this country from Europe. He was a young man with a fierce determination to get ahead. He was working his way through law school, willingly enduring the physical hardships of insufficient food and sleep in order to do so. He was brilliant, witty, nervously energetic. He was attracted to Diane partly because of her higher social status.

Diane's parents did not like him. Like many mobile people he had little respect for old ways, nor for people who clung to old ways. He resembled Fred Bright in that he was not in the habit of asking counsel from his elders. But where Fred simply never thought of doing so, Link deliberately avoided seeking advice. He went out of his way to show his scorn of ideas that he thought old-fashioned. He had broken away entirely from his own early environment and from his parents. He had little respect either for them or for authority in general.

He showed no interest in meeting Diane's parents while he was courting her. He ignored other members of Diane's large, close family. He failed to show the deference that the older folk felt was their due. He dominated conversations, refused to take part in the Sunday visiting that was traditional in the family. None of this endeared him to Diane's parents. They were also concerned about an age difference. Link was twenty-eight, Diane only nineteen.

Despite objections at home, Diane agreed to marry him. Her reason for an early marriage was probably the least reliable she could have picked: she was "in love" with him.

She would have been wiser to wait a few years. Just out of high school, she had not yet known many men well. She had no one against whom to compare Link, no frame of reference by which to judge the likelihood of his making her happy for the rest of her life. Her parents had not taught her much about sex and marriage. She had not gone through a period of observing and testing with men—during which she could watch her own emotions at work, finding out what she wanted in a husband and what kinds of men might best be counted on to satisfy these wants. She had not tested a number of men's willingness to consider her point of view. She was happy in the conviction that if she was nice to people they would treat her in the same way.

If Diane had experienced sexual attraction to other men, if she had learned what the emotion is like and how it may be controlled, it would not have been as likely to overwhelm her when Link came on the scene. As it happened, the emotion did overwhelm her—a heady mixture of sexual attraction and romantic infatuation. As a result, she failed to think clearly and carefully about the marriage, about its chances of success or failure. Because of Diane's obviously overwhelming romantic and sexual attraction to Link, her parents grudgingly accepted her marriage to him. They feared she may already have begun an affair and felt it was better for her to make it legal than to continue on her present course.

After the wedding Link and Diane rented an apartment in New York City. It had been agreed between them that his education was now all-important. Accordingly Diane went to work as a filing clerk, paying the rent and buying the groceries while he finished his last two years of law school.

When the two years were over Link joined a law firm in the city, quickly showed himself to be a brilliant young man, broke away from the firm and set up his own law practice in the city. At first the going was rough, but these were happy years for Diane. She and Link associated with old friends from her home town and new friends in the city. Most of the couples in this young married set were like Link and Diane: struggling to pay the rent, but full of high hopes and big dreams for the future.

In time Link's clientele began to expand. He attracted as clients some bright young people like himself: junior executives, career women, even a few young successes from the entertainment world. He found their company stimulating. Often he entertained them at night, bringing them home to the apartment or asking Diane to join the group at a restaurant. But then Diane became pregnant. More frequently after that, Link entertained his clients by himself.

Diane left work to have her baby. Link, who had always taken charge of the family finances, now inaugurated a system in which he gave her a weekly household allowance and spoke little to her about other aspects of financial affairs. He told her he wanted her to be feminine and domestic; he wanted to feel he was taking care of her, saving her from the worry over money which he felt was man's province. This suited Diane well, though she was sometimes irritated at being kept in the dark about the family's income and expenses. The weekly amount was adequate.

When the baby was ten months old and another was on the way, Link decided it was time to buy a house. Diane was surprised when he showed a liking for a twenty-five-thousand-dollar house in the suburbs. She hadn't thought his income was yet high enough to support such a mortgage. She was even more surprised when he took care of the down payment by dealing out six one-thousand-dollar bills. She had never seen a one-thousand-dollar bill before. It was incredible to her that Link could have made that much money. When she questioned him about it, he merely grinned and remarked that business had been good lately.

Diane settled down in the new house. Occasionally she missed the bright life of the city, felt twinges of envy at the enormous fun Link was obviously reaping from his work. Yet she was content. She was fulfilling her role as a woman; she had a husband who provided for her and often said he loved her; and one day, when the children were grown, she would see more of Link and of the outside world. These solitary days and nights were inevitable, she thought, for the wife of a rising young professional man. They were the price she had to pay for a husband, home, family and economic security. In her view, the price was fair.

Happily, Diane was not totally deprived of social life. She and Link had, by chance, bought a house in a neighborhood whose families, mostly young, were alert to their own need for fun and friendship. There were frequent weekend parties, barbecues, occasionally a block dance. Link often worked in the city on weekends, but on Friday and Saturday nights when he was home, he and Diane participated in the neighborhood social activities. When he wasn't home, she occasionally went to the gatherings by herself, sharing the expense of a babysitter with a neighbor.

A shyly charming girl, Diane drew men to her at such gatherings. There was one handsome, boyish young executive named Jack who seemed particularly interested in her. Jack was enjoying moderate success in his career, but it was more a result of charm and luck than persistent effort. His primary interest was in having a good time. His wife, whom he had married right after high school, had grown discontented with his cavalier attitude toward life and had divorced him to marry an older, more solidly successful executive. Jack now lived with his widowed mother, who cared for him and his infant daughter.

Jack and Diane met often at neighborhood social events. But she firmly rebuffed his attempts to make their acquaintance more than casual. She refused to let him take her out to dinner or escort her home after evening parties.

He persisted, and one New Year's Eve he almost succeeded. Diane and Link had gone to a party at a neighbor's home. Link was moody, unwilling to sink into the convivial spirit of the evening. He seemed to find this suburban social circle—these discussions of children, houses, gardening—less stimulating than the literary and artistic world of his clients in the city. Diane was angry. As the cocktails began to relax her inhibitions, she deliberately ignored Link and attached herself to Jack. There was dancing downstairs in the playroom. As Diane danced with Jack she found, to her bewilderment, that she was becoming sexually excited.

This should not have surprised her. Like most human beings, Diane needed variety and responded to new things with pleasure and excitement. Any adventure—be it sexual relations or mountain climbing or anything else—repeated with the same companion in the same way, over and over again, eventually can cease to be an adventure. It may pall. Diane's husband was not an imaginative lovemaker. He did not try to make the experience varied or interesting for her. Possibly this was because he was already finding the variety he himself needed with other women. His advances to his wife were becoming less and less frequent. In any event, Diane's sexual enjoyment with him had long since begun to dull. She felt that the romance was going out of her marriage. She had reached a point where any small variation would give her pleasure. Such a variation was the act of dancing with a man who, though she lacked the experience to recognize the fact, was on the make.

The small sex liberties that our mobile society allows—dancing, jokes about sex, lighthearted flirtation at social gatherings—can be used sensibly. A husband and wife whose own excitement with each other has begun to wear at the edges may sometimes find sexual stimulation among other people. They go home and consummate their aroused desires with each other. In this way, two people who are relatively unskilled at lovemaking may keep the spice in their marriage.

Unfortunately a ubiquitous problem of mobile people here often rears its busy head: the problem of a carry-over in the training, the attitudes and the moral values that were designed for another, more stable world. In that world, married people were taught that sexual feelings were wrong when directed toward anybody but one's lawful spouse. Some religions warned, further, that the prime object of sexual intercourse should be the production of offspring. These were sensible, useful teachings, for they helped to hold the family and the stable society together. Knowing that extramarital flirtations were taboo even when carried on in the imagination, people tended to shun them, deliberately avoiding the arousal and the temptation that could lead to severe disapproval, the ducking stool, the stocks, banishment or worse.

In the mobile world of today, however, these teachings are considerably harder to obey. Instead of living our lives with the same people, people who are as familiar, pleasant and bland to us as bread, and whom we have learned by sheer habit not to look upon as sexual objects, we are subjected to a continual stream of new, diverse people. Our senses are jarred awake constantly by the impact of sheer variety. To enlarge the problem, sex intrudes upon us through the mass-communication media that have played so great a part in creating this mobile world. It has been discovered by businessmen not only that sex is salable by itself, but also that it can aid in the sale of other merchandise. Virile men and voluptuous women leer at us from advertisements; passionate love scenes smolder on our TV and movie screens; even earthier matter appears in novels. The entertainment world has gone so far as to create a whole new fictitious society with its own whole new moral code, a code that is simply a huge green light: Go Ahead. The typical members of this imaginary society—our modern folk hero and heroine—are the private eye and the fashion model, libertines both, walking from bed to bed in broad daylight.

Thus there is a continual smoldering of sexual arousal in us. The result can be emotionally disturbing, particularly to women. Women are bound to the old teachings far more strongly than men. There is a double standard—one for each sex. In our society, boys learn early that the physical euphoria of sexual activity is a goal to be sought by itself. A boy who has had sexual intercourse is a hero to his friends and may even earn a proud wink, along with the cautionary lecture, from his father. Girls are trained by a different standard. They are taught that sex is not worthwhile as a mere physical pleasure but should be used only as an expression of love. A girl who has had premarital intercourse is not likely to brag about it and will almost certainly try to hide the fact from her parents. This life-long training persists strongly into married life. A husband who finds himself aroused by a woman other than his wife may feel annoyed, amused, temporarily frustrated. A wife in the same situation may react with vastly more painful emotions. If she is a woman such as Diane, brought up on strict stable-world virtues, she may be shocked and overwhelmed by guilt. This arousal goes against all that she has been taught. It is wrong, evil.

Diane, dancing with Jack, felt just these emotions arising in her. She continued dancing with him for a few minutes, for the physical stimulation was temporarily too great to abandon. Then midnight struck. It was time for the traditional New Year's Eve kiss. At this, Diane's sexual excitement rose so high that it frightened her. She broke away from Jack and fled to her husband. She begged him to take her home immediately.

Link, angered by his wife's over-obvious show of fondness for the divorced young executive, was in no mood to make love to her that night. Thus she lay in the dark, frustrated and swamped by guilt. She did not understand the social and psychological causes of her predicament. She knew only that desires had been aroused in her by a man who was not her husband, and that this was wrong. She had not had a premarital testing period during which, by socializing with men, she could have developed greater awareness, understanding and control of her passions. Not having learned to recognize simple physical arousal, such as boys learn, she felt that she desired the man, Jack, not merely the act.

She was sure that her husband must know. He was punishing her for her infidelity.

Link was going to punish her much more severely in another year. His course was already set; the end of their marriage was going to come in any case. But Diane's adventure with Jack made the outcome harder for her than it might have been.

From that day on, Diane avoided social gatherings, afraid to go out lest she meet the man who had aroused her. She avoided even talking with other men. She attended only daytime gatherings of women, shielding herself with comforting woman-talk: babies, shopping, mumps and measles.

Diane did nothing to prepare herself for the blow that was coming. Like an investor who bets his all on a single company's stock, she was leaning her entire life against Link. If that single support should be snatched away by death or divorce—two common eventualities in an increasingly mobile world—her whole structure would collapse.

Diane did not foresee that Link would change. Once again, she was going by the teachings of the stable world. The leopard, that world was fond of saying, cannot change his spots. No doubt he couldn't in those days. In that world, one's environment stayed the same; so did the people who shaped one's life. But in today's world, environments and friends flicker by in endless variety. Whirled along in all this change, individual men and women change, too. Their attitudes and intentions are continually reshaped. This year's passionate beliefs may be next year's jokes. Vows, sincerely and earnestly spoken, may eventually get in the way and have to be trampled underfoot.

Link had found a whole new way of life in New York City. He had met challenging men and had sharpened his personality against theirs. He had met stimulating women. Exciting new vistas of literature and art had been opened to him. New ways of thinking about things had penetrated his mind. He had learned. He had grown. And now that his law practice was solidly on its feet, he found that some of his women clients were prepared to become more than clients to him.

When a wealthy, troubled divorcee indicated her willingness to share her life with his, Link did not hesitate in mapping his future course. Long ago, he had rebelled against what he thought of as old-fashioned moral values. He considered himself a liberated thinker. He subscribed to the modern cult that urges the individual to seek self-fulfillment no matter what the cost to others. He felt that people should not repress their natural urges lest they become, in some obscure way, neurotic.

His announcement that he wanted a separation stunned Diane. What followed left her utterly helpless. For while growing in other ways, Link had also become sophisticated in financial and, of course, legal matters. He knew exactly how to accomplish the separation with minimum inconvenience to himself. Diane, not having been out in the world of business, was comparatively ignorant of such matters. She was not aware of the rights which women, through centuries of fighting, have won for themselves. She had not studied the divorce and separation laws. She did not know what rights she had, what she could demand from Link, what could be made to stick and what couldn't. Nor was she equipped to defend those rights she did know of. In any case her surprise and shock, her emotional upheaval were too great for her to think clearly.

In a daze, without even seeking legal counsel, she signed a separation agreement which bound Link to do only one thing: pay a conscience balm of fifteen dollars a week for her and each of her two children. Any good lawyer could have made him pay several times that amount after a thorough investigation of his income. Any good lawyer, too, would have extracted from him more than an unwitnessed verbal agreement to continue mortgage payments on the house and to leave her the car.

The house and car were, of course, registered in his name. The bank accounts were in his name. Without a lawyer to help her, Diane could not make him give her any of these things.

He did not try to take the car. But he refused to allow her access to the bank accounts. And in a few months, he reconsidered his promise to keep up payments on the house. The expense was unrealistic and unnecessary, he said. Over the phone, when she complained, he suggested that she go to live with her mother—then hung up. Having sold the house, he mailed her another conscience balm: a check for one-third the net receipts.

Diane took her children back to her parents' home. She was deeply depressed, tormented by a feeling that the break-up was somehow her own fault. She hadn't been bright enough for him; she hadn't stimulated him enough intellectually, emotionally or physically; she had been unfaithful to him. She felt that she was a failure as a woman. Shattered and hopeless, Diane shrank into her mother's home to live with guilt and loneliness.

Thus a perfectly normal girl, a girl with no childhood traumatization, was left with a severe emotional problem because she was poorly prepared for life in the changeful mobile world. Her story illustrates the power for good and bad that the husband may wield over a feminine, dependent woman in modern marriage. It is economic power. He wields it because he is so much less dependent on her for support than she on him. The wife risks much when, like Diane, she fails to seek ways of making herself independent should the occasion arise. We shall see, later on, a great difference in Diane's ability to cope with problems—once she has been helped to become more independent financially and socially.

On a Lonely Beach

The lot of the husbandless young wife in Disturbia, especially if she has children to care for, is not likely to be an enviable one. Whether she is widowed, divorced, or separated like Diane, she may face many kinds of stress. If she is as poorly prepared as Diane to stand alone, if she has rested her entire future on her husband, the stresses may be such as to plunge her into severe emotional disturbance.

One of her biggest problems is likely to be economic. Even if, unlike Diane, she has a career skill with which to support herself and the children, the chances are that she will not be able to earn as much as her husband did. Though new areas of employment are continually opening up for women, their opportunities in business are still a long way from equaling men's. Thus the young husbandless wife may have to sink to a lower standard of living. She must watch as her old friends, still married, continue to improve their economic well-being. One by one they move to other, wealthier suburbs.

Her problems in finding a rewarding social life may also be acute. A single woman in a community of couples, she may seldom be invited to play bridge or go to a dance—and even when she is invited, she may lack money to pay a babysitter.

There are only a few conditions under which her chances of remarrying are good. Her best chances lie in being wealthy—having money from her husband or some other source, like the divorcee who had attracted Link. She is in a fairly good position if she is young, attractive and without children. Otherwise, the odds do not favor her.

The law of supply and demand stands in her way. The simple fact is that there are more women in search of husbands than there are men to marry them—and the problem, from the women's point of view, grows worse with each successive year of age.

Men in the United States die younger than women. The Census Bureau's 1958 estimates show there were over three million more women in the country aged twenty-five or older than men at that time.

Thus the older woman who tries to attract a husband is selling in a buyer's market. This in itself is hard enough. What makes it harder is that wife-seeking men of these more mature ages, favored by the law of supply and demand, can and often do pick younger women. The woman with several children, like Diane, is at a considerable disadvantage.

The attractive husbandless wife will have suitors, but her suitors' intentions often won't be honorable. Men tend to think of widows and divorcees as easy prey for the wandering wolf, possibly on the theory that such a woman, having had sexual experience, won't object to a little more—and might, indeed, want or need it. One troubled young divorcee in Bergen County had six unsolicited propositions from her husband's friends in the month after her decree became final.

The wolves' theory may be, in part, valid. The once-married woman who has learned to enjoy sex has a far greater problem in managing her sexual adjustment than, for example, the uninitiated teen-age girl. The husbandless wife knows what she is missing, has less hope of remarriage, and may often be exposed to experienced, worldly-wise men. Society is justly less condemning of a discreet affair conducted by such a woman than of similar behavior in a teen-age girl or a married woman. Nonetheless the widow or divorcee who has an affair with a man may feel guilty and ashamed. Her needs for sexual gratification and companionship are great, yet she feels wrong in fulfilling them.

With all these problems upon her, the husbandless wife may feel like a piece of driftwood washed up on a lonely beach. The tides of life have left her there and receded. It is a stressful situation and often ends in emotional disturbance. Great numbers of widowed, divorced and separated women become in-patients in psychiatric hospitals.

In a sampling of normal people aged eighteen to forty-four, 0.8 per cent were widows. But in a group of psychiatric in-patients in that age group, 3.5 per cent were widows. Divorced and separated women were also far more heavily represented among the disturbed than in the general population. In the normal population sampling, 2.4 per cent of people aged eighteen to forty-four were divorced or separated women. Among the in-patients: 7.5 per cent.

Not only do husbandless wives become emotionally upset in large numbers, but their disturbances are likely to be severe, hard to alleviate and sometimes wholly intractable. The woman who has a husband has someone to help when she is upset. He at least gives her economic support. The future may look considerably less bleak to her than to a woman who must stand alone against an overwhelming onslaught of stress.

The table below tells this story in numbers. It covers women aged eighteen to fifty-nine who were admitted to a state mental hospital as psychiatric patients during a six-month period. It shows the percentage of women in each marital category who were still in the hospital at the end of the period. The married women were cured or discharged on convalescent status considerably more quickly than the husbandless:

	Young (18-44)	*Middle-aged (45-59)*
Married	29% still in	28% still in
Widowed	—	43% " "
Divorced or Separated	33% " "	50% " "

Widows and divorcees who have no special career skills and are primarily home- and family-oriented often find themselves in a particularly difficult position. Emotionally dependent upon children's and family's affections, they often find themselves trying harder and harder to please in order to receive a kind word. Children and other relatives soon learn they can take advantage of this psychological need of the husbandless wife who has not learned to seek economic and emotional security from the world at large. Women who are not prepared to earn a position of strength in the world of business and community affairs petition their families' affections from a position of weakness. This weakness can be, and frequently is, exploited.

CHAPTER 6

Children and Adolescents

Grief in Paradise

Among the reasons that bring a typical climber family to the suburbs, children rank high. A better life for the whole family, man and woman, boy and girl: this is what the suburbs promise. To the casual observer, indeed, these pretty green towns might seem like a children's paradise, a nearly perfect compromise between city and country life. Here the kids can have fine schools and other advantages made possible by a concentrated middle-income population, and here also they can have abundant sunshine and running room. Here, without penning them in a labyrinth of city walls, a man can be close to the high-paying commercial and industrial jobs that buy college educations.

It has been said that American culture is child-centered. If this is true, it is hardly more noticeable anywhere than in the suburbs. Nothing seems too good for the youngsters. Suburbanites morosely but voluntarily take on heavy tax burdens for schools. It is often hard to sell a house that lacks a playroom. Problems of child psychology are discussed at every party and back-fence gathering. In summer, three or four ice cream trucks may tinkle their bells along the same streets on the same day, and all do a howling business. "I'm fed up with commuting," you can hear men growl on the buses and trains. "If it weren't for the kids. . . ."

It is sad to discover, in the light of all this, that our mobile suburbs are still far from being a kid's paradise. There are bright, happy children here, certainly—as there are in all towns of all prosperous nations. But there are also more unhappy children than there should be, more delinquents, more who are failing in school, more who are having difficulties in their sexual and social lives.

Bergen County's high delinquency rates—forty boys per thousand, five girls per thousand—are alarming enough in themselves. What is equally alarming is the high ratio of delinquent boys to girls: eight-to-one (compared with four-to-one in the rural comparison county).

There are more delinquent boys than girls in virtually all towns, stable or mobile, for boys are more likely than girls to show emotional trouble in this particular way. The rural county's four-to-one is not a high ratio. But the suburban county's eight-to-one is. It's as high as in some of the roughest city slum areas.

A high boy-girl ratio among emotionally disturbed youngsters is a danger signal, an indicator of trouble in the community. It often indicates social disintegration such as might be found in a slum neighborhood, and is generally associated with such neighborhoods. Into these blighted, crowded areas, by economic osmosis, drift struggling immigrants and many of society's least successful families. In the slums, the delinquent or disturbed boy often has a father who can't or won't live up to his responsibilities as wage-earner and family head. The mother may be fighting to hold the family together, or she, too, may have abandoned her responsibilities. The home is not an attractive place for the boy. He spends much time away from it. With not enough fatherly help in the difficult business of becoming a man in a rough, competitive world, not enough guidance in the right directions and too much invitation toward the wrong ones, he is in danger of emotional disturbance and delinquency.

The high boy-girl ratio stems from the fact that a girl in such a neighborhood typically has less trouble. Until she is married she can get away with being unassertive. Unlike her brother, she can be passive and gentle without fearing that she will lose her friends' respect or society's applause. She can usually make herself useful around the home and thus can find some reason and reward for being there. Too, she can more easily channel her energies into school work and other intellectual or artistic activities. Her brother has a harder time doing so, for in his mixed-up world, high classroom grades or a skilled artist's brush are not outstanding marks of manliness—or, therefore, of success.

For these reasons and others documented in sociological and psychological literature, slum areas are often marked by high delinquency rates and a high boy-girl ratio in the roster of the troubled. Now the same phenomena seem to have arisen in the bright, sunny, spacious, well-heeled suburbs.

Obviously something is wrong in the mobile world. Something is troubling the youngsters.

Absentee Fathers

Something, particularly, is troubling the boys. One of their major problems, perhaps the most important, is a lack of good, solid guidance from their fathers.

Every child needs an adult of his own sex to guide him and serve as his model in growing up. A boy's job is to become a man, and he can't easily do it by himself. He needs men to teach him, by precept and example, how men in that particular society must act if they are to enjoy rewarding, successful lives. In the mobile society he has many lessons to learn: the importance of education, how to study, how to assert oneself without making enemies, how to persevere in tasks that may be hard and unpleasant, how to act considerately yet competitively toward women and other men, how to control and direct anger and fear in oneself and cope with these emotions in others. These and other things must be learned, and a boy learns them best from his father. His mother may be able to teach some of them, but not usually as well as a man can. She has difficulty in teaching masculine self-assertiveness, for example. Nor can she teach many of the small aspects of masculine attitude and mannerism that will help a boy win his friends' respect. Nor can she usually teach him how to throw a baseball or handle a saw. Nor does she usually fully understand the masculine attitude toward sex.

Many boys of mobile suburban families lack the close fatherly guidance they need. The father leaves home after breakfast and doesn't come back until just before the evening meal. Like Fred Bright, he may recognize that his boy needs him, but he is usually too tired to do anything about it, and other matters may occupy him even when he is rested. A house needs a lot of attention and requires a lot of time, particularly from a man who, like Carl Hager, has spent his life in apartments and must learn from scratch how to use tools, repair plaster and wiring, fix a leaky basement. Caught up in the business of getting ahead, hounded by household chores, tired and tense, a mobile father may absent himself almost totally from his boy's life.

Compare this with the situation in a typical farm family, which epitomizes the life of a small rural town—the traditional life of Americans when the nation was younger. In this family a boy was an essential part of his father's life. He was indispensable to the business of earning a living. His father showed him how to run farm machinery, how to care for animals, how to sow and reap and store and sell. He did these things with the boy not because he felt it was his duty but because he honestly needed the boy's help. He looked forward to a time when he could slowly step back from the farm's management and let his son take over.

In the typical mobile family, the business of earning a living is far removed from the life of the home. A boy has little or no connection with his father's work and may, indeed, have only the vaguest notion of what that work is. He doesn't help his father earn a living. He may instead, in his father's view, be a hindrance. The father wants to relax at night, to prepare himself for the next day's battle, but he feels obliged to haul himself wearily from his armchair and play with the boy. The boy is a distraction, extraneous to the important business of getting ahead.

The idealized farm family is, of course, the extreme opposite of the mobile suburban family. Rural towns have fathers who commute to jobs away from home, too. They seldom commute as far as suburban fathers, however, and typically their jobs are in the same town as their homes. Often they not only are home in the late afternoon, but also for lunch. More important, they are not striving so hard to get ahead. They are home more both in body and spirit.

Thus many a suburban boy grows up without enough father or father-substitute. He may seek guidance from older, uncontrolled boys at school, using them as his model. With no firm man's hand to guide and discipline him, he may drift toward delinquency like Alice Hager's boys, trying to win rewards from life by bullying, stealing and cheating. He may do badly in his schoolwork, for no one has insisted that he study or rewarded him well for doing so. He may take his mother as his model or fail to find any pattern for himself at all, becoming confused, ineffectual and weak like Fred Bright's boy.

The importance of firm fatherly guidance in a boy's life can be shown in numbers. In Bergen County's population at large, 11.5 per cent of homes have no father present. Among girl psychiatric patients in one sampling, the proportion with no father in the home was 10 per cent—roughly the same as in the general population, indicating that an absentee father is not usually a problem to a girl. But among boy psychiatric patients, 17 per cent were without fathers. And among delinquent boys, 30 per cent were fatherless.

The suburban boy's problems go still further than this. Compared to him, the typical small-town boy was doubly lucky. Not only did the rural lad have his father more. He needed his father less.

For one thing, the rural youngster was surrounded by a large family. When his father wasn't there, other men were: grandfathers, uncles, cousins. These were men whom the boy knew well. They were around all the time; they didn't merely come to visit at Christmas. They helped teach and manage the lad, just as female members of the family helped with the girls.

In the suburban family—the small, wandering unit that has detached itself from its kin—the whole burden of child management falls on the two parents, particularly on the mother. Grandpa is only an occasional visitor. He wants the boy to like him and doesn't propose to spoil their brief hours together by walloping him for misbehavior. Rather than helping to teach, grandparents of mobile youngsters are more likely to spoil. They are gift-bringers. The average child quickly learns they can be pushed around. In front of them, the most hair-raising display of rudeness, selfishness, temper and other obnoxious behavior will elicit only an indulgent chuckle. If the typical rural lad had put on such a display, Grandpa would have dusted him off smartly.

Not only did the small-town boy have more men about to guide him; he had society itself. He lived in an integrated town. He and his friends had common backgrounds. The majority of their families were old residents. There were community traditions, founded solidly in generations of time. Kids learned these traditions from each other. The newcomer or upstart was soon initiated into the rules. Year after year, older kids taught younger kids how to play immies, hold a baseball bat, build a treehouse. There was a dominant, clearly apparent pattern of male behavior for every boy to follow, a pattern maintained and policed by the boys themselves. These boys didn't need their fathers to be "pals."

In this town you could gather a group of boys at random, and for every one who didn't play mumbly-peg there'd be five or six who did. In other integrated towns there were other games, handed down from sixth-grader to third-grader in endless progression. But when you assemble a young group in a mobile suburban neighborhood and name a game such as mumbly-peg, you find five or six boys who don't know it for every one who does. These youngsters come from all over the country. They come with different cultural backgrounds, different interests and traditions, different games.

Unlike the stable-town kids, these mobile lads have no ready-made pattern of behavior to follow. They stand around on an idle afternoon, wondering what to do: an Irish Catholic boy from Boston, a Jewish youngster from New York, a Protestant kid from Nebraska. Each has his own idea of what constitutes a good time. Each has a playroom stacked high with manufactured games—the mobile world's substitute for mumbly-peg—which are supposed to develop his eye-hand coordination, encourage his self-expression and otherwise mix education with fun. These games seldom engage the boys' attention for long, for no one game has a large enough following; proficiency in it will not win the town-wide or school-wide applause that could be won with the games that the stable-town kids knew. Even if these mobile boys are lucky enough to have an open field nearby, or a park that isn't crowded with other kids, not all may even know how to play national games such as baseball.

They live in a disintegrated world. To a much bigger extent than the mumbly-peg kids, they have to devise their own games, make their own rules, build their own social structures. Since many of them lack firm control by their parents and the community, they may work out games and rules and structures that will get them into trouble.

This is why adults can't leave them alone as the kids of another era were left alone. Mothers must be amateur psychiatrists, fathers, pals. Boy Scout troops and Little League teams are a necessary substitute for the ready-made social structure of the integrated town. Without adults to help them, mobile suburban boys may have a hard time finding their way to successful manhood.

The "Gimme" Kids

Many of the problems of mobile youngsters, boys and girls alike, spring at least partly from the fact that the Disturbia society is too giving to them. The feeling is in the air that children and teen-agers should be fed a steady diet of love—by which is often meant coddling, protection from what is rough and unpleasant, showering with material treats. Many mobile parents have a notion that it may harm children's personalities in some way to say no to them, to frustrate them, repress their urges or spank them.

This excess of giving springs from many causes. One is prosperity itself. Studies by sociologists have shown that people of the laboring classes are typically less disciplined in their expression of emotions and more lenient with their children than people of middle-class backgrounds. During the past two decades, millions of people have risen from the lower to the middle classes and bought homes in the suburbs. They have brought their values with them, not having had time yet to absorb those of the older middle class. They have more money than they ever dreamed of having, and their tendency is to lavish it on themselves and their children in a less disciplined way than more seasoned members of the middle class.

This orgy of spending is not confined to climbers from the laboring classes, however. This is an era of plenty. A get-rich-quick atmosphere surrounds us. Around every corner is the possibility of a profitable investment, a quick promotion to a high salary bracket. In an age when the fruit of success seems waiting to be plucked from trees, the old middle-class virtues of hard work, thrift and patience—virtues which helped people get ahead in a less bountiful era—no longer seem so important. Many parents, even those of solid middle-class descent, fail to teach these virtues to their children. The times are easy, and parents want to make life easy for the young.

Another reason for the prevailing give-to-children attitude is the fact that so many mobile homes lack masculine firmness. The mother, trained for a more stable world in which self-assertiveness was not required of women, fails to discipline her children. Like Alice Hager she backs down to them, gives in to their tantrums and sulkiness, lets them do and have whatever they want.

The result is that the suburbs are full of obedient parents and spoiled, lazy, materialistic children. No one has cracked down on them. They take what they want because their parents have not insisted that they earn it. On unwrapping the last of a pile of Christmas packages, they look up and ask whether that is all. They go to museums—not to learn, but to make their parents buy them souvenirs. They are not used to hard work, nor are they willing to try it. They have not been made to feel a sense of responsibility. Their parents run errands for them, pick up after them, do their chores for them—if, indeed, chores are assigned at all. They are inconsiderate of others because they have not been made to consider anything but their own desires. Life has been given to them on a silver platter, and they expect the handout to continue. These are the gimme kids.

It is the gimme kids who most often become school behavior problems or delinquents in the suburbs. It has become fashionable to refer to such uncontrolled youngsters as having deep problems. A youngster himself, hauled before a teacher or a judge for some irresponsible act, will frequently hide behind the adult attitude and complain that he is sick, sick, sick—that what he does is not his fault but springs from a lack of love, perhaps, or too much violence on TV, or too much pornography. Usually the problem is not that oblique. All that is wrong, most often, is that the kid is spoiled.

Even parents who try to bring up their children with more firmness may have difficulty. Disturbia does not support firmness. A youngster whose playroom is not cluttered with expensive toys will complain bitterly because his friends' playrooms are. A parent who reprimands a neighbor's spoiled youngster for rudeness may later get an angry call from the neighbor. A boy or girl who wants to do well in school may find it hard because his friends, who are gimme kids, do not admire, and may even scorn, hard-working students. Thus parents who want their children to be self-reliant, considerate, responsible—who see that these are keys to success in the mobile world—may actually have to buck the community to do so. As the Connings and the Brights were ambushed by the older generation, these parents are ambushed by the younger. There are many hapless parents who are ambushed from both sides, with older and younger generations demanding that they give until they can hardly give any more.

The feeling in the air that one should constantly give to children, that one should gratify all their desires and allow them free expression of all their emotions, represents a swing of the pendulum to the opposite extreme from the Spartan attitude of men like Fred Bright. Fred bottled in his emotions, refused to admit pain. This had been his training as a boy. Tough men like Fred are bringing up children who admit pain freely—jump up and down screaming, in fact, at every small frustration.

Neither extreme seems to produce useful results. Children must be made to work for their rewards, to respect other people's rights and feelings, to restrain their emotions. They must learn to persevere, to be patient, to tolerate frustration. If they don't learn these things they are likely, sooner or later and in one form or another, to get into conflict with society.

Disturbia's obedient parents will have to get out of the habit of giving. They will have to recognize that children, once in a while, must be frustrated.

The Personality Crafts

Girls are luckier than boys. They have their mothers as models. Though a mother may be tired, tense and angry, she is at least there in the home. She can teach, at least by example, many of the things girls need to know as they grow to womanhood. The training may not be as good or as firm as that of the calm, happy small-town mother with her platoon of assistants, the grandmothers and aunts and cousins. But it is usually more thorough than the training of the suburban boy. The girl learns to cook and sew; she learns to be attentive.

Like the girl in the blighted city neighborhood, the suburban girl is less likely than her brother to drift into delinquency even though she lacks adequate parental guidance. In our society, teen-age girls are not pushed into being aggressive; they can win praise and husbands by being soft and feminine.

But they *are* expected to be popular, to have attractive personalities and many boyfriends. It is this, perhaps as much as anything else, that may land the suburban girl in trouble.

The personality crafts are studied throughout the length and breadth of the mobile world. Many mobile people have correctly seen that it is important in this world to be liked. It was important in the old integrated towns, too, but people there had years to get to know one another. In the mobile world, we move about; we continually meet new people and must make new friends. Alice Hager was one woman who failed to do so, and she became emotionally disturbed. Thus we are probably more concerned than small-town people were with the impression we make on others.

Small-town people liked one another for qualities of basic goodness and service to society: kindness and usefulness. These are still qualities of superior importance. But many mobile people, in their impatience to make everything happen quickly, have become concerned instead with superficialities, with appearances. The personality crafts are a part of the façade syndrome. Just as a mobile man buys a house and car beyond his means, to create a façade of wealth before the wealth exists, so do many mobile people try to make themselves seem what they have not yet become. They study the personality crafts.

Fred Bright, for example, took a course in personality development. He hoped he would learn quickly thereby to impress people as a confident, dynamic young executive. He could have accomplished the same end more thoroughly, and felt much more secure about it, if he had concentrated instead on learning to do his job well—if he had studied how best to serve the business society to which he belonged. But this wasn't quick enough for Fred. He didn't want to take time to learn his job—he wanted to move up to another job as fast as possible. So he concentrated on learning the appearance of confidence rather than on building confidence itself.

Like Fred, many mobile people search endlessly for some magic formula that will produce personal magnetism overnight, some jar or package of Instant Popularity. Speed is the essential thing; thus they work on the surface rather than on the slower-building fundamentals. They take public-speaking courses, ignoring what every good speaking instructor points out during the first lesson: that the real secret is having something interesting to say. At cocktail parties the tendency is to chatter brightly, never mind about what. Surface brightness is the thing cultivated, rather than a well-stocked mind—which will draw as many listeners but takes longer to develop.

In the same way that they seek popularity for themselves, many suburban parents, like Eve Bright, seek it for their children—particularly for their daughters. Girls are urged to begin studying the personality crafts early, particularly those which will one day serve to attract the right man. A girl who doesn't have a date every weekend is thought somehow to be unsuccessful, even though she is yet in her early teens. Many a suburban mother becomes exasperated when her daughter occasionally shows a preference for reading rather than for learning social graces. In the upper income groups, it is not uncommon for lavish parties to be thrown for boys and girls who have not even reached puberty. A girl who is popular is her parents' pride; they wear her like a badge.

All this is well meant and springs from need. The mobile world can be a lonely place to one who cannot make friends. But, as everywhere else in climber society, there is too much emphasis on speed, on building a façade rather than the real thing. A girl who starts dating in her late teens will have time enough to become popular. If she is not physically unattractive, has an alert, interested mind, and is involved with well-guided youngsters in useful activities, she will suffer no disadvantage for having failed to learn the crafts at the age of ten or twelve. Children whose parents push them into heterosexual contacts at that early an age are likely to drift into trouble. By the time they reach the mid-teens, they are often old hands at petting and perhaps more.

The high-school girl who becomes pregnant is often badly confused. She went out with boys because her mother wanted her to. Consequences resulted which she felt powerless to prevent and which, in her view, her mother might have foreseen. But now that the final results are in, mother is angry. Why?

Attitudes toward sex today are more lenient than they were fifty or even twenty-five years ago. In some respects this liberation has been useful. Fright and frigidity in women, the bugaboo of many marriages earlier in the century, is becoming less common. The majority of modern girls bring to their honeymoons a more complete sexual education than their grandmothers or mothers typically did. Most have had some sex experience—at least petting, if not full intercourse—before marriage. Many have talked frankly of the subject with their mothers. For those with unanswered questions, there are available many excellent books on intercourse techniques.

Many teen-agers, however, have taken this liberation too much to heart. They have aped their parents' notion that it is inadvisable to repress urges. The gimme kids, particularly, feel that they may do anything they like without thought of the consequences —for, in their lives, there have usually been no consequences.

But the joys of genital gymnastics are not essential to the enrichment of a teen-ager's education. A tropical-island society in which food may be had for the plucking can—and some of these societies do—condone sexual liberty without marriage. But in our harder world, where food and shelter must be produced with toil and sweat, society must maintain stricter regulations to insure that nobody produces children who isn't prepared to support them. Our society is not generally greatly concerned over a discreet affair between a mature unmarried man and woman, for they can be presumed to know what they are doing. Teen-agers, however, particularly in this era of the gimme kids, cannot always be counted on to look forward to future consequences or to be responsible for them.

Teen-age marriage is a poor solution to the problem of overemphasis on sex. Many such marriages are unsuccessful; the younger the couple, the less stable the marriage. A marriage of a teen-age bride is roughly three times as likely to end in divorce as one in which the bride is aged twenty-two to twenty-four. This is particularly disturbing since forty-seven per cent of the brides of 1959 were nineteen or under.

Success and Failure in School

Most climber parents are keenly aware of the need for education in the mobile world—not simply training for a single vocation, but a broad, general education. In the rural community of old, a youngster often could make a fairly good guess about the future course of his life. The harness-maker's son figured he'd probably be a harness-maker; the girl guessed she'd be a housewife. But the mobile world is a vastly more uncertain place. Circumstances and people change. A good basic schooling is essential to equip a boy or girl for fast footwork in later life.

Diversity is one of the keys to success in the mobile world. The salesman must know something of personnel relations in case he is pushed up to an executive job. The executive must understand the scientific principles behind his company's products. The husband must have a knowledge of child psychology so that he can help his wife in the home. The housewife must have a career skill in case she is widowed or divorced. Education creates diversity as well as preparing the student for his basic career goals.

Unhappily the mobile society sometimes frustrates the effort to get an education. Probably the most common problem is that represented by the gimme kids. No one has insisted that they study; they have been showered with gifts whether they studied or not. No one has shown them the value and purposes of education. They are not willing to work. "We won't study," they tell the nation's educators, "unless you make the lesson so entertaining that it won't be work." Some schools, like parents, have been obedient to the gimme kids' demands. Instead of cracking down on the kids and making them work, as most teachers still do, some have wracked their brains to fill the classroom sessions with stunts and gimmicks. But sugar-coated education is self-defeating. Part of the value of education is the sheer experience of work, learning the habit of sticking with a task even though it *isn't* fun. Children who lack this training are likely to have difficulty making a place for themselves later in the competitive mobile world.

The gimme kid may be an anti-student. He may show off to his friends by deliberately defying his teachers; he feels that his refusal to study makes him a hero. He partakes of the get-rich-quick attitude in the prosperous society around him: success can be achieved without effort. His attitude may infect others in the classroom. He and his friends scorn learning as kid stuff, jeer at those who do study, tempt wavering students into their camp.

Another common problem is that of a boy or girl who has been moved from one school to another as his or her parents climbed. Each time he made friends; each time he was pulled away from them. If he is an unassertive youngster who finds friend-making difficult, he may have severe emotional trouble on the second or third move—sometimes even on the first. He arrives at the new school and finds friendship cliques already formed. Like adult clubs, they may be inhospitable to newcomers.

The newcomer, if she is a girl, may react to this situation by getting into sex trouble. If she has previously had a good deal of dating experience, if she has learned personality crafts and feels fairly sure of herself with boys, she may try to use sex as a lever for gaining entree into a clique. She may quite deliberately create for herself a reputation of not being prudish, hoping that the boys, at least, will give her the fun and companionship she craves.

Or the newcomer may simply abandon the effort to make friends. He or she may retire home, perhaps to withdraw into the world of books.

Either way the youngster's schoolwork is likely to suffer. The girl who chooses the first course will probably find most favor among the delinquents, gimme kids and anti-students. The youngster who chooses the second may fall into equally bad trouble. More than younger children, teen-agers need to be surrounded by a peer group, friends with whom to have fun and from whom to get recognition and applause. The applause of parents and teachers is not enough for the teen-ager. The lonely boy or girl may grow too unhappy to study. Falling grades may add to the emotional turmoil; it becomes self-feeding. Occasionally teenagers caught in this kind of trap will make half-hearted, but sometimes successful, attempts at suicide.

A third common problem is that of the boy or girl whose family lacks the tradition of respect for education. Such a youngster often doesn't respect it himself. He isn't motivated to study. Even if he does become motivated—perhaps by an inspiring teacher, a friend or friends with the climber's fever—the going may still be tough. He wants to go to college, but his father wants him to abandon education after high school and come into the family construction business. The argument may make studying difficult. To defy one's parents' wishes, to have one's achievements in learning met by indifference or worse, to be denied funds or given them only grudgingly—these things create stress.

The youngster whose parents are themselves not well educated may also lack the cultural enrichment that many other boys and girls have. A child of educated parents hears them talking of many things; they are equipped to answer many of his questions; they get him into the habit of thinking, inquiring, looking facts up in books. When he goes to school the subjects presented to him are not brand-new. He has a broad base on which to build his understanding of them. Thus his schoolwork comes to him more easily.

Many children are well motivated to learn, but lack cultural enrichment and find the task difficult. Others, gimme kids, may have plenty of enrichment in their homes but may lack the needed motivation to buckle down and study. Parents who wish their youngsters to do well in school must provide both enrichment and firmness.

Alec Green, whose story follows, was a boy who had little

affectionate guidance, enrichment or firmness. His story illustrates many of the problems of middle-class children and teen-agers in Disturbia.

The Joyrider

He wears a brilliant silk basketball jacket, though he doesn't play basketball or any other sport very well. He smokes cigarettes to make himself look tough, but his fingers tremble. When with his gang he has an arrogant swagger and an insolent gaze. But when you face him alone he has a furtive look; he avoids your eyes and shuffles his feet. With his friends around him, on the street corner or in a car, he makes remarks about sex to girls passing by. Alone with a girl he is awkward and shy. He is in trouble with the police for joyriding in stolen cars with his friends. He is rude to his mother, enjoys bullying younger and weaker kids. But he will back down very quickly when anyone his own size makes a threatening move in his direction.

This is the typical suburban delinquent—all brass and brashness outside, soft inside. He is not the kind of delinquent who usually makes headlines. The headline delinquent is more often the lower-class boy from a slum or semi-slum area, and he is more often a really tough young man. He wears a leather jacket because it lasts longer than silk and won't tear so easily. He is ready to fight anybody at the drop of a hat. He has known hunger and privation, and he correctly sees that, if he is to make a place for himself in a difficult world, he must fight hard. His mistake is that he is fighting for the wrong things with the wrong weapons.

The delinquent from the mobile suburban society is not that way at all. He has all the food he can eat, all the physical comforts he can ask for. He may have his own car and more spending money than he knows what to do with. He could have college ahead of him and a chance at a bright career if he would think about his future and apply himself. Life has been handed to him like a gift. Yet he is unhappy and frustrated, and has few friends.

The story of young Alec Green shows why. Alec's father, Burt, was an accountant. He was badly overworked, tense, tired and irritable. Severe headaches tormented him; acute indigestion made him unpleasant company at many meals. He had come from an Old World home in which his own father was undisputed head of the household, and he himself exhibited some of the same patriarchal bossiness. Both he and his father had worked hard to get ahead. His father had started as a cutter in a garment factory and had moved up to establish his own clothing business. Burt had gone to college at night to learn business administration and accountancy. His long, hard struggle upward had left its mark on his disposition. When he came home in the evening he wanted only to be served his meal and left alone. He spoke gruffly or not at all to his wife, Alec's mother, and sometimes, when his head hurt and his business worries bothered him more than usual, he barked at her rudely.

Thus young Alec saw that it was permissible to push Mom around. She was a quiet, calm woman with a sweet disposition and a vast capacity for forgiveness. She was a well-educated college graduate who believed in the power of reason and "talking things out." When her husband was discourteous to her she "understood," him, appreciating the tension under which he worked. When Alec misbehaved as a little boy she wondered whether "something was bothering him." She tried to reason with him gently instead of firmly enforcing the rules. When he was extra bad she threatened to tell his father, but both she and Alec learned after a while that the threat meant little. If Burt, dragging himself wearily through the front door at night, was met with a recital of domestic problems, he usually reacted angrily. "Leave me out of it!" he would grumble. "I have problems enough of my own!"

For Burt believed that the raising of his son was a domestic problem and hence entirely his wife's concern. He worked like a dog all day trying to make his family a living. The least he could expect, he felt, was peace and quiet when he got home.

Burt was trying to live in a new society by rules that were developed for an older one. In the old stable communities a man could, without risking unfortunate consequences, wash his hands of responsibility for raising his children. For his wife had other helpers than he. She was supported in her domestic and child-raising tasks by the larger family around her and by the firm rule-enforcement of the community itself. In the nuclear mobile family, the wife whose husband refuses to help must often carry the entire burden by herself. Few women, particularly ineffectual intellectuals like Alec's mother, are prepared to take on so huge a responsibility.

Even on weekends, Burt would have little to do with his son. There was much to do around the house and yard, and Alec got in the way and slowed things down. The words "no" and "don't" and "go away" were the most frequent communication from father to son. If Burt had been a little more patient, he would have discovered that Alec could actually help with the chores. Even a six-year-old boy can do a fine job with a power lawn-mower or a paint brush, provided someone takes the time to teach him how. But since nobody taught Alec, he was clumsy and no help at all.

The result of all this was that Alec was filled with anger. Like most small boys he wanted to do what his father did. He wanted to learn how to saw wood, drill holes, paint, slop cement, light the barbecue fire. His father had been his hero; he wanted to be close to him, help him, learn from him, win his admiration. But Burt pushed the boy away. Alec was hurt and resentful.

Still he imitated his father—what little of his father he saw—for that is how boys learn to be men. He copied Burt's discourteous, rather domineering ways without copying any of the more useful traits that he seldom saw. In time he became a caricature of his father: arrogant, bullying, rude.

Both his father and mother wanted to be good parents, and they felt this meant that they had to give Alec everything. They didn't want him to be deprived. As is typical in the mobile society, they put too much importance on money and merchandise. They felt that this was what Alec must have. The playroom and cellar were cluttered with toys; the garage with bikes and wagons and scooters. Every time Alec demanded something else, he got it. Burt thought he was being a good father by giving his family an abundant supply of money—more and more each year.

Alec was not learning that, to achieve success in the mobile world, you must produce. His parents did not insist that he study hard in school, do chores, earn some of the money before he got a new bike. Alec was not being made familiar with the system of rewards that the world doles out: rewards for those who produce, but not for those who don't. He had been punished by angry snarls for trying to help his father and learn things from him. He had been rewarded with toys for shouting, screaming and stamping his foot. The system was topsy-turvy. From Alec's point of view, it didn't seem to make any difference whether you learned or not, whether you were considerate or not. The way to get things was simply to take them, to be rough and tough.

Yet Alec was not a tough boy. His mother, knowing no other way, tried to raise him as she herself had been raised for a more stable world. She protected him too much. She worried constantly that he might fall, get a scratch or bruise, catch a cold. She wouldn't let him play outdoors in cold weather, chauffeured him to school when it rained. When he got in fights with other boys—which, in his arrogance, he was bound to do often—she dashed out of the house and chased them away, or called their mothers and demanded that they be warned off. When he got a minor cut she hugged and kissed him, so that he exaggerated the pain and cried for more sympathy. He was not learning to stand on his own feet, to endure. Alec was soft.

If there had been a man about the house he would probably not have stood for any of this. The man need only have been there in the evenings, as long as he had been willing to listen to the day's problems and spend time helping to solve them. But there was no such man in Alec's house. Things might even have been different if Alec had had male teachers. But all his teachers were women. Or if he had formed a close relationship with an athletic coach. But Alec was not proficient in sports. Or if he had had a male Boy Scout leader or swimming instructor. But in Alec's community the men were too tired and too busy; most after-school activities were managed by women.

What Alec needed was a man's guiding hand on his shoulder and, once in a while, on the seat of his pants. He needed someone to teach him how to live successfully with others, how to make his way in the world without stepping on people and, in turn, being stepped on. He needed someone to reward him for learning—not only with merchandise but with companionship, praise, a man-to-man slap on the back—and to punish him fairly but firmly, guide him away from troublesome kinds of behavior that would not be useful to him in his later life. This is how boys learn to take on the responsibilities and win the joys of manhood. They can't learn these things by themselves, for our society is complex and rapidly growing more so. They must be taught.

It is a rare woman who can do this teaching adequately. Alec's mother couldn't, any more than Alice Hager or Eve Bright.

Alec took into his teens the attitude that the world owed him a living. He had not been given a good reason to feel otherwise. He felt no need to work. When he wanted something, the world would give. There was no reason to study in school. There was no reason to learn useful social conduct, ways of making people like you, methods of cooperation and compromise. The world was his, to do with as he pleased. Alec saw life as a joyride—for free, for fun.

He began by stealing money from his mother's purse. She noticed that the money was gone, gently asked him about it. He lied glibly. She did not press the inquiry, and she didn't tell Burt for fear of upsetting him.

It was easy. You just took what you wanted, did what you wanted. Life was indeed a joyride.

When he was about fourteen, Alec had an adventure with fire. Fire has a powerful fascination for many people, and boys seem more fascinated than most. The wise father recognizes this in his boy and makes sure that the youngster has a safe outlet for his fire-lighting urge. Like any other potentially dangerous urge, it can be turned in safe, useful channels much more easily and surely than it can be quashed—if, indeed, it can be quashed at all. The wise father doesn't tell his son: "You must not play with fire." Instead he says: "You can light all the fires we need as long as your mother or I am here, but you must never light a fire when we're not here." With adult instruction and supervision even a five-year-old can safely be allowed to light a barbecue fire, burn trash and leaves. In this way he satisfies his urge. If he isn't allowed to do it with supervision, one day he may try to do it without. The results could be disastrous.

It is the same with alcohol, sex, guns, cars. Youngsters are curious about these things and are likely to experiment with them, given the opportunity, whether or not they have parental permission. The parent who satisfies a teen-ager's curiosity about these things, teaches him how to use them properly and without harmful consequences, gives him firm rules in their use, is likely to achieve better results than either the parent who tries to quash the curiosity or the parent who allows complete liberty.

Alec's father had never had the time or patience to teach Alec about fire. As he grew up, Alec and his friends played with fire a number of times, lighting small bonfires in the town park or in someone's garage. In their early teens they finally learned what fire can do.

It became known to them one night that some of the neighborhood girls were having a slumber party. Alec and two of his friends went to the house where the party was being held, intending to perpetrate mischief of some kind. They crept around the house, trying to look into the windows. Then Alec noticed that a cellar window was open. Wouldn't it be fun, he suggested, to light a small but very smoky fire down there on the concrete floor? It would fill the house with smoke and scare all the girls outside.

They squirmed through the window and into the cellar. They found some newspapers and old rags, made a small pile in the middle of the floor and lit it. It flared up much faster and higher than they had expected. Sparks flew into the dry wooden joists above. By the time they realized their mistake, tongues of flame were bursting out in the subflooring.

They held a short, fierce debate: warn the girls or simply get out? Alec was hysterical with fright. He bolted for the window and began scrambling through it. One friend followed him. The other stayed behind long enough to shout "Fire!" until the girls heard; then he, too, made for the window. By the time he was out and running, the girls were also beginning to run from the house. Some of them saw and recognized him.

Fortunately the owner of the house had a fire-extinguisher unit. He ran down and smothered the flames before any serious damage was done. Then he let the matter drop. He didn't want to antagonize the boys' parents, whom he didn't know. He had had experience before with chastising other people's uncontrolled children and having the parents land on him, demanding that he stop mistreating and frightening their poor little kids. If this had been an integrated community he wouldn't have hesitated to handle the matter more firmly. In such a community there would have been a single clear set of rules on child behavior. Everyone would have known the rules, and all would have cooperated in enforcing them. In Disturbia, no parent knows which rules the parents next door are operating by.

Alec continued to behave as the whim seized him. One night, he and some older boys noticed that a car parked on a neighbor's driveway had keys in the ignition lock. They thought it would be fun to borrow the car for an hour or so. They drove through town at seventy-five miles an hour. A police patrol car stopped them, and the whole story came out. But this neighbor didn't press charges either. He, too, was a giver-to-children; he didn't want to make things hard on the boy. He was also afraid of having trouble with Alec's parents.

When Alec's mother heard of the incident she sighed sadly. His father was too tired to do more than merely shout at him for a few minutes. Alec learned, once more, that he could get away with almost anything.

The school authorities were similarly hesitant about cracking down on Alec and other undisciplined youngsters. Every now and then a teacher or the principal, harried beyond endurance by rudeness, disruptive behavior in class, refusal to work or other defiance of the rules, lost patience and subjected a gimme kid to a really smart dressing-down or a heavy assignment of after-school duty. Often such an affair was followed by the appearance at the school of an enraged or tearful mother who would complain that her little one was being treated unfairly, or that the school authorities did not understand his deep problems. The school people's hands were tied. The community was not supporting their attempt at firmness. Teachers once used to make disobedient students straighten out in a hurry by threatening to call in parents. Today, in many cases, the threat is meaningless.

Alec and his friends in the wolf pack bragged to each other a lot about their conquests of girls. Few, in truth, had made such conquests. Alec usually felt lame and tongue-tied when he was alone with a girl. The girls he liked most—the ones from the country-club set, who had all kinds of parties and all kinds of fun—seemed to consider him dirt beneath their feet. He and his friends generally had to be satisfied with second-choice girls from the lower strata of the school's complex society. But they pretended to each other that these were the girls they really wanted; these were the girls who, it was reputed, "put out." By the time he was sixteen, Alec had petted to climax a few times but had never had complete intercourse, despite his frequent loud suggestions to the contrary. The truth was, he didn't quite know how intercourse was accomplished. Certain mechanical problems bothered him. These are things that a boy can learn from his father, but Alec had long since ceased trying to learn anything from Burt. He hesitated to ask his friends, for they would then know how inexperienced he was, and his status among them would sink. (In all probability, many of them were wondering about the same things themselves.)

Alec's trouble with sex illustrates a typical problem of many mobile suburban families. There is not enough time, in these families, for the long, leisurely, probing talk by which people can settle problems and have questions answered. A man's discussion with his wife about money, a father's with his son about sex, are likely to have a hurried, deadlined feeling about them. They are also likely to be attended by embarrassment and tenseness, for these are people who are not used to holding long, serious conversations with each other. In the less hurried stable world, a father and son may have spent long hours working in the fields with each other, or fishing, or simply walking. They had more time. The habit of comfortable, companionable talk was more likely to be ingrained in them. The subject of sex (which a boy often learned about, in any case, by watching farm animals) could be brought up with a minimum of hemming and hawing and in a natural atmosphere. But when the hard-working suburban father decides the time has come to explain about sex—how to control one's urges so as not to become a victim of them, harm others and get into trouble—he may have to make a formal appointment with his son. As the two sit down opposite one another, they squirm. They have never done this before. They are strangers.

As Alec and his friends used the protection of their group to make themselves brave in other areas, they began using it for sex. Crowded around a phone booth, they called girls up and said things that none would have dared to say face-to-face, alone. Together, never alone, they picked up girls at movies or bowling alleys. They were using the psychological principle that an individual can face fear more confidently when he is accompanied by others, whether or not they are braver than he. This principle is useful in helping fearful children, shy wives and anxious psychiatric patients. But it can also be used in harmful ways, as in a teen-age gang.

One night Alec and two of his friends went to the home of a more or less willing fifteen-year-old girl to conduct what was known in their circle as a "gang-bang." It was Alec's first attempt at complete sexual intercourse. Worried that he would do something wrong, afraid to ask advice, tense and frightened, he botched his chance ludicrously. The experience left him frustrated and miserable, full of new doubts about his sexual capacities.

The party was still in progress when the girl's parents unexpectedly came home. Hearing them open the door, the girl quickly devised a way to protect her reputation and escape blame. She screamed, "Rape!"

Thus Alec came before a juvenile court. Reporters writing of the case and others discussing it pictured Alec and his friends as, variously, hard-boiled young toughs or deeply disturbed boys who should be handled with love and pity. They were, in fact, neither. They were simply soft, spoiled, undisciplined gimme kids.

Gimme kids *can* be directed into more constructive and wholesome patterns of living, as we shall see in Part Two. But the task is a slow, arduous one. How much better it would be if parents could forestall the "gimme" problem with firmer discipline in the home.

CHAPTER 7

The Single

Foursomes, Twosomes and Lonesomes

In great areas of suburban territory, the single man or woman is something of a rarity. The suburbs are not designed for the single, but for married couples and their children. There are whole vast housing developments, in fact, in which the adult population is not only predominantly married but also predominantly within the same ten-year age bracket. The random mixture of age groups and marital states which is typical of the integrated town, and which helps make life happy in that town, is absent in many suburban neighborhoods. (This apparent sameness of suburban neighbors has given rise to a notion among non-suburbanites that these neighborhoods are "homogenous." Except in age, marital status, income and house design they are considerably less homogenous than the neighborhoods of integrated communities—and in this very fact lie many of the suburbs' emotional problems.)

To the bachelor or bachelor-girl who comes into a metropolitan area to work, the most interesting place to live is usually the central city. The city offers a full, exciting life. This is where you find bright lights, concerts and museums and theatres, universities and vocational schools, cultural and hobby groups, other bachelors and bachelor-girls. Also, from a purely practical point of view, why commute farther than you have to? A single man or woman, having no need to worry about schools and safe play areas for children, may, with a little luck, find an apartment only ten or fifteen minutes away from the plant or office.

It is hard to live a gay unmarried life while residing in a suburban house or apartment. In fact, it is easy to become quite lonely. All around are married couples. Their spare-time activities often are based on multiples of the number two. They enjoy bridge, dancing and other activities designed for even-numbered groups of people. Marriedness dominates the community atmosphere. Little or nothing is done to provide social activities for single people beyond high-school age. Even when the bachelor is invited to a cocktail party or a barbecue, the talk may not be interesting or even intelligible to him. It may embarrass him. To hear women frankly and publicly discussing their experiences in childbirth, while perhaps boring to husbands, can be shocking to the unmarried man or woman. If he hastily leaves the women and seeks refuge in a group of men, he is likely to find an equally esoteric discussion in progress. The prices of homes and the best way to splice BX cable are not topics of discussion on which the bachelor can usually hope to scintillate.

Thus, by and large, single men and women gravitate to the central city. There are some, however, who find themselves stranded in the suburbs. They are primarily men and women who were born or went to school in these particular towns and simply stayed, living with their parents, when they became adults. It is in this latter group—the stay-homers—that a good deal of emotional trouble arises.

It arises particularly among the men. While the most frequently troubled *married* people in the mobile suburb are young women, the most frequently troubled single people are young men.

It is not hard to understand why. The single man's life in the mobile world is typically harder than the single girl's. He must compete, and he will be under stress if circumstances or his nature make competition difficult for him. The single girl in American mobile society can often avoid the need to compete, except for a husband—and she is likely to find that a gentle, feminine nature is as useful in that particular arena as a stronger, more assertive personality. If she is moderately attractive and moderately lucky, life for her can be balmy until she gets married.

The Husbandless

The single woman typically grows troubled when she begins to fear that she won't marry. The upset grows stronger as age advances and the law of supply and demand makes marriage progressively less likely. This is probably the most common precipitator of emotional trouble among single women in their thirties and older. Among a group of fifty-four single men and sixty-one single women who were psychiatric office patients, forty-six per cent of women's problems were precipitated by unhappy love affairs, as compared to twenty-two per cent of the single men's difficulties.

Marriage is still the primary career goal of most women. Normally unable to earn incomes as high as men, the husbandless may feel economically insecure. If most of their friends are married and climbing they may feel lonely, particularly if they live in the suburbs. Stress piles up as the years roll by and the chances of winning a husband diminish.

When single women do become disturbed, their troubles are often more severe and more intractable than those of married women. The reasons are basically the same as those in the situation of the widow or divorcee. The single woman has no husband to provide for her. This being a mobile world, she typically has no large, close family to fall back upon. Her sisters, cousins, and friends may be far away and scattered. She doesn't want to burden any of them by asking them to support her. She feels she is her own sole source of support. Typically she is in the lower white-collar job group—one of the groups with high mortality in heart disease. If she becomes sick and unable to work for a long period, she may fear that her job will disappear. Thus her chances of quick recovery from emotional disturbance are not usually as good as a wife's.

The table below portrays this fact. It tells the story of one hundred and eight married women and seventy-five single women who were admitted to the psychiatric division of a state hospital in a six-month period. It shows what percentage of women in each age and marital category were still in the hospital at the period's end.

	Young (18-44)	*Middle-Aged* (45-59)	*Older* (60+)
Married	29% still in	37.5% still in	50% still in
Single	39% " "	53% " "	79% " "

It appears that there are two things that may help a woman recover quickly from a severe disturbance: being young, and being married.

The Chronic Losers

The single man, meanwhile, may be running into trouble while the single girl is still enjoying the springtime of life. The fact that he is a suburban stay-homer and the fact that he is unmarried may both stem from a lack of aggressiveness in him. Throughout his life he has been out-competed. He has had a hard time getting an education, a job and a girl. The chronic loser is the most common type of disturbed single man in the mobile suburbs.

His difficulty may have begun in grade school or high school. The successful student is the boy whose parents have shown him that rewards are won in our society by self-discipline, perseverance and an attitude of considerate self-assertiveness. He has learned that there is a middle ground between a pushy, inconsiderate aggressiveness, which antagonizes people and makes life more difficult than necessary, and a lack of protective self-assertiveness, which allows one to be walked upon. He has learned that hard work and competition are built into the mobile world and can hardly be avoided. He does well in his schoolwork, is liked by his classmates of both sexes, learns useful skills in constructive groups, capably shoulders responsibilities.

For various reasons, another boy may fail to learn these lessons. He may either drift toward a delinquent way of life, like Alec Green, or simply grow up weak like Fred Bright's boy, unfit for the rough-and-tumble of the mobile life.

Unless someone helps him straighten out his attitudes, these traits stay with him as he grows to manhood. The delinquent youth may become a delinquent man. He may try to bully and steal his way through life, usually with painful results to himself and others. The weak boy may become a weak man, a chronic loser. He often fails to get married, for more competitive men steal his girls away—if indeed he has any to begin with.

There are many reasons why men choose to remain single. Most single men lead happy, rewarding lives. It is the man whose unmarried status results largely from his weakness who most commonly has emotional trouble. All kinds of stresses are on him. His friends have moved up and away from him. Better-educated, more aggressive men get the jobs he wants. He may try to improve his education by going to college, but the poor study habits and emotional interference that defeated him in high school will probably defeat him here. He may try to keep up with his more able competitors by taking on a standard or an even heavier burden of college courses, thus overloading himself. Often he flunks out, and another piece of his self-confidence erodes away.

Chronic losers are often young men whose parents have been unable to help them adjust to the society in which they live. Many are sons of foreign-born parents. The father of such a boy doesn't teach him American sports and may not even encourage him to learn them, so that he is denied this means of winning recognition and gaining confidence. His parents may not have absorbed the American middle-class tradition of respecting education, and may not support him enough in his efforts at school. Even if they are eager to have him learn they may not be equipped to help him. Their English vocabulary may be limited, and they may not be familiar with many of the subjects taught in American schools. The boy, confused about whether to copy his father's foreign mannerisms and attitudes or those of his classmates, may never quite decide and may remain awkward. His schoolmates may think of him as a little strange, may poke fun at him and continually undermine his efforts at gaining self-assurance.

Sons of foreign-born fathers bulk large among emotionally disturbed single men in the suburbs. In a group of single girls who were psychiatric patients, ten per cent had foreign-born fathers. In a group of single men patients, fifty-three per cent had fathers who were born overseas. There were no differences in the birthplaces of their mothers. The feminine role can be taught as well by European-born as American-born mothers.

Troubled single men vary widely in their symptoms. Some become deeply depressed. Others, feeling that society is persecuting them (which in a way it is), get the quite understandable idea that this persecution is deliberate and specific, rather than merely a random phenomenon of the competitive world. Many get into trouble with the law for sex acts such as exhibitionism, voyeurism, homosexuality and writing pornographic letters.

The case study that follows is an examination of this kind of man—in this case a voyeur, or peeping Tom. He is a man who, in a quieter and less competitive society, might easily have made a useful, happy life for himself. In the mobile world he failed to make the grade.

The Cultural Squeeze

A confused and unhappy young man was picked up by police one summer night in a rural Pennsylvania town, far from his home in Bergen County. A housewife. sitting on her porch in the dark, had seen him climb onto a low roof across the street and peer into a second-floor window. Slits of light showed that the venetian blind covering the window was not fully closed. Inside the room, a woman was undressing for bed.

The housewife on the porch called the police. They hauled the young man off the roof. He was tall and thin, had big protruding ears and a weak, pale face. He gave his age as twenty-six and his name as Tom Krazinkow. Stuttering and incoherent, he tried to explain that he was an FBI agent on the track of a sinister Communist spy ring. The woman he had been watching possessed the formula for making a new explosive, deadlier than the hydrogen bomb, out of ordinary household items such as talcum powder and salt. Halfheartedly he asked the police to let him go and keep the matter secret; the fate of the nation depended on it.

The police kindly offered to let him stay in their jail that night, safe from the enemy. The peaceful Pennsylvania community was shocked. A dangerous madman had come into their midst. They could have been murdered in their beds! Their daughters weren't safe even at home, let alone on the streets!

In truth, however, Tom Krazinkow was one of the most harmless of men. He sought this outlet for his sexual urges because he lacked the aggressiveness to satisfy the need through normal methods. For Tom Krazinkow was a chronic loser. He was a man who had been trampled and left behind by the mobile society.

Tom had lived all his life with his two younger sisters in Bergen County. His father was a European-born mechanic, a big, beefy, red-faced man with a heavy accent, loud voice and strong opinions. He spent much of his free time in a neighborhood bar with his friends from the factory, or in a club of men from the old country. Tom's mother was a small, nervous woman who cultivated a façade of intellectualism. She was given to espousing strange new causes and philosophies. She belonged to a society whose members composed and read to each other weird poetry, incomprehensible to outsiders. They claimed to understand each other and gained a feeling of superiority from the fact that nobody else did. At one time in her life she had admired the philosophic ideals of Communism, but since that had ceased to be fashionable, she had turned her attention to Yoga and Zen Buddhism. Since she seldom did more than study the surface features of these things, their façades, she seldom understood them well. She was quite sensitive, easily reduced to tears by supposed slights.

With her husband out of the house much of the time, she took on the major burden of bringing up her children. She subscribed to the popular modern notion that a child should be allowed to "find himself"—that adults shouldn't exert their will on him for fear of damaging his personality and undermining his self-confidence. She avoided guiding her children and encouraging them into constructive interests. She liked to tell her friends that the children were surrounded by a permissive atmosphere in which their personalities could flower without restraint. Actually her sensitiveness produced in Tom continued anxiety that he might do something to hurt her feelings.

She did not stop to ask herself how a child is to "find himself" without being shown where to look. A youngster without firm adult guidance is a ship without a rudder. Lacking the intelligence and experience to do it for himself, he needs adults to introduce him to constructive interests, to help him learn, to help him develop self-discipline for his life in the competitive mobile world. He doesn't just discover these things for himself. The mobile society does not automatically teach them to a child—it may, in fact, teach just the opposite.

Tom's mother was worried that her children's self-confidence might suffer if she disciplined and guided them firmly. Actually she was risking more damage to their self-confidence by failing to be firm with them. For self-confidence does not exist in a vacuum. It comes into existence only as a result of efforts that have succeeded. Tom was not succeeding in his efforts because his parents were not making sure that he tried hard. His mother allowed him to give up when discouraged in schoolwork or games instead of urging him on to greater effort. He was not learning perseverance, the willingness to stick with a task until it was finished and rewards could be garnered. He was not learning to tolerate frustration. Either he got his rewards immediately or he quit. Thus he was not building in himself an awareness that he could achieve his aspirations by his own efforts, and naturally he had little of the related self-confidence.

With his mother hovering anxiously about, waiting for him to find himself, Tom merely drifted nervously. He had no hobbies, played no sports, was seldom interested in any one thing for more than a few days. His grades in school were below average and barely passing, for nobody was guiding or encouraging him or giving him the necessary mild prodding. The teachers tried; but in motivating children to learn, teachers need support from home. In Tom's case they lacked this support and eventually gave Tom up as a hopeless case.

Tom was a bed-wetter until he was sixteen, and even after that he lost control of his bladder in periods of tension. This, again, was a matter of learning self-discipline. Fearing that she would frustrate him if she tried too hard to train him, his mother mostly waited for him to train himself. He didn't. Children learn bladder control when they are shown a good reason for doing so—when they are rewarded for waking up dry and mildly but firmly disapproved when they lose control. An affectionate hug or a pat on the back is usually enough reward. After a few months of trying, the youngster teaches himself to wake up whenever the nerve endings in the sphincter muscle, the valve that closes the bladder, signal by hurting that the vessel is full. The process becomes automatic. The average adult goes to bed fully confident that he will wake up dry; he doesn't need to think about it.

Tom had a hard time learning even this much discipline. It was made even harder for him by the fact that he was tense. The bladder is a muscle, and like other muscles will often tighten under emotional stress. This tightening squeezes liquid against the sphincter, urging the valve to open even when the bladder is not full. When people are acutely frightened—when under enemy fire in wartime, for example—they will sometimes lose control even though wide awake. Thus the chronically tense youngster has more difficulty with his bladder than the tranquil, happy child.

Tom's tension sprang from many causes. One was his father. The senior Krazinkow came from an Old World stable community, where fathers could and often did stay away from the business of raising children. The senior Krazinkow did not pay much attention to Tom. When he did, it was more often to discourage the boy than help him. Tom's father considered baseball, basketball and football silly games. He wanted Tom to spend more time at the Old World club, where boys practiced muscle-building exercises and played old-country games. This, of course, did not help Tom achieve success or win applause among his American friends. He was trapped in a cultural squeeze.

Tom's non-athletic interests also died in the bud. One of the few things that seemed to hold his weakly focused attention for any appreciable length of time was horticulture. He enjoyed raising plants in pots that he kept in his room, tending them and watching them grow. His mother and two younger sisters had the same interest. Tom's father laughed at this as a sissy pursuit. He came from a family of men who had earned their bread as laborers, and in that society it was useful, if not essential, for a boy to grow big and strong. Non-muscular kinds of education were not highly respected.

Tom's interest in plants might have given him many of the things he needed—fun, a sense of accomplishment, a taste of success, self-confidence—and it might have led, through biology or other avenues, to a fine career. Tom's mother might have encouraged his interest despite his father's scorn. But she lacked the assertiveness to stand up to the senior Krazinkow. And when she saw Tom's interest in plants beginning to fade, her philosophy of letting him find himself argued against her trying to intervene to keep the interest alive.

With his father away from home so much, Tom did not have enough opportunity to learn masculine traits and attitudes. Not only did Tom lack his father's guidance, but his parents made no effort to get Tom into contact with men who might have served as partial substitutes: Boy Scout leaders, perhaps, or athletic coaches. There was one uncle who took an interest in Tom—his mother's brother Harry, who had no son. Uncle Harry owned a drugstore in a small town several hours' ride from Tom's home. But Tom seldom saw this more Americanized uncle. Tom was with women—his mother and teachers—much more than with men. Women were his pattern. His gestures and attitudes, his way of running and throwing a ball, were girlish and awkward.

Tom's father dealt out lessons erratically and sometimes harshly. Months would go by when he hardly appeared to notice the youngster. Then suddenly a weekend would come when hope and anger would boil up in him, and he would swear grimly that he was going to make Tom into a man. He would then try to accomplish this purpose in a day. To teach Tom to swim, for example, he pulled the boy into deep water and let go of him. When some neighborhood boys threatened to take Tom's pants off on the way to school and Tom was terrified to leave the house, his father ordered him into the car and drove him to where the boys were walking together. He forced Tom out of the car and ordered him to stand up to the bullies like a man. Then he drove away in disgust, leaving Tom shrinking with terror on the sidewalk.

This kind of teaching did little but fill Tom with fear and with enormous frustration at his inability to live up to his father's standards. Learning of any kind, whether it is learning arithmetic or learning to overcome fear, must proceed step by step. A reward at the end of each step encourages the learner to tackle the next longer step. A little anxiety, a small fear of punishment for failure to accomplish, teams up with the expectation of reward and keeps him striving. If either the pull of reward or the prod of anxiety is too weak, the learning process may falter. Too much inappropriate reward, too indiscriminately lavished, and too little anxiety about falling below the standards, may help produce a gimme kid like Alec Green. Too much anxiety and insufficient reward may produce a fearful, withdrawn boy. Such was Tom Krazinkow.

Tom was also tense in school and among his few playmates. He sometimes felt unable to cope with the schoolwork. He often had the idea that his playmates were avoiding him or laughing at him. The idea was not unrealistic. They teased him and tormented him, called him Krazy-Kow, deliberately excluded him from their games.

His two younger sisters, meanwhile, were far less troubled. They had their mother from whom to learn womanhood. They lacked direction and self-assertiveness and were somewhat wishy-washy in their thinking, but these had not yet proved great handicaps.

Tom's difficulties grew more serious when he reached his late teens, around 1950. This was the period when Bergen County began filling rapidly with mobile, hard-driving newcomers. The high school filled with new competitors for Tom: some of them boys like Alec Green who enjoyed picking on the weak; some of them boys whose parents had drummed into them a fierce desire to get ahead and who studied as competitively as their fathers worked. Tom grew more and more troubled and withdrawn as he tried to hold up his head in the mounting competition. His school grades slipped, picked up, slipped again.

Tom's parents were ill-prepared to answer his questions about history, nature, mathematics. Their discussions did not provoke his curiosity nor stimulate his interest in the world around him. The family often spoke in the father's native tongue. Tom's own vocabulary lacked the enrichment of stimulating conversation and wide reading. He assimilated little learning from his home environment, thus had to study harder in school to keep up with his more fortunate schoolmates.

He had never dated girls very much. He was so shy, so rigidly polite, that most girls were either bored or embarrassed in his presence. He was afraid of girls. He didn't really know what they were all about. He had had no guidance from his father on the subject of sex. He had never made a pass at a girl nor even tried to hold hands with one. He lacked the needed self-confidence. When the nature of the community began to change in the 1950's, the few girls who had been willing to go out with him were whisked away by more aggressive boys. He stopped dating entirely.

He was a badly frustrated youth. Like everyone else, he needed an outlet for his sexual desires—but he could not find a normal outlet. Conditions at home added to his turmoil. It was compatible with his mother's confused cult of modern emancipation for her to go about the house naked. Tom frequently saw her breasts. His father, too, an aggressive man who was little concerned with modesty, made only token efforts to insure privacy when he was intimate with Tom's mother. These occasional exposures excited and increasingly confused the frustrated adolescent.

In addition to sexual release, Tom needed a sense of accomplishment, admiration instead of scorn from his fellow human beings. He began to spend time daydreaming alone in his room—first minutes, then hours, then whole afternoons and evenings. He lay on his bed, chain-smoking cigarettes and building grandiose fantasies in which he was a big, strong man like his father. He was an Oriental potentate, an FBI agent, a great scientist. Usually girls were involved in these fantasies. Sometimes they were girls he knew at school. At other times they were imaginary: glamorous lady spies, princesses in far-off lands. All of them loved him, for he gave them sexual gratification such as no other man on earth could give. Women's breasts played a large part in these fantasies. He imagined himself fondling them, squeezing them, sometimes stamping on them.

Though he became sexually stimulated during these daydreams he seldom relieved himself through masturbation. His father, who had once surprised him in the act, had told him angrily and disgustedly that masturbation is morally wrong, a sign of weakness and a prelude to insanity. Thus Tom carried a constant burden of sexual tensions.

Often, after a period of arousal without release, Tom suffered severe cramp-like pains in his genital area. This condition (known in young male circles as "stony gullions" or "lover's nuts") is caused simply by the automatic tightening of muscles lining the male genital tract upon secretions produced during sexual arousal. It is a universal hazard of bachelor life. Though painful, it is probably harmless. Tom, however, was frightened of it. Guilt-ridden and confused, with nobody to consult, he had no idea that the affliction was so common. He thought it was doing damage to his manly organs.

Occasionally he did succumb and relieve himself through masturbation, but only with feelings of great shame, guilt and fear. After such release, his genital cramps went away, but he was too fearful to notice the fact.

There was always the real world to wake up to after the daydreams. After scraping through high school, Tom was drafted into the army. He was discharged a few months later for bed-wetting and general unadaptability. His mother and he now felt that it would be a good idea if he went to college. Though his father had little respect for education, he did recognize that, in American mobile society, the college degree is a milestone of success. He had grudging respect for the façade of education, for the sheepskin as a passport into high-paying jobs. After some grumbling he agreed to let Tom go to college. Tom managed to get into a small, struggling institution where the scholastic standards were not too high.

He decided to major in biology, perhaps later going on to study medicine. (In some of his fantasies he had been a great surgeon.) But his ambitions were unrealistic. If he had been content to get his degree in five or six years instead of four, taking two or three courses a semester and perhaps working in his free time, he might have made it. But he and his parents were in too great a hurry. Tom signed up for a course load that would have been difficult even for a good student to carry. To Tom, who had a poor educational background in home and class, who had never been trained to study hard and well, who lacked the ability to strive through difficulty, the load was impossible. He flunked out in his freshman year.

The educators were concerned with crowded classes and schedules. They had more applicants for admission than they could handle. They could give little time or thought to understanding Tom's particular problem and trying to help him continue. They could not worry over the consequences to Tom's morale of his latest failure. The demand for education is greater than the spaces available in colleges, and the student who can't keep up is often out of luck.

Tom came back home to look for a job. If this had been a stable society, he might have found a marginal but comfortable adjustment somewhere. He would not have been among climbers and hence would not have sensed so great a gap between what he could do and what his high school classmates were doing. Most of them had left home and were making names for themselves in colleges and business. His few friends were gone, probably never to return. His sisters were happy and successful, making average grades in school, well supplied with dates. Soon they would marry and, like his friends, depart. Tom felt left behind, inadequate, a failure. He was sure people were laughing at him, talking about him, calling him insulting names.

In the mobile suburb, the feeling was in the air that one had to climb to be successful and happy. Thus Tom tried to get jobs for which he was not equipped. He tried to be a salesman and failed utterly. He signed on as a clerk-trainee in an insurance company's actuarial department, but was soon fired. The company found him too slow to learn, not alert enough and not eager enough to be a fit candidate for advancement. Finally he got a job as a hardware store clerk in a town near his home.

This was a job in which he might easily have been secure had he only been born a hundred years back. It was a steady, interesting, easygoing job, paying fair wages. But Tom could never be happy in it, for he came from a middle-class home in a mobile society. More, much more, was expected of him.

Tom was an acutely unhappy young man. He had suffered so many defeats and frustrations that he had now become chronically discouraged. He did not know how to succeed against tough competition in studying, working, making friends, attracting girls. His efforts had met so regularly with failure that he had lost interest in trying. He doubted that he could achieve, and he distrusted anyone who showed an interest in helping him. He grew lethargic and aimless; no effort of any kind seemed worthwhile. He withdrew ever more deeply into his world of fantasy.

He spent more and more of his evenings alone in his room, building his fantasies into vast new complexity. When this palled, he began taking long night drives in the family car, going nowhere in particular, just driving. It was another way of escaping the world that had no place for him. Sometimes he parked the car in a strange town and walked around the streets.

It was while doing this one night, in a suburban town not far from home, that he came to a garden apartment development. It was late. Most of the apartments were dark, but a few lights still shone. Tom at the time was building a fantasy: he was a private detective on the track of a dangerous jewel thief. He peered into some of the ground-floor windows, saw men and women sitting about reading, talking, watching television. Then he happened to find a bedroom window where the shade was not drawn completely down. Through the slit at the bottom he saw a woman putting on her nightgown.

Tom had never seen a nude woman before, except his mother and pictures in photography magazines. The sight made him wildly excited. From then on, he prowled about the neighborhood after dark several nights a week, seeking the same thrill. If he had been less reluctant to relieve himself in private he might not have felt so compelled to look into windows, risking trouble with the police or angry homeowners. He was aware of the risks he was running, and he trembled with fear every time he crept across lawns and through shrubbery in the dark. Nonetheless he continued his nocturnal seeking. His fantasies grew richer as he tried ever more desperately to escape the real world. His car excursions grew longer as he hunted new territories to roam. Three or four times he disappeared with the car for several days. The police, alerted by his worried parents, found him once far north in New York State. On other occasions he returned home by himself. He could never clearly remember where he had been or what he had done. His emotional torment was interfering with his ability to think rationally. He was concentrating so hard on his worries and on his fantasies that, like Alice Hager, he was losing touch with the real world.

Eventually the night came, in Pennsylvania, when the police arrested him for peeping. He did not deliberately lie when he told them he was an FBI man chasing spies. He was frightened and confused. He no longer knew what was real and what wasn't.

Tom Krazinkow was not a productive member of society. He could have been, and therein lay his tragedy. He was not lacking in intelligence, but it never had a chance to be used. His interest in biology might have led him to a fine career. His close family connection with Europe and his ability to speak a foreign tongue might have been made useful to the nation in government, business, or military affairs. But because Tom was so poorly prepared for life in Disturbia, he became a chronic loser—until the efforts of his uncle intervened (Part Two) to start him on the road to a more normal existence.

CHAPTER 8

The Middle-Aged and Older

Unemployed Wives

Young married women such as Alice Hager and Gina Conning are the most frequent patients of psychiatrists in the fast-growing suburbs. But they are not, as a group, the most badly hurt. The most tragic cases among women, the emotional disasters, are most often those of middle-aged or older women.

Even severely troubled young wives can usually handle their problems quite quickly, quite simply, without hospitalization. For these are typically problems of growth, and in such cases there is abundant hope. When a young wife seeks psychiatric help, it is often because she has temporarily overloaded herself; she has bitten off more independence than she can chew. But there are ways of unloading the burden. The young wife's social and family situation is usually flexible and can be changed. Normally she has economic security, the first requirement of serenity. There are people around her—her husband for one—who can be asked to help her. She has a future for which to plan. She and her husband are moving upward, and with a little care they can learn to go at it in such a way that neither will have emotional trouble again.

Older women in the suburbs are not as likely to have problems resulting from the overloading of upward mobility. If a woman is going to have such a problem at all, she will in all likelihood have it in her early years as a housewife, while her children are young. By the time she reaches middle age, the chances that she will overload herself in this fashion are fewer. Her children are grown. If she is in the lucky majority group, her husband's income is higher than it used to be, so that he and she can pursue their out-of-house interests more freely. She is freer to move about, finding things in the community that interest her.

When an older woman does have a problem, it is more likely to be a tough one. When she seeks or is brought in for psychiatric help, often as not it is because she has found herself trapped in a situation that seems like a dead end.

The older woman's emotional trouble usually stems from one or more of four main sources—often from all four:

First, she may be worried by an economic decline, or perhaps by a failure to get ahead as fast as her friends. A typical situation is one in which the middle-aged husband has come up against sharp competition from younger, more energetic men. Another typical situation is that of the widow or divorcee, living on a meager dole of life insurance or alimony and a low-white-collar job. In one group of troubled Bergen County divorcees, forty-one per cent were downwardly mobile, compared to eight per cent of normal county residents. Among older women psychiatric patients who had no work skills, twenty-six per cent had to be hospitalized. But among those who had worked and still could, only ten per cent needed psychiatric hospital care.

Second, she worries about her body: failing health, loss of physical attractiveness, declining or halted sexual activity. These are often realistic worries, not hypochondria. As shown before (Chapter Three), psychiatric patients have far more physical illness in their own and their families' lives than do normal people.

Third, she is being hurt by the loss of loved ones. She has lost her husband, perhaps, through divorce or death. Or she has lost him to the business world. Or she senses—or knows for certain—that her husband is having affairs with younger or more exciting women out in that business world. She is losing her children as they grow, become more independent of her, eventually marry and move away. Her parents, brothers and sisters, other relatives, are dying.

Fourth, as the older woman's children become teen-agers and then adults, she may lose the one thing she had left—usefulness. She finds herself unemployed, lacking any constructive role in life. Her husband, her children, her sons- and daughters-in-law may treat her more as a nuisance than anything else. Her service to society is done; she is laid off. In a group of middle-aged women psychiatric patients whose children had grown up and left the county, forty-one per cent became so ill as to need care in a psychiatric hospital. But among patients whose children remained near home, only seventeen per cent had to be hospitalized.

Such a situation may be hard to handle. For unlike the typical young wife's problem, the older woman's consists largely of stubborn or seemingly irreversible facts: Husband dead, divorced or drifting. Health, beauty and sex appeal declining or gone. Children independent. Economic position insecure. These are the present-day external problems that have precipitated the emotional disturbance. It is very hard to calm down the disturbance permanently as long as the external problems remain.

It is because of this—because of the apparent hopelessness of some older women's problems—that the middle-aged and older are more likely to contemplate and commit suicide in Disturbia than the younger women are. In Bergen County, suicides of younger women have actually become less frequent since the late 1940's even though the county's population has grown. The young mobile people who have poured into the county lead lives that, though often painfully stressful, nonetheless usually have elements of hope. Alice Hager, for example, severely disturbed though she was, struggled to protect herself from her imagined enemies and had no thought of self-destruction. Teen-agers sometimes stage suicide attempts, but often this is an exaggerated form of sulking, a bid for sympathy or attention; the attempt is not intended to be successful. Older women, however, have committed suicide more frequently as the county has grown more mobile. Though the percentage of older women in the county's general population dropped slightly in the 1950's, their percentage among suicides rose sharply.

SUICIDES OF WOMEN, BERGEN COUNTY

	1948-50 % of total	1954-56 % of total
Women:		
Young (18-44)	50%	24%
Middle-aged and older (45-64)	50	76
	100%	100%

All this is a picture peculiar to today's mobile world. In the integrated communities of the past, middle-aged and older women had a far easier time. When a woman's husband died or walked out, she automatically went to live with a sister, a daughter or other relatives in her town. When her children grew up and married, they didn't seek to be independent of her. They lived nearby, asking her counsel and help with babies, marital problems, sickness. When she wasn't busy with them, community activities occupied her time—in fact, demanded it. There were jobs in the community that were the special bailiwick of women in just her position: preparing the church supper, sewing costumes for the Fourth of July parade, making the rounds to help when new babies arrived. In those days, too, more articles for family use were produced by hand: canned foods, clothing, confections. The middle-aged or older woman was always needed.

Nor did financial insecurity loom so large and ugly in this community as it does in today's mobile world. These were people who, unlike most suburbanites, admitted their dependence on each other. When you fell upon hard times, relatives supported you. That is what families were for. The mobile world's substitute for the economic benefits of big-family togetherness is life insurance, and it is not a very complete substitute. It is useful only to the widow. It doesn't help the woman whose husband has left her or is being squeezed out of his job by younger, fiercer climbers.

Discontented Husbands

The middle-aged or older man, like his wife, may face grave emotional dangers in the mobile society. The most common danger is that of economic discontent. Middle age is the time in a man's life when he takes stock of himself and his accomplishments. He may find on doing so that he hasn't come as far as the men who went to school with him or started work with him. He may have come to a standstill while his friends still climb, while younger men catch up with him and pass him. He may, indeed, be declining, unable as his body ages to keep up with the long hours and punishing workload demanded by the competition or by his aggressive, competitive boss. Or he may be in a fast-changing business, unable to keep up with the new knowledge being developed.

He remembers the dreams of his young manhood. He measures the distance that still remains between his accomplishments and his ambitions. His hope of traversing that distance diminishes as each year passes.

He compares his house with those of his friends who have moved away. He finds it small and shabby. His wife, perhaps, reminds him that so-and-so has bought a retirement home in Florida and somebody else goes to Europe every summer. He opens the newspaper one morning and notes that a half-forgotten acquaintance has been made sales manager of a large corporation.

This is the kind of middle-aged man who, if life has put many stresses on him, most commonly has emotional trouble in the suburbs. Like his wife, he is more likely to have trouble than his counterpart in the stable community where climbing is not so important, where there are other ways to win success and applause, where competition does not underline deficiencies and aging. Among eighty-three men past middle age who sought psychiatric help in Disturbia, forty-one per cent of those who were suffering economic decline needed care in a psychiatric hospital. But only twelve per cent of those with no economic decline had to be hospitalized.

Also like his wife, the middle-aged man in Suburbia is likely to have a disturbance that is more difficult to handle than that of a younger man who still has hope. Though the percentage of middle-aged men in the county's population has dropped since 1950, they are more likely than younger men to commit suicide in Bergen County now that the county has grown more mobile:

	1948-50 % of total	1954-56 % of total
Male suicides:		
Young (18-44)	41½%	28%
Middle-aged and older (45-64)	58½	72
	100%	100%

Though economic decline or dead-ending is the most common factor in emotional trouble among suburban middle-aged men, it is not, of course, the only common one. Another typical picture is that of a man who has succeeded and found that this was not what he wanted after all. He has all the money he needs; he has outdone his friends in climb, house and Cadillacs. Yet his life is stale and empty. He lacks purpose, direction, goals, recognition. He can't understand why.

One reason may be that, having succeeded at making money, he has no other arena in which to try himself. He finds nothing else to challenge and stimulate him. He has spent his adult life working; he hasn't taken time to learn about other things—hobbies, sports, cultural interests. Even if he does have such interests, he lives in a community that reserves its main applause for economic success. He is in a trap: he is tired of working, but work is all he has. He may find that he isn't getting the recognition and affection he wants. He has been too busy to win the love of his family, peers, subordinates.

For such a man, retirement may come as a shock. Now the one thing he had is stripped from him. He feels lost, lonely and useless. Many corporations have taken note of this problem, and some have tried to do something about it. Some retire executives by degrees, providing progressively longer vacations as retirement age approaches. Others have worked out arrangements whereby a retired man continues to work sporadically as a consultant to the company. All this is valuable, provided the man himself makes use of it in the right way. Often he finds it hard to do so. He finds it hard to switch values overnight, to turn from making money to making furniture, from watching market reports to watching birds. Ideally, a man should begin preparing for retirement on the day he lands his first job. He should sustain his off-the-job interests, continuing to win recognition from them as well as from his rise in business. Then, when he does retire, he is not suddenly stripped of all goals and all applause.

Retirement and Beyond

Older men and women—those near or beyond retirement age—have relatively less trouble in the mobile suburb than in the stable community. This table tells the story in terms of psychiatric inpatients in two hospitals in 1957-58.

	SUBURBAN HOSPITAL % of total			RURAL HOSPITAL % of total		
Age	*Men*	*Women*		*Men*	*Women*	
Young (18-44)	22%	34%		26%	19%	
Middle-aged (45-59)	14	19		10	10	
Older (60 plus)	6	5		18	17	
Total	42	58	(100%)	54	46	(100%)

The difference is striking. In the suburban hospital, older psychiatric patients made up only a little more than one-tenth of the total. In the rural hospital they accounted for more than a third.

Part of the difference is undoubtedly due to the simple fact that proportionately fewer people aged sixty and more live in the mobile suburbs. These towns are still a relatively new phenomenon. Most of the people who have poured into them during their great growth since World War II have been young men and women, couples with young children. In time, the proportion of older people in these towns will probably grow until it more nearly parallels the national proportion. The percentage of older people in suburban psychiatric wards may then rise slightly.

But population distribution is not the only reason behind these hospital percentages. A principal reason is the sheer amount of stress to which young and middle-aged people are subjected in the mobile society. They develop emotional difficulty in such large numbers, compared with the stable community, that they overshadow the older men and women.

There is another very direct reason that may have something to do with this higher percentage of older patients in the rural psychiatric hospital. In today's remaining integrated communities, older people are affected obliquely by mobility. In the process of dwindling to a small fraction of the national population, rural communities have continually lost younger people to the mobile world outside. As each year's crop of youngsters graduates from high school, the more ambitious and energetic leave for colleges and cities. Their more stable home town has not been sheltered from the magnetism of the mobile world. They have heard its siren song. In magazines and newspapers, on movie and TV screens, they have learned of fortunes to be made—wealth unattainable within the home town itself. They have listened wide-eyed while far travelers from last year's graduating class returned and told of distant cities where success and romance run like wine in the streets. So they are bitten. They have the climber's fever. They pack up and go, leaving the old folk behind—and, sometimes, leaving them with emotional problems. In the rural community, as young people leave and older ones die, life can become demoralizing for older folks who stay behind. Thus the disintegration of mobility reaches into even the most sequestered country village.

When older men and women in Disturbia have emotional trouble, it is often bad trouble. Older people are subject to stresses that aren't shared, or at least aren't felt so keenly or so often, by the younger. There may be worry over an existing or feared illness, for example. There may be fear of or worry about death—one's own or that of a loved one. Friends may be dying off in the clubs to which the older man or woman belongs, and the energy to join new clubs may be lacking. For the older man there may be the shock of retirement, the lack of a suitable substitute for work. These tensions may combine with others such as that of economic discontent or decline and bring on an emotional disturbance. When such a disturbance does seize an older man or woman, it is typically harder to handle than the problems of younger or middle-aged people. Even more than with the middle-aged, older people's problems are likely to contain irreversible elements: declining health, economic dead end, loss of loved ones by death.

The table below covers all women who were admitted to a state mental hospital during the first half of 1958, and shows what percentage in each category had not been discharged by the end of the period. Older women—particularly widows and the single—were far more likely than the others to be hospitalized for a long time:

	Young (*18-44*)	*Middle-aged* (*45-59*)	*Older* (*60 and over*)
Married	29% still in	38% still in	50% still in
Divorced or Separated	33 " "	50 " "	67 " "
Widowed	— " "	43 " "	84 " "
Single	39 " "	53 " "	79 " "

Older people in the stable communities of another era did not typically share all the problems of those in present-day America. In those towns, Granddad and Grandma were not cast away as useless; they became respected counselors to the younger generation. Economic dead-ending was not likely to trouble them severely, for these were not climber communities.

The case study that follows is the story of two middle-aged people who were prepared for a stable life in an integrated community. As their community changed, they failed to find an adjustment.

The Nobodies

The case of Martha Kohler is a tragedy of the mobile world. It is an example of the way in which relentless external forces—forces created by the national urge to get ahead—can hurl a strong woman down.

Martha Kohler was in her early fifties. As a child, she had spent several frightening years going in and out of hospitals battling cystitis, a chronic bladder infection. This traumatic experience sensitized her emotionally, but it also taught her to withstand pain and hardship without complaining. Though her parents were sympathetic they became irritable when she cried. She learned that she could win the reward of their affection by hiding the discomfort of the disease. She grew up strong-minded, cheerful and independent.

She married George Kohler in the early 1930's. George had been an only child, born in Bergen County. His parents were both dead, and he had been living as a bachelor in the home they had left him: a small, creaky old house on five acres of what had once been farmland. George was a genial, friendly man with a boyish face, well liked by almost everyone who knew him. He lacked assertiveness. He preferred to make his way in the world by friendliness rather than by a driving, competitive attitude.

George worked for a small electrical repair shop. It paid a comfortable wage, and George enjoyed the work thoroughly. He was an accomplished tinkerer. He loved to take machines and devices apart to see what made them tick. He spent much of his free time with the neighborhood boys, building wagons and kites, playing baseball, repairing broken toys.

During the first year after they were married and Martha moved into the old house with him, she suggested a few times that he try to advance himself. But George was not interested. He was happy where he was. The climber's fever had not yet bitten him. Martha did not press the point, for she, too, became very happy in the community. She involved herself in activities centered around the church, made many friends. She and George had two children, a boy and a girl.

After World War II, the owners of the electrical repair shop decided to expand into appliance sales. George was made assistant manager of the new, larger establishment. He did not enjoy the administrative side of his new job, but the extra money was welcome. He discovered, also, that he was a natural salesman.

Those were good times for appliance stores. The customers were hungry; they'd been starved of luxuries during the war, and now they had plenty of money to lavish upon themselves. No hard sell was necessary. The store made more money than really seemed right. In 1950 George was elevated to the job of manager, with a share in the profits. He and Martha had plenty of money, plenty of friends and a bright future.

But in the early 1950's, the county suffered a change. Newcomers flooded in; business rushed in after them to provide their needs, and suddenly the appliance business was alive with hard-driving climbers. New stores opened—discount houses, highway bargain marts—owned and staffed by tough, competitive men who were ready to stay on their feet twelve hours a day and sweat for every sale. George lacked the stamina, the drive to keep up with them. Slowly but perceptibly, the store's business began to slacken.

The owners of the store, studying the problem, decided that one of their major troubles was location. If they could move into a shinier, larger store in one of the big new shopping centers that were attracting so many customers, they would be in a better position to compete with the newcomers. But they lacked capital to make the move. To bring capital into the business they offered to sell a share of it to George.

George by now had caught the fever. Many of his old friends had climbed away from him. He had had a taste of money, and now he wanted more. He wanted to move out of his old house and buy a bigger, more fashionable one as befitted his rising status in the business world. To raise the money he needed to buy into the business, he sold the five acres of land that he owned, all except the quarter-acre on which the house stood. He sold it without seeking advice or studying the situation, to a man for whose son he had done many favors. He assumed that the man, as a friend, would deal fairly. He did not realize that people move about and change rapidly in Disturbia. There is no certainty that a man for whom you have done a favor will stay around to return it, or will even want to return it when the time comes.

The man to whom George sold the land knew something that George had not taken care to find out: that parts of that end of town were shortly to be rezoned for business, and that the street on which George's house stood was being considered for widening into a four-lane county road. A year after George sold his land, the buyer re-sold it to a development corporation for use as a shopping center. The buyer more than doubled the money he had paid George.

The move of the appliance store to a new location did not help as much as George and the other owners had hoped. The competition was too keen. The relationship between George and

Martha began to deteriorate under the economic stress. George became irritable. His amiable disposition gave way to fits of sullenness. As the store's business grew worse and his tensions mounted, he began to drink more heavily than usual. He stayed out late at night, often not troubling to tell Martha he wouldn't be home for dinner and usually mumbling something about "business" by way of explanation.

Martha felt that she was losing George, and she felt that it was mostly her own fault. She was losing her attractiveness as a woman; she wasn't being good enough to George. In an attempt to solve the problem she went to all lengths to please him. She never questioned him when he came home late with liquor on his breath, tried to meet his sullen moods with affectionate understanding. But George did not respond. He was facing failure.

In a slower-paced environment, a society that was content to make a comfortable living and let it go at that, the likeable George probably would have succeeded well in managing a store. But this was a society in which it was not often possible to manage a business in a leisurely way. Either you got ahead or you moved backward. George's competitors were racing ahead of him. His and Martha's old friends were moving up and away. The challenge was too big for him. He was trying to escape through drink.

While this economic stress was growing, Martha's children were moving away from her. Her son had gone to college and then to an engineering job on the West Coast. Soon after leaving high school her daughter, Joan, had married a mobile young man whose company had since transferred him and his wife to the Midwest.

Martha felt lonely, neglected and jobless. With too few interesting activities to occupy her mind, she began to brood over her problems. She was badly worried about financial security—she wondered what would happen if George lost his job at the store. She was also worried about her health. Her experience with hospitals as a child had made her more than normally concerned about sickness.

One of her worries sprang from the fact that her appetite had decreased as her anxieties mounted, and she had recently lost weight. Her concern was probably needless. In our society of abundance most people can stand to lose a good deal of weight before trouble is indicated. It is possible that the human body is adjusted to gain weight when food is plentiful. In early history, before the development of homes that could be kept warm in winter, survival may have depended to some extent on people's putting on fat during the summer when plant foods were abundant and hunting was easier. Today we live in perpetual summer, and as a result we are, as a nation, heavier than we need to be.

Martha was also worried about her eyes. They had become extremely sensitive to bright light and tired easily. She thought some obscure disease might have afflicted them, but actually the trouble was probably a simple result of chronic tension. When people are tense their muscles tighten, and these may include the ciliary muscles controlling the eye lenses, and the muscles controlling the pupils. One result may be that the eyes are hard to focus. They also may ache and feel tired, as does any muscle that is tense for a long time. Another result may be that the pupil is held open wider than necessary for any given degree of brightness, so that a greater than normal amount of light is admitted to the eye. And the nervous system, chronically excited, may be hyperalert. All this would tend to make the eye hypersensitive. (It may be for this reason that many chronically tense people wear dark glasses.)

The same hypersensitivity may afflict the ears when muscles controlling the eardrum and the bones of the middle ear are tense. To ears thus affected, sounds would appear louder than to the same ears when more relaxed. This may be one reason why chronically tense people have less tolerance of noise, find it hard to think when children are playing nearby, jump at sudden sounds.

Martha was also afraid she was beginning to grow senile before her time. It isn't hard to see where the idea came from. One of her grandmothers, who had lived with Martha's parents when Martha was a girl, had become senile in her last years of life. Martha's mother had taken on the burden of caring for her as she grew more and more helpless. Thus Martha knew what senility was like and was scared of it. With her husband sunk in his business problems and her children gone, she became obsessed with the thought that she was now old and unattractive, ripe for abandonment. She then began to notice that she was having trouble remembering names, faces, telephone numbers, shopping lists.

The real reason for this seeming memory loss was simply that she was concentrating on more important matters—her very real economic and social problems. The mind can't function lucidly in two areas at once, and when it is dwelling strongly on a particular problem it will perform unreliably when asked to do other things. This is why the absent-minded professor neglects to put on his tie—he is preoccupied with other things. Martha, however, took her faulting memory as a sign of approaching senility. This added to her turmoil. Like Alice Hager's, it became a self-feeding thing. The symptoms became causes.

Martha went to a doctor. He found nothing wrong with her except a slight degree of high blood pressure. It wasn't serious, but it seemed so to Martha. She became frantic with worry over her health. She found it harder and harder to cheer George out of his fits of gloominess over his business. His increasing irritability and drinking were additional stresses to her. He, in turn, was worried about her growing unhappiness. Each was adding to the other's burden of worry.

Martha sought refuge in her church. She went there every day to pray with the old clergyman. The hours spent with him in the quiet of the church, away from the overwhelming world outside, were comforting to her. But the world was always waiting each day when she left the church. The problems were still there.

Martha came to depend on the church and the clergyman. They were her only comfort in a cruel, lonely world.

Then, without warning, the old clergyman died of a heart attack. Martha felt that the last prop had been knocked out from under her. She grew deeply depressed, lay awake crying all night, talked of suicide. The comfort and emotional security she had obtained from prayer were gone. And with the clergyman's death, a new dimension was added to her concerns about disease.

As her depression deepened, she consulted her doctor. Arrangements were made for her to enter a hospital. There she was given electric shock treatments. Shock treatment is, for people with emotional problems, something like surgery for ulcer patients. It is a more drastic measure than psychotherapy or medicines, but sometimes a necessary one. Its effect is to break an emotional short-circuit so that logical thinking can gain control. It helps reestablish constructive behavior and a state of mind in which solutions to problems can be found.

The shock treatments helped her. The downward spiral of her depression was broken. She went home thinking quite clearly, casting about in her mind for ways to relieve her loneliness and insecurity.

But then a new blow struck her. George, driving home one night, smashed into another car. The blame for the accident seemed about equally divided. George, though driving at a moderate speed, had been drinking and was not as alert as he should have been. The other driver, a young father who may have been much like Fred Bright in his compulsive hurrying, was driving beyond the speed limit. The young father was not seriously injured. George, however, was knocked unconscious for half an hour and taken to a hospital, where it was discovered that he had a concussion.

George returned home from the hospital suffering from a post-concussion syndrome: light-headedness, dizziness, difficulty in concentrating and in coordinating movements. The syndrome generally passes away in time, as the patient retrains his brain to function normally. But George was too discouraged to face life any more. He felt that the auto accident was the last blow, the final defeat. Worried about business, mounting debts, Martha, he felt unable to go on. Like Tom Krazinkow, he felt that further effort was futile. He was wearing his brain in a sling, unwilling to begin retraining it. Coupled with this discouragement was a new fear of riding in cars. There was no way for George to get to work except by car, but the thought of driving filled him with panic.

He dreaded returning to his job at the appliance store. He filed for sickness compensation on medical grounds: post-concussion syndrome and post-traumatic neurosis.

Martha now began to worry about what might happen to her if George died. She would be all alone, without husband, without children, without anyone. How would she support herself? And suppose she became ill and had to go to a hospital? Who would pay the bills? She and George were desperately in need of comfort, affection and security from each other. But neither could offer the other any help.

Martha's depression returned more strongly than before. Again she sank into lethargy—a common characteristic of people who are severely depressed. She wouldn't move, nor speak, nor eat. She sat in a chair, staring ahead of her.

Financially insecure, lonely, jobless, she was one of life's orphans. Amid the storm of her emotions now was a new element, the fear of hospitals and electric shock treatment. Looking toward the years ahead of her, she saw herself returning to the hospital again and again for the experience. She saw herself growing steadily worse, senile, insane.

Strong-minded people often think of suicide in seemingly hopeless situations such as Martha's. The strong tend to believe that their misfortunes are largely their own doing, while the weak will more often blame others—people real or imaginary, or mysterious agencies that are influencing their lives from afar. The strong often feel that they are dragging others down, that they are burdensome and hence should remove themselves. This was Martha Kohler's thinking. She saw herself as not only useless, but worse. In her mounting difficulties, she was weighing too heavily on George and might become a burden to her children.

Martha swallowed a bottle of sleeping pills. Thc ambulance got her to a hospital in time. Her stomach was pumped out; the suicide attempt was thwarted. But Martha didn't even seem to care. Life appeared to hold no more promise for her. She and George felt they were nobodies, defeated and trampled by the mobile society. Only later were they helped to realize the many ways in which they could contribute valuable services to their mobile community. The treatment of their problem will be discussed later in a subsequent section of the book.

CHAPTER 9

The Creeping Decadence

Life on the Golden Plateau

They were all climbing, trying to climb, or trying to hold their own: Alice and Carl Hager, Gina and John Conning, the Brights, the R. Lincoln Webers, Alec Green's parents, Tom Krazinkow, the middle-aged Kohlers. They all wanted wealth and the better life that wealth can open up. All were reaching for the golden plateau.

All assumed that wealth could automatically bring them happiness and peace. They were wrong. Wealth can, and with intelligent handling usually will, bring the full, rich, contented life Americans dream about. But this happy ending to the story of mobility is not guaranteed. The climber's life, the very life that moves toward wealth, has attached to it like parasites some factors that may prevent the enjoyment of wealth. It nourishes the agents of its own frustration.

The American suburbs have in their populace many middle-aged people who, unlike George and Martha, have succeeded in the climb. Some are happy. But some, having pulled themselves up over the edge of the plateau, have looked around and discovered to their poignant dismay that this is not where they really wanted to be after all. Their years of backbreaking effort, they now see, have gained them only a barren wasteland.

Harley Tragg was such a man, and this is his story.

In material things, Harley had plenty to show for his life. He had the presidency and majority ownership of a prosperous manufacturing business. He and his wife lived in a seventy-five-thousand-dollar house on two beautifully landscaped acres in one of Bergen County's wealthiest towns—a house and grounds that not even a real estate advertisement could exaggerate. Each had a Cadillac; their twenty-four-year-old son had a bright red foreign sports car, and their twenty-year-old daughter had a startling mauve convertible. They had the economic position that millions of mobile people are striving for.

But Harley Tragg was not a happy man. He had a severe obsession. He was terrified that he would one day throw himself in front of a moving vehicle—a train, bus, car. Whenever he saw a vehicle approaching he had a powerful, frightening impulse to jump beneath its wheels. He did not know where the impulse came from and he did not believe he could control it. Every day he thought: yesterday I conquered it but today, perhaps, I won't. He went to all lengths to avoid standing where vehicles passed, seldom took a bus or train, drove his own car whenever possible and broke into a chill sweat whenever it was necessary for him to walk along a city sidewalk or hail a taxicab.

Even when he was away from traffic, Harley could get no fun out of life. Nothing interested him; all seemed stale and gray. The finest foods were no more exciting to him than dry crackers. His wife and children irritated him. The mistress he kept in New York City failed to satisfy his needs. He was not permitted to drink much because of high blood pressure, but this was no loss to him, for even liquor failed to produce the sense of well-being that he craved. A doctor had suggested a hobby, and he'd bought several expensive kits: photography, woodcarving, painting. He couldn't develop an interest in any of them. The kits lay dusty on shelves in the cellar.

Harley was confused and hurt. He felt that life had played a shabby trick on him. A man in his position, a man who had succeeded to this extent, should be happy. Why wasn't he?

Harley had caught the climber's fever early in life. As a youth in rural Pennsylvania, where his father barely supported the family by operating a general store, he read avidly of a fabulous place called Wall Street where fortunes could be made overnight. He thought about Wall Street all the time he was working in the store. The work was hard. Harley's mother was a semi-invalid and unable to help, and Harley had to leave high school without graduating in order to keep the struggling store alive. He worked there from morning till night, had little time off, few friends, no real hobbies or sports or other interests. Finally, when he was about twenty, he escaped. He took a train to New York and got a job as a clerk in a Wall Street bank.

He was a hard and diligent worker, got to be known as a serious-minded young man, soon moved up to be chief clerk of his department. But as his pay rose from meager to low, he began to think that a man such as he, without much education and without friends and family in high places, could hardly succeed except by having his own business.

A chance to succeed came along. Among the few girls he had met was one named Audrey, whose father had built up a small business manufacturing electrical equipment. Audrey was plain and had little fun in her, but this was all right with Harley. He was uncomfortable in the presence of pretty, fun-loving girls, who often teased him about his businesslike matter-of-factness.

He and Audrey were not notably attracted to one another, but when Harley and Audrey's father met, it was economic love at first sight. The older man was growing tired, wanted to pull back from the management of his little company. He had no son of his own to install at the helm, but he wanted the profits and control of the business to stay in the family. Harley Tragg impressed him as being just the answer: a smart, level-headed, hard-working young fellow with no nonsense about him, eager to learn, anxious to make something of himself. Harley was equally pleased at the prospect of joining the family business. With Audrey's father assisting in the wooing, Harley proceeded, in businesslike fashion, to win himself a bride.

It was more a business merger than a marriage, but Audrey was not displeased. She had few suitors. She shrewdly saw that Harley represented the best chance of marriage that had come her way in a long time—or, indeed, might ever come again. She did wish that he were more romantic (he and her father spent the wedding reception discussing the stock market), but she considered the bargain a good one.

Her father considered it the best deal he had made in his life. Harley threw himself into the business, worked from early morning until late at night, soon was able to help the old man with management problems, finally took over the management altogether. The Depression came, and Harley worked frantically to keep the business alive. He used every weapon at his command: gifts in high places, money slipped under the table. Sometimes he slept on a couch in his office several nights in a row. During those desperate years he saw many of his competitors fold up. He saw many human tragedies of economic decline. One former competitor came to him, hat in hand, to ask for a job. A cousin whom Harley had once known well, a stock market speculator who had lost his shirt in the 1929 crash, committed suicide by throwing himself under a train. These things left a lasting mark on Harley. But he was tough. He swore that no such thing would ever happen to him. He worked himself to exhaustion every day to hold his business together.

When business improved in the middle 1930's, Harley reluctantly agreed to sire the children that he and Audrey had been postponing. Sexual intercourse had always been rare between them, by mutual consent. There was no real interest on either part. But now the idea of having children seemed to make sense. Audrey was bored. She complained more bitterly each year that Harley never paid any attention to her, that she had nothing to do but sit home and brood. Harley thought that children, by giving her something to do, might make her more content.

When World War II broke out and Harley's competitors rushed to Washington to get contracts, they found that Harley had been in ahead of them, distributing payola, making whispered deals. His business grew fast through the war and through the peacetime boom that followed. In 1946 he, Audrey and their two children moved into a home in Bergen County. A few years later they bought a bigger home. In the mid-1950's they bought a palatial one. Harley had reached the golden plateau. He was rich. His struggle was over.

By this time his father had died, but his invalid mother continued to linger on. Audrey didn't want to be bothered with the old lady, so Harley had her put in a nearby nursing home. She was now seriously ill with high blood pressure and was partially paralyzed after a stroke. She was confined to a wheelchair, helpless, embarrassed by uncontrolled soiling. Harley visited her weekly at the nursing home, where he saw other sick, lonely old people. The visits depressed him. By the time his mother died, in the late 1950's, he had a horror of becoming ill. He wondered what would happen to him if, in his older years, he became helpless like his mother. He wondered who would care for him.

For he had realized, quite suddenly and with something close to terror, that nobody seemed to love him.

All his life he had done little else but work. Work and its

product, money, had been his religion, his all. Instead of giving his wife affection and understanding he had given her money. When his children had got in his hair he had given them expensive gifts. He had supposed that money was all anybody needed. Now his wife, son and daughter were almost strangers to him.

The family lacked a sense of unity and direction. None of the members knew or cared much what the others were doing. None could feel himself to be engaged in challenging, constructive work for which society might applaud and reward him.

Audrey felt ignored and unloved by her husband and children. She spent much of her time at the country club, eating too much and drinking too many cocktails, seeking the temporary sense of well-being that comes from indulgence in food and drink. She was overweight and had a pasty complexion. She was angry, bitter and disappointed. She had expected that wealth would bring her recognition, failing to see that this is not a feudal society but a mobile democracy which, in general and in the long run, rewards only those who produce something for it. Audrey had not produced.

Her only real interest was in a national society of women who claimed to be descended from Americans of Revolutionary times. She had spent several years trying to prove her genealogy for membership in this society. She was not concerned with becoming involved in the useful work the society was doing—orphanages, scholarships—but with the façade of importance that she hoped membership would provide. Once again her thinking was feudal. She failed to understand that a society of climbers, a society in which people gain social position through their own efforts, does not give universal recognition to inherited position and may, in fact, resent it.

She was no stranger to resentment. In her anger at society for failing to give her the recognition to which she felt entitled, she had become overbearing and loud of voice. The librarians whom she harassed in her hunt for bona fide ancestors deliberately failed to cooperate with her the way they did with more patient, friendly patrons. The local tradesmen, whom she tried to terrorize, went out of their way to annoy her.

Harley's son and daughter were also failing to see that the mobile society rewards producers. Nobody had ever taught them this monumentally important fact. Harley produced, but they never saw him at it. They saw only the materialistic side of his nature, the reaching for wealth without the hard, useful work that had created the wealth.

Harley's son, Jerry, was a playboy. He had never been shown why he must study, or work, or observe the rules by which people live in harmony together. He had been expelled from a prep school and two colleges. He was constantly in trouble with the police for speeding in his red sports car. He spent much of his time playing tennis and swimming. His position in society was that of a freeloader. He had never learned a skill that society could use. Harley had tried to bring him in to the family business but the attempt had been a fiasco—Jerry simply didn't want to work.

Harley's daughter, Mona, was a dilettante novelist. She spent her time with a group of fringe beatniks who cluttered up the house and drank Harley's expensive liquor. They, too, were freeloaders. Mona was overweight like her mother. She had little literary ability because she had not been willing to go through the long, patient training that the craft requires. She and her friends produced nothing worthwhile, pretended to be rebelling against middle-class values although they weren't really convinced about anything, won hollow recognition from each other and grumbled because the world didn't understand them. The world understood them, all right. It just didn't want to be bothered with them.

Harley was the only member of the family who, through his work, was producing anything for society. Even his productiveness, however, was less useful than it might have been. The success of his company was founded not only on the quality of its products, but also on secret deals and under-the-table payments to customers' employees, government officials and others in a position to smooth the company's road. Harley was constantly being made to realize that a man bought for money can be bought again, by someone else, for more money. Thus his company's position was not as secure as it would have been if Harley had been content to succeed a little more slowly, on the basis of quality and usefulness.

There were other reasons why his work gave him little pleasure. His employees disliked him thoroughly. In the Depression years he'd kept the company alive by driving the employees mercilessly, and they'd had to stay and take it because jobs were scarce. Times were better now, but he kept driving; it was in his blood. Fear still goaded him. He felt guilty when he wasn't hard at work himself, and he felt uncomfortable when he saw an employee standing idle. He didn't know how to make work enjoyable for himself or others. There was no fun in him. His face was gray, deeply lined and sour. Valued employees quit continually. The company was always in the agitated state of hunting new key men.

The business and its economic and scientific environment had grown so complex since the war that Harley had been forced to bring in two high-salaried vice presidents, an accountant and an electronics engineer. These two men also learned to dislike Harley, and the fact that employees ran to them with grievances against Harley made matters worse. Unlike Harley, they expected to milk some enjoyment out of their work. Occasionally, when tensions were high, for instance, the two of them had a long, leisurely lunch together. Harley would not have joined them if invited, but the fact that he wasn't invited made him angry. He also felt left out of their conversations, for the only thing he could talk about was work, while they had other interests—golf, hobbies, their kids. He felt that they did not respect him. He argued and fought with them constantly. They gave him the feeling that they could run the business without him, while he was sure he couldn't run it without them. The days were gone when he was desperately needed to hold the company together. He no longer had a goal. He could only work for the sake of working.

Like many other top executives, Harley found his pinnacle of power frighteningly lonely. He had no one in whom to confide, no one with whom to discuss his personal and business problems, no one to slap him on the back and tell him he was doing a good job. This loneliness probably would not have developed if he had lived in a stable society where people knew each other. The stable community would have been around him, looking up to him, demanding his services as a skilled business administrator for all kinds of local activities. In his mobile suburban town, such activities were handled by an overloaded few. They needed help but didn't know where to find it among all the strangers around them. They would have welcomed Harley if he had come forward on his own, but since they didn't know him they didn't think of coming to him and asking him to contribute his services.

It was in this state of aching loneliness and fear for the future that Harley met Joni. A business acquaintance introduced them. Joni was twenty-three. She had come to New York ostensibly to seek a career as an actress, but she wasn't really interested in working. She came from a broken home, had never seen the pleasant side of family life and had no interest in marriage. Her aim was simply to have a good time without expending effort. Her name, her platinum-blonde hair, her snake-like walk were all patently and unashamedly phony, but the result was a brilliant exaggeration of female sexuality. She hit Harley like a thunderbolt, stirring long-forgotten and sharply pleasurable sensations within him.

He was surprised when she accepted his mumbled invitation to lunch. He needn't have been, for Joni was no fool. She had quickly diagnosed his need as dovetailing with hers. It need not have surprised him, either—though it did—when he found himself in her apartment a few weeks later, fumblingly helping her to undress. A month later, after a few pointed hints from Joni, he set her up in a much bigger, much more expensive apartment with furs, a poodle and a handsome weekly allowance.

Harley had not known many girls as a young man, and since his marriage he had hardly even spoken to any woman except Audrey. Sexual intercourse with her had been so unsatisfactory that during the past ten years he had been almost celibate. Thus Joni had a powerful impact on him. She revived and completely satisfied his sexual desires. Equally important, she listened to him while he talked of his problems and fears. Being clever, she recognized that this was part of the deal; if she wished to hold onto him as a source of money, she must give sympathy as well as sex.

A wiser, more experienced man would not have become so emotionally entangled with a girl like Joni. Such a man, having learned through practice to recognize, understand and control his own emotions, would have been aware that Joni aroused only his sexual desires and had little else to offer. Understanding this, he would not have felt compelled to be with Joni herself, but could have carried his aroused desires home to his wife. Harley, however, lacked experience with his emotions. Aroused sexually by Joni, he thought that he must have her, that no other woman could possibly satisfy him. He did not recognize that, in truth, she satisfied only a small fraction of his needs. He was overwhelmed by her. He thought he couldn't live without her.

Joni saw all this quite clearly. She began to demand more money of him. She refused to organize her life to suit his convenience, and often when he visited the apartment he found other men and women there. Her friends were mainly second-rate models, untalented, non-producing artists and unemployed people who labeled themselves actors and actresses. They weren't interested in Harley, except to touch him for loans (which were never repaid). Nor was Harley interested in them. He was a man who had spent his life building something; he had been a producer. He needed the society of other producers to give him what he was trying to get from Joni. He needed somebody to give him new goals to replace the goal of making money. But Joni and her friends did not have the kind of goals he could understand—if, indeed, they had any at all. Their society was unproductive. It could not give Harley the feeling of usefulness and purpose, the encouragement and applause, the affection and respect that he needed.

Harley was not as clever with people as Joni, but he was not a fool. He had a fairly clear idea of Joni's motives. He knew that it was his money, more than he himself, that attracted and held her. The knowledge hurt and angered him, but it scarcely lessened his addiction to her. He felt hopelessly trapped. Bitter experience with his own family had shown him that money cannot be relied upon to make people do what you want them to do. He worried incessantly that Joni might one day find another man, a man just as wealthy but perhaps younger and more attractive than he. What would he do then? To whom could he go? Would he, he wondered, commit suicide like his cousin in the Depression?

He worried more and more about his fleeting years, about a lonely, helpless old age, about illness. He became a diet faddist. He ran from one doctor to another, seeking medicines for complaints both real and imaginary. When his stomach ached he fancied that he had cancer. Every common cold and tension headache was translated in his mind to a dread disease. He read in a businessman's journal that middle-aged men sometimes have heart attacks in the midst of sexual intercourse, but almost never with their own wives. This made him tense and fearful when he was with Joni, adding emotional stress to the physical exertion that naturally made his heart beat hard during intercourse. He became afraid to visit her, yet he could not stay away.

She became more and more independent in her relationship with him. Several times he found young men alone with her when he visited. Once, ringing the bell, he heard a sudden scuffling sound inside, as though someone had leaped to his feet and run into hiding. Through the closed door Joni told Harley that she was sick and couldn't see him that night.

Harley was gnawed by jealousy. Any day, he thought, a more attractive man might come along and take Joni away. Indeed, maybe it was happening already.

One night he had a dream in which a man committed suicide in Joni's apartment. He awoke terrified, sweating, his heart pounding. From then on he thought of suicide more and more often. It seemed to him that if Joni left him, if he became ill, if no one came forward to help him, suicide might look like the only way out. Like his cousin, he might throw himself beneath a train.

Harley was not a weak man and did not like to admit the existence of fear in himself. He told himself that he would never do so cowardly a thing as to take his own life. He fought the thought, fought the whole idea of fear. Yet whether he consciously admitted it to himself or not, he was afraid; his body was going through the physical reactions of fear. Back during the Depression, these reactions had been associated in his mind with the idea of suicide, just as the smell of rubbing alcohol might be associated in one's mind with the thought of doctors, sickness, needles. Now the idea came back every time the bodily reactions set in. Harley did not understand this. He didn't know why the thought of suicide returned every time an unpleasant event occurred—every time Joni or his vice presidents or his wife or children treated him badly. He didn't understand that the sequence was automatic: event, fear reactions, suicide idea.

Harley would have been much better off if he had admitted his fears to himself. In wartime, men usually lived through front-line dangers relatively well when they were told beforehand that they were going to be scared stiff, that their thoughts would be confused, that their hearts would pound and their legs tremble, that they would have headaches and stomach aches. Recognizing and understanding his fear, a man was in a better position to cope with it. Not understanding it or not admitting it, the soldier would have sought other reasons to explain the unusual things that were going on in his body. He would have thought that his weakened, trembling legs were succumbing to some mysterious paralysis, or that his headaches and confused thoughts were caused by enemy radar. He would have ended in a rear zone mental hospital with paralyzed legs or hallucinations.

If Harley had understood that he was lonely and scared, he would probably have recognized his suicidal thoughts as part of the phenomenon of fear. He might not have understood the mind-and-body mechanism completely, but at least he would have had a sound basis for speculating on where the troublesome thought originated. Not having such a basis, he thought his suicide ideas came from some deep, mysterious part of his personality that actually wanted to die. He had heard of people with split personalities and of something called a "death wish." He imagined himself to be battling with a hidden man inside him who was in the grip of this macabre wish.

The thought came to him every time a wheeled vehicle passed. He mistook the thought for the wish. He completely rearranged his travel habits so that he would never have to stand and watch any vehicle go by.

Then two things happened. Joni, as was probably inevitable, threw him over for another, younger executive. And Harley had a mild heart attack.

It seemed to him, as he left the hospital, that his worst expectations were being confirmed. He was utterly alone. He was on the way to becoming sick and helpless. The idea of suicide came more often and more strongly than before. He became mortally afraid, now, to go near a car or train, even to ride in one. He could not go to his office, but shut himself up at home. He now frankly admitted his terror. But he admitted it over the wrong thing, the thing that was not really dangerous—the recurring thought of suicide.

This is how one man found the golden plateau to be. It seemed hardly worth the climb.

The Freeloaders

This country was built by tough, industrious people. Like the pioneers who settled the West, the men and women who have poured into the suburbs during the past twenty years have been predominantly people of strong fiber. They have not been afraid to strive for the things they have wanted. Hardship has not stopped them. They have made mistakes; they have gone about certain things in the wrong ways, as Harley did. But primarily their wish has been to earn—not to be given—their place in the sun.

Unfortunately, these same tough, industrious men and women are, in many cases, raising children like Jerry and Mona Tragg. Harley's son and daughter were parasitic. They were enemies of our society. They were not enemies as criminals are—they perpetrated no violence and were not sought by the police except for traffic violations. They belonged to a more numerous, better camouflaged and therefore perhaps more dangerous army of enemies: the nonproducers, the freeloaders.

You could see this kind of individual beginning to develop in Alice Hager's sons and in the teen-aged Alec Green. These were boys who had not been guided firmly enough. They got what they wanted by other means than earning. They had not been made to respect other people's rights, needs or feelings. They had a particularly arrogant attitude toward women, who, they had learned early, could be pushed around. They did not produce; they expected society to produce for them.

These are the non-builders who are being shaped, ironically, by our society of builders. Carl Hager, Burt Green and Harley Tragg are the kinds of men who have helped make America big. Their sons and daughters may help destroy it. They represent the softening in America, the weakening of moral fiber that has been so widely observed. Their way of thinking is a debilitating disease of our culture: the something-for-nothing syndrome.

The non-producer is the kind of man who, if his father is rich, becomes a playboy. If he must support himself he typically bounces from job to job, selling himself through the personality crafts. In either case, he isn't willing to work. He wants money to be given him but he plans to do as little as possible in return.

He is the kind of man who cheats, for this seems easier than contributing to society. He is behind the reported increase of cheating in school and college exams. When he marries, he cheats on his wife. When he tires of his responsibilities as family head, he leaves her and his children. He may go through life marrying and divorcing as cavalierly as one buys and discards clothes. He uses people but feels no debt to them.

He is arrogant, conceited. He feels that the laws of society are for other people, not him. He cheats on his income tax, lets others bear the burden. He drives his car as fast as he pleases. He freely makes use of lying and deceit when he can gain by them. When caught and exposed, he is angry or tries to bribe the policeman, but he is not ashamed.

He is everywhere. He is the fashionably dressed fellow who sells you a house with a leaky cellar, a car with the speedometer turned back, a defective television set. When you seek later to remind him of his beautifully worded guarantee he has disappeared or is hiding behind fine print on a legal document. He is the politician who fixes tickets and swings government contracts for his paying friends. He is the rigger of television quiz shows, the payer and taker of disc-jockey payola. His female counterpart is the parasitic Joni or the Eve Bright who drives her husband to surround her with a façade of material things. The freeloader will do almost anything for reward except produce something useful for society. He wants something for nothing.

The danger in the something-for-nothing syndrome is that it does not seem big or shocking, like crime. People tend to shrug their shoulders at it. It is not uncommon in the mobile suburbs and the world they epitomize to see otherwise clear-thinking men and women grinning in admiration as someone relates how he has cheated on his taxes, or smuggled a camera into the country without paying the duty, or figured out a tricky way of evading turnpike tolls. Thus even producers are tainted with the attitude; they give it implied approval. It is unfashionable to display too strict a moral code. When a man brags that he is cheating on his wife, the popular thing to do is wink knowingly.

This is the weakness in our culture. The climber life tends to breed spoiled, semi-delinquent kids who become spoiled, nonproducing adults. It is a dangerous weakness, a harbinger of softening and decadence such as have wrecked other cultures in the past.

We are in competition today with new, tough nations that have arisen in once remote parts of the world. Russia and China are climber nations. Like ours, their mobility is breeding emotional problems. But their mobility has not yet progressed as far as ours. Their people are only now beginning to struggle up to the equivalent of American middle-class prosperity. They are builders. They are willing to work hard for what they want.

Against this tough-minded determination only a sturdy people can compete successfully. We have been sturdy in the past, but a softening has set in. We will not be sturdy enough if the something-for-nothing syndrome weakens us much further.

These newly risen nations, particularly China, believe that our softening has already progressed far. They are constantly testing us, prodding us to see how far they can go. They will run roughshod over us if we allow them to. This we must not do. We must grant them their place in the sun; we can't hold them down any more than the older, established cliques in our own society have been able to hold down hard-climbing newcomers. But we must remain tough, protectively self-assertive, to make sure that what we have will not be taken away from us.

This is why non-producers are the enemies of our society. They are not helping to build our industry or to harvest our still vast resources. They are soft; they would rather have luxuries than pay taxes to support the nation's advance in protective military power, space exploration, scientific research. A boy like Alec Green or Jerry Tragg will scheme to avoid military service, even feigning emotional disorder if he has to. Freeloaders will not provide this nation with the strength it needs to live successfully in an increasingly tough, competitive world.

Other nations in Europe, Asia, Africa and Latin America are climbing as they become industrialized and urbanized. They will look to us, as the highest climbers, for leadership in the difficult decades ahead. Men like Alec and Jerry, women like Joni and Eve, are not going to provide leadership of high enough quality.

The best leadership will come from men and women who produce and respect productiveness in others, who are considerate and helpful. It is important to find ways of dealing with the emotional problems that have afflicted such people in the mobile society, to help them release themselves from emotional interference so that they can produce more effectively. It is important, too, to find means by which they can raise tougher, harder-working, more productive children.

Part Two

NINE TECHNIQUES OF EMOTIONAL ADJUSTMENT

CHAPTER 10

Can Stresses Be Subtracted?

The preceding studies of unhappy people have shown some important facts about emotional disturbance. We can think of stresses in much the same way as an engineer thinks of them. He knows an engine will fail if it is overloaded (active stress) or if oiling and other maintenance are neglected (passive stress). The human mechanism is similar. It can function normally under only so much abuse; then it begins to act abnormally.

Stresses are cumulative. For those who aren't prepared to handle difficult situations, each sensitizer, pressurizer and precipitator strains the organism a little more, until finally the breaking point is reached. The study of childbearing women in Bergen County (Chapter Three) showed this. It is not simply the nature of stresses, but also the weight and shock of them, that determine whether a man or woman will give way emotionally. When too much difficulty piles up too fast, the individual may be overwhelmed. The mothers with fewer than five major stress factors were not likely to have the baby blues, and the blues they did have were likely to be relatively mild. Those with more than ten were almost sure to have trouble, and it was likely to be severe trouble.

The case studies showed, further, that there are more stresses, active and passive, lurking in this new mobile life. Statistically, the chances are greater in this life that people will accumulate the number of stresses that add up to emotional disturbance.

Now the question arises: Is it possible to lighten the burden of stresses an individual carries, or (what amounts to the same thing) help him carry them more easily? Better yet, can emotional trouble be prevented? Can stresses be lifted off? Can the individual be helped to adjust to them, before the trouble starts?

Even better than that, can people cut their load of stresses by themselves?

The answer to all these questions is, demonstrably, yes.

If emotional difficulty is to be cured or prevented, the sensitizers, pressurizers and precipitators in people's lives must somehow be reduced in number or effect. How can this be done?

The sensitizers are obviously hard to deal with. These are typically experiences that have happened in the past and cannot be repealed—parental discord, for example. You can use deep probing psychotherapy on such a stress, uncovering the past and helping the sufferer reorganize his inner feelings about his unhappy experiences. But this requires professional help and a heavy financial outlay. It seems quicker for mobile people to let such old wounds remain unprobed. The present-day stresses, the pressurizers and precipitators, offer easier hand-holds. These can often be alleviated without exhaustive and expensive probing to uncover the past. The patient's problem can be attacked through the external circumstances of his life instead of through his inner feelings.

There are, of course, people whose early sensitizing has been so great that their best hope lies in the probing or uncovering kind of psychotherapy. But the tremendous increase of emotional difficulty in the mobile world has come principally from an increase in pressurizers and precipitators—the realistic, obvious, day-to-day stresses associated with social mobility. The majority of mobile people who have emotional trouble are suffering from an overload of these present-day stresses. Such stresses can overload not only those who have been sensitized in their past lives, but also those who were previously well adjusted—people such as Diane Weber and George Kohler. To give a troubled individual insight into his sensitizers—the background features that shaped his personality—is not likely to help much when he is repeatedly traumatized in his present life.

To deal with the ongoing, practical stresses of the mobile world, a new realm of medical and behavioral science has been developed: social psychiatry. It deals with the individual's social environment rather than directly with his inner feelings. It is concerned with both the troubled and the normal mobile individual—and with both treatment and prevention. Its effort is to help the individual improve his emotional adjustment by helping him unload problems or cope with them more effectively. It concentrates on practical problems of the present rather than those from the past.

Social psychotherapy has been effective with mobile people. Between 1953 and 1959, a series of comparisons was made in Bergen County of deep-probing or uncovering therapy, and social therapy. The table below tells the story of nearly one thousand patients. It shows the percentage of patients who undertook treatment and were helped successfully by the two approaches:

	PERCENTAGE OF PATIENTS HELPED	
	Uncovering	*Social*
Childbearing women	43%	84%
Other young married women	23	94
Young married men	70	76
Young single women	60	61
Young single men	40	66
Middle-aged and older women	20	47
Middle-aged and older men	23	45
Girls	94	95
Boys	80	94

Note that, while some groups such as young wives were helped far more effectively by the new approach, others showed little improvement. Among these were young single women. Their present-day problems were harder to handle because they often had no one who could help them—no husband, no family nearby. The circumstances of their lives were less easy to change than those of married people; thus social therapy could not be used as effectively with them. For the same general reasons, older men and women, though they fared twice as well with social as with uncovering therapy, were less successful than younger men and women. Older people's problems were more likely to involve irreversible facts. Children and teen-agers, by contrast, were readily helped when parents and schools cooperated, even when there were very severe problems and morbid symptoms.

In general, social therapy was more successful with mobile people than with the less mobile. Among childbearing women who had lived in Bergen County five years or longer (a crude index of non-mobility), the rate of success in social psychotherapy was fifty-four per cent. Among newcomers—the more mobile women who had been in the county less than five years—the rate was nearly one hundred per cent. The problems of mobile and less mobile people are likely to differ. The less mobile do not have emotional difficulty nearly so often; but when they do, the difficulty is often a severe problem related mainly to early sensitizing. The mobile, by far the more numerous among disturbed people in Bergen County, typically suffer from stresses of the present. It is much easier to do something about these stresses than to correct a condition of oversensitiveness that began in the past and is rooted deeply in the personality.

Social therapy has the advantage of economy. Even severely troubled people can often be treated in relatively few psychiatric office sessions. Among 243 Bergen people who were treated with uncovering therapy, twenty per cent were successfully helped in fewer than twenty sessions. Among 252 who were treated with social therapy, forty-three per cent were discharged as successful before the twentieth visit.

The greatest advantage of social psychiatry, however, is that its principles can be understood and applied by the layman.

The various general solutions that mobile people in Bergen County have found to their problems can be grouped into categories that might be called techniques. These techniques are the substance of the social psychotherapy that has proved successful with Bergen's mobile people, and they can be applied by all individuals in the suburbs—and cities, too—of America.

The people whose case histories are discussed here had to learn of the techniques in psychiatric office visits. The psychiatrist, however, did not cure these people. He was needed mainly to identify their problems and to explain the techniques found successful by similar people with similar problems. Once given an understanding of the techniques, the patients and their families, friends and associates chose which combinations were practicable in their particular lives, made the necessary adjustments and cured themselves.

Specific applications of the techniques are illustrated here, as they apply to the people in the eight case histories. Other people will, of course, find different applications that suit their own particular circumstances.

CHAPTER 11

The First Technique: Help and Understanding

One of the most striking attributes of mobile Americans is their dogged independence of spirit. They are determined to go it alone. The suburbs are populated not by whole families but by wandering, spun-off nuclei. Mobile mothers try to manage homes and bring up children by themselves. Mobile men plunge into new jobs without first seeking training or advice. There is a feeling in the air that one must not "be a burden" on anybody.

But this pseudo independence works only until a stressful situation comes along. Much of the mobile world's emotional stress comes from the fact that people have won pseudo independence and found it unworkable. The gentle Southerner, Alice Hager, tried to live without her larger family and ended huddled fearfully in a closet. Fred Bright's employer and his own ambition pushed him untutored into an unfamiliar job and left him there, struggling alone and developing an ulcer.

These people could begin to regain their lost happiness once they sought and accepted help. Their first need in the acute emergency was for a strong, propping-up, crutch-like, very practical support. They needed this because they were emotionally disturbed, full of fears and worries that made them incapable of facing life on their own. Later, as the immediate emergency subsided for each of them, the propping-up help could be slowly replaced by a broader, more permanent environment of mutual assistance. This second kind of help was engineered to keep their troubles from coming back. Had it existed in the first place, few if any of them would have had such severe trouble. Life in the older stable communities was carried on in a permanent environment of mutual help. Today, mobile people can prevent emotional trouble by creating a similar environment for themselves.

Alice and Carl Hager

For the disturbed, however, propping-up help is the first requirement. When the intellectual Carl Hager came home and found his gentle Southern wife, Alice, huddled in a closet, he knew he would have to make some changes in his attitudes. Carl was tough; he'd come up the hard way. What he hadn't realized was that his wife needed to be tough, too, if she was to find a successful life in Disturbia. She needed someone to teach her how to be tough. That someone, Carl gradually realized, must be he.

He slowly withdrew slightly from his preoccupation with getting ahead in order to spend more time at home. He reduced his evening classes from three evenings a week to one. His attitude toward Alice changed gradually from irritability at her ineffectiveness to sympathetic understanding. He praised her heroic effort to carry on without any support. He arranged for a kindly older woman, whose own children had grown up and left the community, to provide Alice with companionship in the mornings and to help get her children off to school and her other duties accomplished. Within a few weeks, with medical tranquilization, Alice's panic had subsided.

Now that some of the larger stresses were diminished, Carl set out to help Alice extinguish her fears—of going outdoors, of the supermarket where she had had anxiety attacks, of the community which she had thought hostile. Carl thought perhaps he might talk her out of her fears, but it quickly became plain to him that words were not potent enough for such a job.

Fears are extinguished only by repeated exposure to the fear-inspiring situation with the danger removed or lessened, and often with a trusted escort to lean upon. When the troubled individual faces larger and larger doses of the feared thing again and again without being hurt, the conditioned fear gradually fades away.

Carl began taking Alice for short walks near home. With his arm around her, he walked with her in the evenings through the quiet suburban streets. Sometimes she was reluctant to go. He didn't force her, but he kept a firm, gentle pressure on her, a steady urging to go out with him and face what she feared. He was careful not to make her feel trapped; he let her know she could turn back and go home if it was absolutely necessary. But he encouraged her to keep going forward. There were times when she did turn back. Once a carload of kids sped by, honking the horn and shouting. Another time a police or fire siren wailed nearby. These things seemed menacing to Alice, and she fled home. But all the time, Carl kept urging her to try again. In spite of setbacks, they gradually moved their sphere of exploration farther and farther from home.

Eventually Carl thought she was ready to go with him to places where there were people. He took her one night to a movie, a light romantic comedy. The idea of jostling crowds frightened her, but he took her by the hand and led her there anyway. When they went into the theatre he carefully found seats on the aisle, near the back, so that Alice wouldn't feel trapped. Twice during the show she wanted to leave. Carl walked out to the lobby with her each time, bought her some popcorn, talked to her and when she calmed, led her back.

A few weeks later he had less of a struggle in getting her into a quiet restaurant. She was tense and anxious at first, but as the meal progressed she gradually relaxed. Carl was congratulating himself on the success of his therapy when suddenly a boisterous party of young couples came into the restaurant and sat at the next table. They had obviously just come from a cocktail party. They sang, laughed, talked loudly. Alice immediately became tense. Carl had to take her home. It was several weeks before he again dragged her out to a restaurant.

It was a long, hard process for both Carl and Alice. There were many setbacks, many days when Carl felt he could no longer bear the tremendous burden of supporting Alice. But he and she stuck with it. Gradually Alice learned that there was nothing to fear in the community as long as Carl was with her.

Carl eventually took her to the supermarket, showed her how to bargain good-humoredly with tradesmen and gently but firmly handle people she had thought were trying to trample on her. When she became more ready to meet people, they joined the local Parent-Teacher Association. Thus, with Carl helping, Alice began to seek friends and pleasures in the community she had hated. No longer required to do battle alone, she gradually lost her feelings of persecution. Her hallucinations ceased.

Carl could not, of course, be expected to prop her up indefinitely. Well-motivated, previously pseudo-independent people take pride in doing things for themselves. With Carl's help, Alice learned gradually to help herself. She hadn't learned it before because she had been almost over-protected much of her earlier life. Then suddenly she had been required to learn everything at once, alone. The requirement had overwhelmed her, and she had collapsed in panic. Now she began to learn step by step. She began to develop more self-assertiveness. She learned not to back down in arguments with tradesmen and neighbors, became able to seek friends by herself. Carl's physical presence was no longer needed; he could now serve more as a consultant. She began to adopt a firmer hand with her unruly sons, supported by Carl's willing management of them when he was home. Each success built confidence for the next effort. She was able to do these things because she knew she had Carl in reserve, ready to come to her support if she needed him. He was ready to talk to her when she needed advice.

Though Carl eventually stopped propping her up, he did not once again plunge into the business of getting ahead and leave her all alone. He and she established a permanent environment of mutual help. Carl spent more time with his sons, disciplining and guiding them, backing up Alice's authority. He continued to participate in community activities with her, constantly widening their circle of friends. Alice began to establish an environment of help with her neighbors, too. She and they started to baby-sit for each other, occasionally got together for coffee during the day to discuss mutual problems.

Thus Alice made a double gain. She gained help. And she became tougher, more able to help herself. Both are essential to a young wife in the mobile community.

Gina and John Conning

Gina Conning, the young Italian-American mother who had run to a police station talking wildly of knives and sexual perversions, was similarly in need of help. Her husband, John, was frantic when he saw her need. He called his mother and begged her to help her daughter-in-law and baby grandson.

The older woman had smoldered with resentments against Gina for a long time. When John first asked her to come and help she balked. Why should she do things for this ungracious, social-climbing young Latin woman who had taken her only son away? But John pleaded hard. He pointed out that the baby would suffer if no one came forward to help in this emergency. This made Mrs. Conning stop and think. She loved the baby boy, thought he looked much like John, had often wished she had more chance to care for him and cuddle him. (Gina, who had lost her mother as a child and didn't realize an older woman could help, had seldom asked Mrs. Conning to help with the baby. Mrs. Conning had taken this as a sign that she was supposed to keep her hands off him.) Moreover, Mrs. Conning, like the depressed, suicidal Martha Kohler and many other middle-aged women, had been suffering from a feeling of uselessness after her son's marriage. She yearned for a chance to serve.

Finally, grudgingly, she agreed to come over to John's and Gina's house and lend a hand. When she arrived and saw Gina sobbing miserably on the living-room couch, she was filled with compassion. No matter what faults Gina might have, the most important thing about her at the moment was that she was in trouble and in need of another woman's help. Mrs. Conning threw her arms around her weeping daughter-in-law. She put Gina to bed with a dose of tranquilizers and sedatives from the doctor. She assured Gina everything was now all right; Mother would take care of the baby and Gina. She told Gina she could sleep without worry. Gina did—for sixteen hours uninterruptedly. She got up for a few hours, saw her house in order, her baby sleeping peacefully, her husband well taken care of. She hugged her mother-in-law and went back to bed. She slept twelve more hours. She awoke a new woman. Her body was finally beginning to get the rest it craved. Her fear of hurting John or the baby was beginning to subside.

She and her mother-in-law now settled down to build a permanent environment of help. The older woman stayed in Gina's home for several weeks, then started a schedule of visiting Gina several days each week to help with the baby and baby-sit. The two women had many arguments at first, stemming from their differences in background. Sometimes Mrs. Conning would storm out of the house, vowing never to come back. But she always returned. Often it was the two men—John and his father—who cooled the women down and got them together again. Slowly Gina and her mother-in-law learned to restrain their emotional outbursts at each other. When people join forces in a higher cause, whether it is serving a baby or fighting a war, small differences are usually put aside. Each woman had much to gain through this teaming-up and much to lose if the arrangement ended.

A tremendous load of work and worry was thus lifted from Gina's shoulders. With Mrs. Conning helping and teaching, she felt less confused about the baby. She was enormously relieved to know the burden was no longer hers alone, that an experienced, reliable mother was on hand. She was now learning motherhood as women have learned it for thousands of non-mobile years—not by herself, but under the eye of an experienced teacher. She was able to rest, relax, sleep for an hour or two each afternoon. Occasionally she went out to seek rewards for her hard work. As her tensions and body aches subsided, she was able to sleep better. Life once again started to look bright to Gina Conning.

Tom Krazinkow

The chronic loser, peeping Tom Krazinkow, also began to feel better when he got appropriate help. His mother's brother, childless Uncle Harry, persuaded Tom's parents and the court to release Tom in his custody. Uncle Harry saw that Tom could not easily get anywhere otherwise.

Uncle Harry took Tom to live with him, gave Tom a part-time job in his drugstore. He was careful not to push him past his limitations. But he encouraged him to talk of his plans, encouraged his thoughts of trying to go back to college. The work at the store was easy, by design; and Tom, for the first time in his life, very slowly began to get a small feeling of success. The thought, "I can succeed," began to flower in his mind. Through this first technique of help and understanding—and, as we shall see later, through several of the other eight techniques—Tom was building the beginnings of self-confidence.

Martha and George Kohler

The middle-aged alcoholic, George Kohler, and his suicidal wife, Martha, were unable to help each other. Their daughter Joan took a leave of absence from her job and husband and rushed to the rescue. Martha's spirits lifted when Joan visited her in the hospital and assured Martha she had not been abandoned. Joan promised to stand by and help her mother and dad as long as necessary.

Martha didn't leave the hospital right away. But slowly, medical treatment with psychic energizers began to counteract her depression. Her doctor assured her she wasn't likely to need more of the electric shock treatments she feared, as long as she had her daughter's help and the new medicines.

Between visits to the hospital, the capable Joan worked on her father. George didn't feel like going back to work or facing the daily struggle of living any more. Some of his friends had advised him to make the most of his automobile accident and resulting concussion syndrome, sue for a fat settlement from the other driver's insurance company and live the rest of his life pensioned off. This sounded good to George. He felt weary and defeated.

Joan saw that, no matter how much her father might like the idea at the moment, being put out to pasture was not the ideal solution for him. She didn't think he'd be happy vegetating uselessly, cut off from the mainstream of human society with no reward but financial security. As Carl Hager gently pressured his shy Southern wife, Alice, Joan urged her father to face what he feared. She wheedled and cajoled him from his armchair, took him for short drives in the car. Gradually he lost his fear of being in a car, was able to take the wheel occasionally and drive short distances on quiet streets, with Joan beside him. There were setbacks and frustrations, of course. Small mistakes and discourtesies by other drivers threw him into panic, and sometimes he refused to drive for days. But Joan stuck with it. Week by week George's fear of driving was extinguished. It was he who drove Martha home from the hospital. His headaches and dizziness gradually subsided.

Eventually Joan suggested that her father drive to the appliance store where he'd worked and have a talk with his employer-partners. George wasn't anxious to do this. He felt he'd failed in his attempt to be the store manager. He was sure his employers wouldn't take him on again as manager. He thought maybe they'd give him a lower-ranking job, and he couldn't make himself face the thought of a drop in pay and prestige.

Finally, however, Joan got him to do what had to be done. His employers knew something of his recent problems and were surprised and pleased to learn he'd driven to the store by himself. They were even more surprised when he asked to have his old job back. Despite his difficulty in keeping up with the competition, George had been a valuable man to have as store manager. The customers liked him; many had been asking about him in his absence. The store owners decided to reinstate George as manager, but with a younger, more energetic man as assistant. They told him to arrange his own schedule, go easy at first, delegate responsibilities so as not to become overburdened again.

George was lucky his employers were farsighted, understanding men. There are some employers who feel they must constantly clean out "dead wood." They aren't inclined to help an emotionally troubled man such as George work his way back to usefulness. Their disinclination not only means personal tragedy for the men concerned, but on a national scale it probably adds up to a vast waste of skilled manpower.

Martha, George, and their daughter now called on the clergyman who had come to their church after the old clergyman had died of a heart attack. He was a well-educated young man who had had previous experience with rapidly changing communities. He quickly understood the Kohlers' problem. He was delighted to see them. He needed them, as long-term pillars of the church, to help him and the community. He had plans. He wanted their church to become the hub of the parish, the place in which community integration could begin. A large new parish house needed to be built, not only for religious purposes but with an auditorium, a stage and a kitchen. Dinners, picnics, bazaars and dances should be organized. There were conference rooms used on Sunday for religious instruction which could serve as meeting places for young people's groups, spinsters' and bachelors' clubs, married couples' groups. A welcoming committee for newcomers and cadres to help organize children's activities were badly needed. The new clergyman was counting on parishioners like Martha and George Kohler to serve on the board of trustees, to chair committees, to help organize the church membership.

Martha and George left their meeting inspired. Their brooding over their own problems had been replaced by planning for a cause larger than themselves. Martha no longer found herself useless. She became too busy to dwell any more on her fears of sickness. She began to relax; her body's complaints dwindled.

Fred and Eve Bright

The tense young father, Fred Bright, out of the hospital with his ulcer on the mend, sought a conference with his boss. He relayed the doctors' orders that he must give his system a chance to calm down. He asked his boss temporarily to postpone increasing his burden of responsibility; to let him have more time to get his present job under comfortable control. This meant, of course, that Fred had to slow down his race for further promotions. It wasn't easy to make this change in attitude. But he understood, now, that it was necessary to get ahead a little more slowly.

Fred's boss, realizing that he himself would be overburdened if one of his lieutenants collapsed, promised to cooperate. Reassured by this attitude, Fred began to feel he could ask his boss for advice and help; he began to confer about difficult problems as they came up. Thus, Fred began to learn less painfully. The façade of dynamic confidence that he had so carefully built was beginning to have some substance behind it. Fred had never understood that such help was necessary or available. Thrown prematurely into the mobile world by his father's death, he had never learned to seek assistance or advice.

Help such as this—help from family, neighbors, community, business associates—can keep even severely disturbed people out of mental hospitals. In the year 1953 a group of 115 troubled suburbanites were treated by psychiatric methods in which family and friends were not usually called in for consultation or asked to help. Twenty-two per cent of the patients had to be hospitalized. In 1958-59, the social-psychiatric factor of help was added, combined with new tranquilizing and energizing drugs, for a new group of 232 patients. Only seven per cent—one-third as many—had to be sent to the mental hospital. Many of the patients recovered after fewer than twenty psychiatric office sessions, and some after only four or five. Some sixteen per cent of these same patients had been hospitalized for emotional disturbance in previous years, when they were not receiving social or community help.

The statistics are still more striking when you consider only new mothers. In a group of maternity psychiatric patients treated in 1953-54, fully forty-three per cent had to be hospitalized. Since the factor of help was added, among more than one hundred disturbed new mothers, fewer than one per cent have had to be sent to a mental hospital.

Statistics can also be made to tell the story in reverse: those with the least help available to them are likely to have the most trouble. In a group of new mothers who came through the maternity experience without emotional upset, only nineteen per cent had no one such as a mother or sister to help with the new baby. In a group of new mothers who did become disturbed, eighty per cent had no experienced women to help them. Lack of help largely explains why single women, widows and divorcees stay in mental hospitals longer, on the average, than married women.

Spun off from their larger families, mobile people must recognize that they need replacements for the help that would have been at hand in an integrated community. This calls for a switching-around of traditional roles in the community. Wives far from their larger families must get more help in the home from their husbands. Husbands must teach their wives how to handle home-maintenance jobs. Children must be taught to help at an early age, as they were in the farm household. They must share some of their parents' workload. Each family member must be diversified, ready to step into another role, so that no one's burden becomes too large. Realistically independent people are interdependent. People with no help in reserve are precariously pseudo-independent.

The need for help goes out beyond the home itself. A wife who understands something of her husband's business, who can counsel him on it and perhaps directly help him in it, lifts a burden off his shoulders and enables him to relax more. A wife who has a career skill other than homemaking can help her husband earn money or can be ready to take over the earning function in an emergency—when he is sick, for example, or loses his job. Similarly a husband who takes part in community activities can help his wife make friends in town, help her get away from the house and children.

Thus the mobile family can begin to build its own new integration in a disintegrated world. The family is no longer split down the middle, with income-earning on one side and home on the other.

Help must also be sought from the community at large. Young mothers must get older women such as Martha Kohler, who need the sense of usefulness, to help with the children and to baby-sit. Older men such as George Kohler, who need recognition, must be engaged to coach and teach the sons of younger fathers such as Carl Hager and Fred Bright, who have less time. Each generation benefits.

Mutual help, mutual service: this is the first step by which a mobile community can begin to replace the emotional satisfactions of the old-time integrated community.

CHAPTER 12

The Second Technique: Producing for Recognition

The people in old-time American stable communities were mostly producers. They got their satisfactions largely from serving each other and society, from doing useful jobs for which they were rewarded materially and in community applause. This was the only way in which the democratic society could function, and the attitude contributed to the nation's growth.

Our mobile society also rewards producers, for without them it would collapse. Economic output and noneconomic community service are still the prime functions of individuals in a society that hopes to maintain or increase its strength. But this monumentally important fact has been obscured somewhat in the dust and turmoil of getting ahead. Mobile people have seen the rewards that are handed out for productiveness: recognition, power, money and the things money buys. These things glitter. People have been in a hurry to grab them, and have tended to try getting them by shortcut methods. They have tried to sidestep the requirement that one produces before one consumes. This is the origin of the façade syndrome.

Fred and Eve Bright

Eve Bright, ulcer-ridden Fred's materialistic wife, accurately noted that many wealthy people were popular, looked up to, applauded. But the prime reason why they were admired—the fact that they had contributed heavily to the growth of the American economy—was obscured from Eve behind a subordinate factor: that they lived in well-appointed homes. So she strove to build a façade of affluence, hoping thus to win the same respect, admiration and acceptance for herself and her family. The mobile suburban community didn't seem, to her, to offer any other road to recognition. What she failed to understand was that it is not usually the wealth itself that wins friends and admirers, but the usefulness, the productiveness from which wealth may result.

While Fred was still in the hospital, he and Eve discussed their predicament—how their striving for the façade of affluence, their constant spending beyond Fred's income, had contributed to the tensions that had brought Fred so close to death. Eve began to see how futile all the spending had been. If she wanted real recognition, she realized, there were two things she could do. She could find ways to make herself useful to the people of the community—by producing for them instead of petitioning for their admiration. And she could help Fred become more productive economically—by helping him reduce his burden of worry, cutting the family's spending, making the children do some of his home-maintenance chores to earn their rewards. In these ways recognition would eventually come, and along with it, perhaps, wealth.

Thus Fred Bright got his wife's help as well as that of his boss. Fred, too, had begun to understand that there is no safe short cut to the rewards that glitter so brightly. If he wished for continued rises in income, he saw, he must make himself increasingly useful to the business community. He had tried before to climb by grabbing at promotions before he was adequately prepared, covering his realistic insecurity with a façade of confidence. This had brought him grief and almost death; it could not bring real security. The way to climb, Fred saw, was to become increasingly productive—to prepare to do more advanced work, and to step up into the next higher job only when qualified to perform it well. Fred's first task was to learn his present job well.

Eve's materialistic mother also had to get off the Brights' back and start producing. There is no reason why children and some older people in our society should ambush the generation in between. Children and retired people can perform many useful services; they need not be freeloaders like Eve's mother and the teen-ager, Alec Green, living on the generosity of young and middle-aged adults. Young couples like Fred and Eve have a right to insist that nobody, young or old, overburden them. Just as Alice and Carl Hager had begun teaching their children to be more helpful, better behaved and less burdensome, so Fred and Eve began suggesting tactfully that Eve's mother baby-sit occasionally, help around the house, stop urging the family to spend. The older woman discovered that as she became more productive, she was more welcome in the family.

Harley and Audrey Tragg

Like Eve, the ancestor-hunting Audrey Tragg, wife of the successful but unhappy businessman, Harley, had to realize that real status is based on achievement and not on a façade. She, too, had to discover that wealth does not automatically bring recognition.

Audrey's first taste of real recognition came when she supported frightened, lonely Harley during the period when he cowered at home, afraid of his "death wish." She gave up visiting the country club to take care of him. When Harley expressed his relief and gratitude, she felt really useful for the first time in many years. As for Harley, it was the first tangible indication he had had in years that anybody cared what happened to him. Just as

Joan Kohler helped her father regain his confidence in driving, Audrey gently pressured Harley out of the house and eventually back to work. After a while, he was able to manage alone. By this time, the relationship between the two was subtly changed. They no longer ignored each other, going separate ways. Each had given the other something. Harley had been shown that somebody might care for him if he grew old and sick, that he might not, after all, be utterly alone. His fear of committing suicide was fading. Audrey had found herself to be worthy in someone else's eyes.

This taste of true appreciation whetted her appetite for more. She began to look around for ways in which she could use her time and money to perform a real service to the community, instead of using them to line up and parade forgotten ancestors. One of her first acts was to present the local library with a set of historical reference books. Like many libraries in fast-growing suburban towns, this one had needs that far exceeded its budget. The chief librarian, once a victim of Audrey's impatient badgering, was delighted with Audrey's interest in the library's needs. The librarian suggested that Audrey attend a forthcoming meeting of the local Friends of the Library.

Audrey went home thinking of ways in which she could help. She was beginning to see, at last, how she could get people to applaud her.

Alec Green

Alec Green, the gimme kid who was caught at a gang-bang party and hauled before a juvenile court on a morals charge, discovered at last that the world wouldn't let him have his own way all the time. The judge gave him an indeterminate sentence and put him on probation, with an evening curfew and an order to report with his parents to a probation officer once a week. If he didn't behave, the judge warned, he would go to a training school.

Alec's parents now began to recognize their responsibility in preparing Alec for successful living. Backed up by the experienced, stern but kindly probation officer, Alec's father, Burt, began the first of many man-to-man talks with the boy. A boy like Alec is handled best with a friendly arm around his shoulders, both to encourage and to control him. Burt showed Alec plainly that the trouble he'd already had was nothing compared to what might happen in the military services or at the hands of employers in later life. Burt promised that he and Alec's mother would gladly help the boy gain what he wanted in rewards and pleasures, but their support would take the form of helping him earn these things himself.

Alec's whole future, Burt pointed out, depended on his willingness and ability to apply himself persistently. He wouldn't always have a family to give him what he wanted or bail him out of trouble. He had lived his entire life in economic boom times, and this had contributed to his unrealistic picture of the world. He must learn to plan ahead for bad times, to save, to think of the future.

Burt realized that sermonizing alone would not rehabilitate his son. Words are useful, but they must have a solid foundation of reality to make them meaningful. Supported by the probation office, Burt set about giving his lectures such a foundation. He shifted some of his attention from crabgrass to Alec. He tried to reorganize Alec's life in such a way that it would teach the lessons Alec needed to learn. Burt encouraged Alec's ineffectual mother to be more firm and supported her efforts.

Alec was a teen-ager, halfway through high school, and it was going to be harder to get him interested in sports, work, studies and group activities than it might have been with a younger boy. Like most older boys, however, Alec needed money for movies, sodas and other pleasures. Burt had been giving him a regular allowance, the same amount each week regardless of Alec's behavior. Burt now cut the allowance, but offered Alec an opportunity to earn a greater amount by mowing the lawn, weeding crabgrass and doing other useful jobs about the house. He told Alec that, from now on, he would have to produce before he consumed. Alec at first grumbled, sulked and refused to work. But Burt was firm. After a few weeks of being broke, Alec slowly started to produce.

Burt gave him all the work he wanted. At first he didn't want much; he earned less than his allowance had been. His transformation wasn't miraculous, but slow and often painful. But eventually, as he began to see that his rewards were directly proportional to his efforts, he was earning half again as much as his allowance.

Tom Krazinkow

Peeping Tom Krazinkow was also starting to realize rewards from productiveness. Unlike Tom's inconsistent father, his Uncle Harry did not become angry when Tom faltered and hesitated, but patiently showed him how to accomplish and then patted him on the back for slow, step-by-step improvements. And unlike Tom's flighty mother, Uncle Harry encouraged him to keep trying even when the going was rough. Tom learned not to expect big things to happen quickly, not to give up when he failed at first to master a skill or an area of knowledge. Each time he achieved a small goal, his perseverance was reinforced; he moved on toward progressively larger accomplishments. There were many setbacks and frustrations, but Uncle Harry kept urging him on. The feeling that he could succeed was becoming ever more firmly planted in him.

In the drugstore his interest in biology led him, with Uncle Harry's encouragement, to an interest in botanicals and other drugs. As his interests in the store broadened, he came to enjoy working there more and more. Busy in his work, he had less time to brood over his sexual and other problems, less time to spend in fantasy or window-peeping. Tom Krazinkow was starting to become a useful member of society, and his rewards were increasing proportionately.

Like the technique of mutual help, with which it is linked, productiveness is a key to happiness in the mobile society. This is one reason why single men do better in social psychotherapy than single women. It is generally easier for the troubled single man to get a job in which he can be productive and happy. Our society doesn't offer the disturbed single girl as good a chance of happiness. Not so many jobs are open to her. When she does get a job she may not be entirely satisfied in it, for her orientation is toward marriage.

Producing is the surest way of getting ahead. The majority of people who are in the mid-middle and upper-middle classes today are there because they have produced something for which society has paid them well. They have been rewarded not only in material things, but also in having the best chances for happiness in the mobile world. Just as men of higher incomes recover more readily from heart attacks, people of higher social and economic stations do better in psychotherapy. They do better because they are in more firm control of their own destinies; they are better able to reorganize their lives to remove stresses and increase rewards. The table below shows how 113 psychiatric patients of various socioeconomic classes fared in therapy:

Success in therapy	*Upper-middle*	*Mid-middle*	*Lower-middle*	*Lower*
Good	50%	33%	20%	0%
Fair	50	43	60	25
Poor	0	24	20	75
	(100%)	(100%)	(100%)	(100%)

None of the upper-middle-class patients did poorly. None of the lower-class patients did very well. Thus it pays to get ahead; the chances of happiness increase on the way up. But it is important to get ahead carefully, by producing.

CHAPTER 13

The Third Technique: Planning and Preparation

Life in the stable society was a good deal simpler than it is today. There was less need for broad education, formal or informal. Planning and preparation for the future could be directed along a single, narrow path.

Our society today is more complex. The mobile man and woman require a broad, continuous education, in and out of school.

Fred and Eve Bright

The ulcer-ridden Fred Bright, for example, slowly realized that he needed more training to do his job better and less painfully. He began to educate himself informally; he asked questions, consulted with more experienced men. He also sensed a need for more formal education, and he arranged a program of courses in a university. Later, as his superiors in the company realized he was taking his studies seriously, as his questions showed understanding and his work improved, they arranged for him to attend classes two afternoons a week with the company paying the tuition. As his knowledge began to expand, his self-confidence grew. Eventually, he was able to handle his job more effectively, accomplishing the same amount of work in less time. He no longer found it urgently necessary to stop at the bar each evening to mend fences; he was becoming more sure his fences were in good repair. He no longer had to jump at every whim of his superiors. He had confidence that he was now making himself too useful to the company to be fired.

Fred was an ambitious man, full of curiosity, anxious to try his hand in new areas of endeavor. In time he recognized that he was ripe for promotion. He had mastered his job, and he foresaw that he might become bored with it. But he now knew better than to leap unprepared into another job. From the company's changed attitude toward him he knew he would receive further promotions in time. He began to prepare himself for the next higher job. And he began to teach two of his more promising subordinates his own job. For the mobile man, the process of education can never stop.

George and Martha Kohler

The alcoholic George Kohler, who had tried to retire from life after his car accident, also began to improve his informal education. In the Little League baseball organization and on the church's board of trustees, he came in contact with businessmen who had been more successful than he. He talked with them, asked them questions, observed the ways in which they handled administrative and financial affairs of the Little League and the church. He learned gradually that it is useful in the mobile world to be not only soft-hearted but also hard-headed—to treat people with kindness but at the same time to make sure they don't walk on you. As manager of the appliance store, George had been too easygoing. He hadn't been firm enough with lazy employees or with customers who failed to pay their bills. With his new businessmen friends as his models, he began to get a firmer grip on the affairs and destiny of his store.

Diane Weber

Diane Weber, after her separation from Link, the husband who had outgrown her, regretted not having a college education. Like many girls, she had built her entire future on her husband. She had no career skill other than that of housewife. She did not know how to be productive except in unskilled clerical work. It was not easy to accept the social decline from successful lawyer's wife to file clerk. Yet she must work rather than sit home and brood. After talking things over with her family, who stood by her and were willing to help with the children, she realized that she must begin now to make the preparations she should have made before marriage. She enrolled in a one-year secretarial school.

Tom Krazinkow

Tom Krazinkow, the chronic loser who ran afoul of the law for window-peeping, had failed to win the position in life he coveted partly because he lacked education. After much talk with his uncle, he enrolled for one night course in his old interest, botany. He concentrated just on making a passing grade. There were times when he wanted to quit, but Uncle Harry made him stick with it. Tom made an effort to meet other students and ask questions about their work and plans. But most important, he and his uncle discussed his work. His uncle answered his questions and suggested outside reading. Tom made a C grade in the course and felt ready for two courses the next semester. After two years' time, Tom was ready for full-time college. As he progressed slowly in the drugstore and in college under his uncle's guidance, he saw himself moving closer toward his goals.

He also broadened his preparation on other fronts. With his Uncle Harry helping, he started learning how to get along with people, how to stand firm against aggression, how to make himself more likable. Tom's continuing progress in college, his widening interests in biology and other subjects, gave him enough that was worthwhile and interesting to talk about so that he did not have to study the personality crafts very hard. He needed only to apply a small amount of polish, learn to stand a little straighter, look people in the eye, have his hair cut more often. Now, working at his uncle's soda fountain, listening to the young people's talk, he learned in a few months to speak back to them knowingly and sometimes humorously.

George and Martha Kohler

The suicidal Martha Kohler, like many middle-aged people, was under stress partly because of worries about her health. These worries had arisen from past experience with illness in her own life and the lives of others close to her. To lay these worries to rest she arranged regular physical checkups, began to understand and respect her body's limitations. Planning thus converted worry into intelligent behavior instead of into physical tension reactions.

People who learn to plan their steps are more likely to succeed without emotional difficulty. They learn not only through formal education, but also by examining their own past mistakes. Their past griefs inspire new useful plans. They also draw upon the experience of others. They consult, discuss.

In the old-time stable communities, people had stable rules to live by. It was possible to live almost by rote. The society didn't change much, and the rules that served grandfather and grandmother were useful to young adults. In our world of rapid change, our mobile melting pot, the useful rules of one old culture are clashing with those of another, and the rules of most old cultures are often failing to serve the new society's needs. Rote living, dogmatically following old answers to life's problems, no longer assures success. For people on the frontiers of change, the surest solutions are coming from creative thought.

No single individual's experience is likely to give him knowledge enough to solve all the problems he meets on these frontiers. Thus he must draw on the experiences of others—not only of older people, as the younger in the stable community could more often do, but also of his own contemporaries. This is necessarily an era of committees and conferences. People of different ages and backgrounds, religious and ethnic groups, ways of thinking, standards and values, must get together to solve mutual problems. The need for talk is everywhere in the mobile society. Talk is a key component of education.

Alec Green

Burt Green started making it a regular habit to talk at length with his juvenile delinquent son, Alec. Burt didn't wait for Alec to come to him; he had learned that youngsters won't always seek on their own to discuss problems with adults.

One of the subjects they discussed most often was sex. Burt made it clear that a fifteen-year-old boy need be in no hurry to prove himself in sexual conquests. There were other areas of life which were far more important at the moment: studies, sports, learning social poise and social skills such as dancing, earning the respect of good friends. When Alec was ready to assume adult responsibilities in the complicated mobile world, when he was prepared to support a wife and family—then would come the time for regularly enjoying the deserved pleasures of maturity.

Burt counseled his son to pay no attention to his friends' boasts about conquests. Most such boasts were grossly exaggerated. Adolescence is a time for learning, getting ready for life. Boys and girls who go steady, especially those who fornicate regularly, are losing precious hours that might be spent far more usefully in learning more productive skills—including the skill of choosing and enjoying productive friends. Burt advised his son to distract himself when sexually aroused and, when necessary, to relieve himself in private.

At the same time, Burt recognized that part of education for life is education in the field of sex. He encouraged Alec to learn all he could about sex, suggested books that he might read on the subject, offered to answer any questions the boy might have. He helped Alec see that there is a difference between being constantly on the prowl for sexual experience and being ready to learn when the opportunity arises. He assured the boy that, as he grew older, continued to meet people and win success in diverse areas of his life, girls would be attracted to him and opportunities for experience would arise.

Burt explained that most girls of Alec's middle-class background were taught not to be anxious for sexual experience at a young age and would remain virgins for a number of years. Alec should never try to force, persuade or emotionally trap a virgin. However, Burt went on, before Alec grew much older he would probably hear about several older single girls whose attitude toward sex was different from that of the majority. If by that time Alec had made himself into a likable young man, if he could command people's respect, then such girls would be delighted to try a few tricks with him. If he failed to make himself worthy of society's admiration, however, relatively few girls would let him get close enough to try. His immediate goal was to learn, to do a good job in school and elsewhere, to win friends and respect.

Burt also started Alec thinking about other long-term rewards. Like many boys, Alec hoped one day to have a car of his own. He had expected to be given one, as he'd always been given anything else he'd wanted. Burt told him, instead, that he would have to earn at least part of the money himself. Thus Alec began to learn that, in the mobile world, it is valuable to plan and prepare for the future.

At Burt's urging, he began a systematic program of saving. He also started to prepare for earning more money the following year. He enrolled in an after-school swimming course which would, he hoped, lead eventually to a lifeguard's certificate. Burt praised him and encouraged him amply during his early efforts at improving his mediocre swimming ability, urged him to keep at it when he felt like quitting. As Alec became a better swimmer, he needed his father's support less often. Recognition was beginning to come from other boys around the swimming pool. As further preparation for the hoped-for car, Burt urged the boy to join a police-sponsored club in which pre-drivers learned auto mechanics and safe driving habits.

Gradually Alec's parents cracked down on his laziness in school. By the same process of encouraging step-by-step improvement, rewarding forward movement but punishing steps backward, they slowly trained him to apply himself hard to his studies. They pushed him, but not past his limitations, letting him climb carefully. In his schoolwork, his swimming and his chores, he was learning to work perseveringly for his rewards. His parents granted or withheld privileges—weekend and weekday curfew hours in particular—according to his efforts at disciplining his behavior, studying, controlling his temper, watching his language, showing respect to his mother and teachers.

The importance of formal and informal education in the mobile world can hardly be exaggerated. The youngster who is studying hard in school and being rewarded for it is not likely to become a delinquent. The adult who has learned useful skills to contribute in his job or in the community need not fall prey to the façade syndrome. The housewife who has learned varied interests need not lead a life of loneliness and drudgery, as Alice Hager did, nor feel helpless like Diane Weber when she loses her husband through divorce or death.

A mobile man's or woman's chances of happiness, in short, are directly proportional to the amount of knowledge he or she has. This can be demonstrated in numbers: the better educated are far more likely to do well in psychotherapy than those with less education. In one group of disturbed young married women, only fifty-two per cent of those with less than high school education responded well to treatment. But of those with high school or higher education, seventy-seven per cent did well. The better educated women had been trained to think more clearly. They were more used to facing and overcoming problems by applying their intellects. More diverse avenues were open to them in which to seek recognition and reward.

Ernest Burgess and Leonard Cottrell, Jr., sociologists who have studied marriage, have found that women's chances of marital happiness increase as their career preparation increases. Teachers do best—there are fewer poorly adjusted marriages among them than in any other group of women. Next come women in other highly regarded professions such as nursing, medicine and law. Next come skilled office workers, then clerical and semi-clerical workers. The worst off, as far as the chances of marital happiness go, are those whose only training has been in domestic or unskilled employment.

As another indication of education's importance in the happiness of the mobile, consider the factor of intelligence. Recent evidence shows that an individual's intelligence, as measured by IQ tests, increases as he trains himself to use it, rather than remaining fixed throughout his life. Thus education would boost intelligence. And the more intelligent an individual is, the better are his chances of solving emotional problems. The table below shows how 148 people of various IQ's fared in psychotherapy:

	WECHLER-BELLEVUE INTELLIGENCE QUOTIENT (IQ)				
	below 90	*90-99*	*100-109*	*110-119*	*120 and over*
Per cent successful in therapy	36%	68%	75%	79%	93%

People who start an education and fail to finish it are often doubly unfortunate. Not only do they lack the education they started out to get; they also carry around with them the frustration of not finishing. The educational quitter, not having succeeded in his learning goals, may lack the feeling that he can succeed in other areas. Tom Krazinkow was an example of this frustration.

Educational quitters bulk large among the emotionally disturbed. According to census figures, about forty-nine per cent of women in Bergen County who began college completed their studies; while in a group of women psychiatric patients only twenty-one per cent of those who began were college graduates. The importance of education shows up, too, in the fact that college graduates throughout the nation are less likely to divorce than people of less schooling.

The technique of planning and preparation is linked with producing, which is linked with the environment of help. All have much to do with the fourth technique, diversity.

CHAPTER 14

The Fourth Technique: Diversity

The mobile world is full of uncertainties. Real security can come only from flexibility and diversity—from having more than one possible career, more than one possible source of income, recognition, reward. Thus, if there is failure in one area, the others will continue to provide support.

Fred and Eve Bright

The need for diversity exists in all areas of the mobile life. Consider the area of jobs and careers, for example. The ulcer-ridden Fred Bright became extremely tense in his job because he saw, all too clearly, that things could change—that he could be relegated to some corporate limbo or fired. All his eggs were in this one basket.

Fred began to see how diversity could improve his position. He began to chat about job possibilities with friends in other companies. He found several job areas in these companies where he might fit if he should ever need to. In this way, he gradually reduced his fear of failure in his own job.

At home, recalling the fun he had had with his own father, he became active with his son in a Boy Scout hiking and nature-study group. This gave him needed relaxation, fun and exercise. It gave him other things to think of besides work. It diversified his means of getting rewards. It brought him into contact with new friends who opened new job vistas to him. Previously, he and his wife, Eve, had pushed themselves at people; but people now sought him out, for they respected the job he was doing with his own son and their sons as well.

His wife, Eve, saw that she could help both herself and Fred by diversifying. She had already diversified her means of getting recognition by joining a citizens' group whose purpose was to keep the town looking neat and pretty. In this group, she had many friends, among them some of the country-club people whom she had previously tried to woo with expensive cocktail parties. They liked her now, for she and they were serving together in a larger cause. With recognition beginning to come from this source, it no longer seemed so important to Eve to create a façade of affluence.

Now she started to diversify further. She enrolled in a series of college courses in interior decoration. She had always been interested in the subject, and she enjoyed the courses thoroughly. Her reputation as a skilled decorator began to spread through her growing circle of friends. She advised them on their home-beautifying problems, taking as her payment their appreciation of her service. Now she was gaining status without needing to build a false front. Moreover, her diversity gave her a new economic security. She was a housewife with auxiliary career skills. In an emergency she could probably earn a good income from interior decoration. This was comforting to Fred; it further eased his fear of losing his job. It was also comforting to Eve. If Fred became ill again, or if he died or divorced her, she would not be in the same straits as Diane Weber.

Eve Bright also applied the technique of diversity to her straying daughters, Franny and Ginny. She saw that a girl who leads a diverse, interesting life, with fun and applause coming from many sources, will feel less need to parade her sexual charms before boys—and, indeed will have less time in which to do so. She encouraged her girls to get involved in worthwhile activities: a school drama group, babysitting, sports.

She began to discourage their going to movies every weekend, taking car rides with boys, hanging around all afternoon at the local soda shop. She did not, of course, cut them off from all contact with boys. But she cracked down on them a little. Without trying to pick their boy friends for them, she discouraged their keeping company with certain boys of the gimme-kid crowd. She established and strictly enforced curfew hours, saw to it that the night-time boy-girl activities they attended—school and country-club dances, for example—were chaperoned by responsible adults. She let them know that they could bring their friends home with them on certain evenings as long as their homework was done, as long as they asked permission first and as long as the parties were reasonably quiet. The lights in the living room were to stay lit. These rules were enforced by granting or denying privileges such as curfew hours. The girls were not allowed to conform to the abnormal norm set by their peers.

The girls were not happy at first with this new state of affairs. There were many tearful scenes, many acts of rebellion. But as their new diverse activities began to absorb them, their precocious sexual interests slowly waned. Stricter rules at home brought about an improvement in their schoolwork, and they began to get applause from this source as well. They were finally learning to be productive.

Diane Weber

Diane Weber, whose husband, Link, had outgrown her and tossed her aside, faced a tough problem. She should have diversified before marriage or while married. She should have prepared for the unforeseen change in Link, making ready to support herself if she should ever be left alone. She would also have been better off if she had been active in the community, if she had had many interests and many friends. The mobile husband or wife who has always kept busy is not likely to be devastated by the loss of a spouse. Unlike the women of the Ganges, who were so totally dependent on their husbands that they threw themselves on their husbands' funeral pyres, the modern diversified woman has many ties to society. She gets economic support, recognition and reward from her husband, but not alone from him. If he dies or leaves, other existing activities and friends keep her from collapsing. Moreover, her wide circle of friends and contacts gives her a better chance of remarriage than if she had stayed cooped up at home.

Such diversity was less necessary in the stable community, where a divorcee or widow had a multi-generation family and a welcoming community to fall back upon. Happily, organizations are developing spontaneously in the moble world to fill some of the void that was created by the disruption of the old multi-generation family. Diane joined one of these: Parents Without Partners, a national club of mothers and fathers who have lost their spouses by separation, divorce, or death. At the local chapter meetings, she met other women and a few men who were in the same boat as she. She conferred with them, worked with them in hunting solutions to the many problems of living and raising children with half the family support gone.

Diane also found a job in the city after graduating from her secretarial course. At the Parents Without Partners meetings and in her new job, Diane slowly began to meet people, find new rewards, rebuild her shattered life.

The divorced young executive, Jack, who had made a play for Diane while she was still married, began to grow attentive again when news reached him of Diane's separation. She was still powerfully attracted to him physically, but she remembered with pain how confused she had become when he had kissed her at the New Year's Eve party. She didn't know what to do. Finally she took her worries to her mother.

Her mother said that companionship with men was just what Diane needed. Diane's disappointment in marriage was due partly to the fact that she hadn't gained enough experience with men before marrying. She had moved too fast with Link and paid for it. But it wasn't too late for her to begin learning now. Her mother encouraged her to become a little more sophisticated in understanding men and their actions as well as herself and her reactions.

Diane accepted a date with Jack. She made it clear, however, that he must keep his distance. It was difficult to tell him this when the physical attraction was so strong. But for the time being, at least, their affair must stay on a platonic basis.

George and Martha Kohler

Just as Diane used Parents Without Partners to help in her adjustment, middle-aged, suicidal Martha Kohler also made use of one of the mobile world's spontaneously developed organizations once she began to regain her self-confidence. Her need to feel useful was being partly satisfied by her growing activities in the church, helping newcomers, chaperoning teen-agers' dances. But this did not occupy enough of her time. She entered an area in which her services were badly needed by younger women in the suburban community. She joined the Homemakers' Service, an organization made up largely of older women such as she, whose own children no longer needed them. The Homemakers filled a role in the community that the old multi-generation family used to fill. They took over the management of a home when the wife was sick and in other times of need. (It was a Homemaker who helped Alice Hager.)

Thus Martha diversified. She now had multiple sources of recognition. She had a source of income in case her husband, George, became ill or died. The money she earned through the Homemakers also helped ease George's fears of economic disaster and furthered his emotional recovery.

George, meanwhile, was working on the church's board of

trustees and with boys' groups. Thus he was also building himself multiple sources of recognition. His status in the community was no longer based solely on his business success and his income. As a result, getting ahead in business was no longer a matter of such desperate urgency to him. Busy, productive, applauded in many areas, he felt less and less need for the oblivion of alcohol.

None of this happened miraculously or overnight. There were many setbacks for both George and Martha. There were days when things didn't go well for George at the appliance store where he worked as manager, and he reverted to alcohol. There were days when Martha's community projects didn't go smoothly, when promised help failed to materialize, when she felt she was fighting a lone battle against community inertia. Sometimes she felt depressed; occasionally the thought of suicide returned. But often George would be feeling good when Martha was blue, and vice versa. They bolstered each other. Their new young clergyman also was a source of strength when his faltering parishioners needed it.

Carl and Alice Hager

The shy Southerner, Alice Hager, meanwhile, was beginning to come out of her shell. Her problem had been that she had only one area of life in which to seek rewards. That area had been her home, and she had found too few rewards there. She needed diversity. At first with her husband's help and then more often alone, she explored the resources of the community. As mobile women must, she became a joiner, a clubwoman. She worked with her neighbors in the PTA. She also became active in organizing programs for a new transferees' club that Carl's company had sponsored in the area. Alice took particular pride in the fact that the club held promise of saving other young transferee wives from her fate.

Alice did not at first enjoy her efforts at being more active and less of a homebody. Life would have been easier for her if she could have been supported as were the women in her old home town. It was hard for Alice to force herself to meet people, to supply the initiative that got committees working, to drive long distances alone in her car, to be firm with her sons. She would much rather have been on a pedestal, protected by her husband, sheltered from the roughness of life. But her terrible emotional experience had shown her very plainly that a young mother can't live successfully in the mobile world by the rules and values of the stable world. Though it was hard, she was grimly determined to become more courageous, a little more rugged, more diverse in her interests and activities. She was able to do it because she now had help and because she now could proceed slowly.

It was also hard for Alice to become more diverse in her friendships. Many of her new acquaintances seemed different from the gentle, gracious folk of her Southern girlhood. She felt that she was stepping down socially to align herself with them. In time, however, Alice got to know people with backgrounds more like her own. As she became their friend and was invited into their homes, her loneliness for her girlhood friends diminished and her status felt more secure. This accomplished, she was more willing to befriend new and different kinds of people.

Alice's husband, the intellectual Carl, also needed diversity. He was a thinker who had never learned to use his hands. As a result, he was constantly irritated by the demands of home maintenance and the bills of repairmen. To learn basic workshop skills, he took a series of adult-education courses in home repair. In addition, by growing more active in the community with Alice, he came in contact with men like the middle-aged George Kohler —men who were handy, could give him advice and help when the cellar leaked or the power lawnmower refused to start. Gradually Carl learned to be more effective about the house. He took time to teach his sons and was surprised to find, in a short while, that they could actually help.

Carl had already slowed down his rush to get ahead. The result of it all was that he had more time to spend with his wife and sons. He slowly became less irritable, more patient, more relaxed, more capable of having fun. At his office and laboratory, too, his disposition was improving.

Harley and Audrey Tragg

The middle-aged businessman Harley Tragg, who had been paralyzed by an obsession with suicide, was a man who had devoted his whole life to work, and this lack of diversity had brought him grief. He had no source of fun or recognition outside the office; and when that single source dried up, Harley was in trouble.

He now wondered whether the community had any recreational facilities where he might find the fun, friendship and respect for which he had been starved. He asked his son, Jerry—who, though he might know little else, knew at least how to play. Jerry said that the community had no public recreation program of any kind for adults. There was, however, a public recreation board that had recently been formed to study the situation.

Harley offered his services to the board. As an experienced businessman he could supply valuable counsel and help in the financial aspects of the board's work. The board, a group of citizens who served without pay, eagerly accepted Harley's help. As Harley plunged into a study of recreational needs and budgets, he began to find that people were noticing him, listening to him. He began to make friends in the community. When eventually he was instrumental in saving the town several thousand dollars in a swimming-pool project, his stock in the community rose high.

Among the men Harley met were several business executives. He and these men got to know each other well, talked over their business problems together, pointed ways to solutions. Harley no longer found his pinnacle of executive power so lonely. He now had someone to whom he could go for advice. He had someone against whom to measure his own success—someone to assure him he was doing a good job.

With other goals to absorb him, Harley no longer drove so hard to push his company ahead. As he began to get more and more enjoyment out of his involvement in the community, he started to mellow. He saw how his driving had antagonized employees and colleagues. He began to relax more with them. He also saw how his former striving had pushed his wife away from him. He began to talk with Audrey more often, found to his surprise that she had a keen mind and was interested in both business and community problems. Her work with the Friends of the Library was bringing her into contact with many of the same people Harley dealt with in his recreation-board work. Harley and Audrey were slowly developing a circle of mutual friends in the community. They began to attend meetings and parties together. They and nine other couples banded together eventually to form a husband-and-wife investment club. The monthly meetings for fun and finance helped create a stronger economic as well as social bond between Harley and his wife.

Diverse lives are more complicated. Diversity requires both originality and orderliness—noting, recording, scheduling to avoid conflict and confusion. It involves clarifying goals, deciding which of several possible activities will be the most truly rewarding in the future. It involves planning, deciding which to do today and what to postpone.

Diversification is an old technique of prudent stock-market investors. It has been developed on Wall Street as protection against the changefulness, the unpredictability, of the market. It serves equally well in the boom-and-bust of the mobile society.

CHAPTER 15

The Fifth Technique: Climbing with Care

Many unhappy people have taken a step toward serenity by asking themselves three questions:

Is it necessary to climb so fast?

Can't I get where I'm going with less stress?

Won't I accomplish more if I take it easier and perhaps live longer?

Fred and Eve Bright

The ulcer-plagued young father, Fred Bright, had been forced to slow his climb by doctor's orders. He climbed with care from then on, for he had now learned to recognize his body's limitations. Ideally he should have recognized them before his ulcer started to form. The body has barometers by which it usually tells us when it is being pushed too hard. When it hurts, that is a signal to slow down. Unfortunately many men in our society tend to disregard the signals. Like Fred, they grit their teeth and keep going until the body finally gives in.

Once slowed down, Fred had to be careful to continue watching his limitations. People who are learning to live successfully after a life of frustration and tension will sometimes become wildly elated by it all, involve themselves in far too many interesting activities and once more overload their systems. Then any small change in the body such as a bad cold or other virus infection, or glandular adjustments during a change of seasons—particularly the famous "spring fever"—may bring on a new upset. (In early spring, ulcers often become active, and psychiatrists frequently notice a sudden increase of severely depressed patients and suicides.) There is a boom-and-bust cycle in psychology as in business: an overloading and overspeculation, followed by a toppling-over.

Carl and Alice Hager

Carl Hager was beginning to enjoy himself with his wife, Alice, and his boys. He had once thought nothing of bringing home a briefcase full of weekend work; it was the thing to do if you wanted to get ahead. Now he avoided doing so except on rare occasions when it was absolutely necessary. He had once gone out of his way to show his superiors he was eager to travel, take on extra duties, do anything for the company. Now he volunteered only for his share. Carl had seen the effects of stress on his wife. Now he began to wonder what might happen to him if he kept driving himself. Fortunately his company was one of many that are beginning to recognize the hardship wrought—particularly on wives—by too frequent transfers and too much travel. Men can often be promoted within geographic locations instead of being shifted back and forth (it's cheaper for the company, too). In these days of efficient and steadily improving telephone service, even an hour-long phone conversation is cheaper than a business trip across the country.

A time came when Carl's company did offer him a promotion-transfer. By now he was having so much fun at home, was learning so much in his slower-paced program of studies at the university, that the offer failed to thrill him as it once would have. He doubted, too, that another move, this soon, would be good for Alice and the boys. He asked that the promotion be postponed until he had landed his master's degree. He also pointed out that the company would benefit if he could finish the project he was working on in the company laboratory. The company officials were grateful for his concern and agreed to postpone the promotion.

It is important to assess carefully the gains that may come from a promotion, transfer or change of employers. Mobile Americans have an optimistic attitude toward change. We tend to feel that, unless the observable facts point the other way, a change must be for the better. We welcome change for its own sake. A lack of change is thought of as "being in a rut." As our ancestors ocean-hopped in search of better things, without any real assurance that the search would be successful, we job-hop, house-hop and spouse-hop. Hopping is built into our culture. When we are dissatisfied or bored, our reaction often is to take off instead of thinking what improvements might be made in the existing situation.

True, such a hop is frequently rewarding. But equally often, the same rewards can be gained, with less disruption and stress, by sticking with the existing situation and improving it. Many men in Harley Tragg's position, for example, dissatisfied with life at home and infatuated with another woman, might see only one solution: divorce. But Harley didn't need a divorce. He was beginning to find new satisfactions in his home community and soon, with patience, would begin to find new satisfactions in his wife. A typical young couple like John and Gina Conning, ambushed by the older generation, might move to the other end of the country to get away from the old folks' interference. But John and Gina were beginning to work things out by staying home, with benefit to them and to the elder Connings. Already Gina and her mother-in-law had formed a friendship in mutual service to the baby. They were giving each other something that neither might have had if the young couple had pulled up stakes. John and his father would also settle their business disagreement soon, by sticking with it and giving it thought.

Change is not automatically for the best. The distant pasture, so green to the eye, may turn out to be a field of thistles. Too much change, too fast, may involve more stress than the body can take.

Hopping is a symptom of the speculative way of life. There is chance-taking all around us. There are hundreds of thousands of tense young men like Fred Bright whose lives are a daily gamble. They bet everything on their ability to hold a job that is too big, pay a debt out of income not yet in existence, reach for the golden plateau before physical collapse sets in. It is a gamble for frighteningly high stakes: happiness, health, even life itself.

The past twenty years have been bonanza years, and in one way this has been unfortunate. Prosperity has increased the tendency of ambitious people to speculate. Every day we hear or read that somebody, somewhere, has struck it rich. A marginal farm on some desolate rocky flat is split by a superhighway, and suddenly the farmer is catapulted to wealth. A starving little company, morosely manufacturing hula hoops in a loft, suddenly finds itself lifted skyward on the crest of a nationwide fad. A girl from nowhere happens to be at the right place at the right time, and a year later she is languidly banking fifty thousand dollars a week for television performances. Such rocket-like climbs to enormous wealth are a part of our complicated, changeful world, and they nurture dreams in men like Fred and women like Eve. They inspire envy and the urge to speculate in the hope of quick, easy money. In the stable society, life was simpler; change mostly took place slowly and bonanzas didn't make daily headlines. It was a more thoroughly accepted fact that if you wanted money you had to work long, hard and patiently.

The dangers of reaching too hard for riches are illustrated starkly by Bergen County's heart-disease statistics. Men who have climbed high too hard and too fast are more likely than lower-income men to have heart attacks early in life.

Mobile people will continue to climb. It is hard to think of many things that could stop them. But they must climb carefully, or they may find themselves too ill to enjoy what they find at the top.

CHAPTER 16

The Sixth Technique: Rest and Reward

It is not always enough merely to produce. Producers are usually rewarded, but not automatically. It is up to each individual to make sure that he is rewarded—to make sure he gets recognition for what he is doing, to insist on fair financial compensation, to guarantee himself fun and relaxation.

Businessman Harley Tragg was a man who had been rewarded financially but in no other way. There are other men who are being rewarded in other ways but not financially, who have worked long and loyally for their employers without seeing to it that their paychecks reflect the fact. There are women who have worked hard for their families but haven't insisted on getting fun out of life in return. Many artists have died poor. Many inventors have seen others milk their patents.

It is essential to be rewarded. Good friends, good times, a more interesting life, a feeling of accomplishment, an occasional pat on the back: to strive without these is to risk emotional disturbance. Rewards counterbalance stresses. A man or woman who is getting plenty of rewards from life can stand a good deal of stress. Parents who help their youngsters earn rewards both inside and outside the home can demand more of them in school and at home. But a youngster who is pushed and disciplined without being rewarded may rebel or develop emotional problems.

Initially rewards should come fairly often. A child learns to persevere by being rewarded frequently for his efforts at first, then less and less often. But if the rewards—the "well-done's," the treats, the outings—come too infrequently, the youngster will be frustrated. He'll cease to feel that all his hard work is worthwhile. Some parents, particularly those who are too busy climbing to spend much time with their kids, try to make the youngsters produce by promising a single big treat at the end of the school term. This is seldom enough to pull a C average up to an A or to make a brat into a model of courtesy. Rewards must come at each step of the road toward improvement. The C-average child needs an encouraging pat on the back for the extra effort that goes into each B paper. Later, when he has begun to establish himself firmly on the B level, when more diligent study has become habitual, rewards for B's can be handed out less regularly. But they should not be spaced out so widely that they exceed the span of his perseverance; otherwise he may slip back to C's.

Adult psychology is the same. Many mobile people, while rewarding their children only too often, reward themselves too little. They have massive perseverance; they can keep driving themselves for great periods of time without a pause for rest and fun. The young husband dreams of the time when he will be an executive and own a big house; the middle-aged man dreams of retiring in Florida. There is one big goal. The climber withholds rewards from himself as he fights doggedly toward it. When he reaches it, he promises himself, he will relax and enjoy life. He nurtures himself on his big dream. But a dream of enjoyment is not half so nourishing as the real thing. After a certain span of time, as stresses pile up and he still has not received his counterbalancing reward, he succumbs to tension problems, ulcers, heart disease. Wives, too: they try to milk happiness from the thought that, one day in the dim future, their children will be in school and there will be freedom to relax and enjoy life. But the span of time is too great; stresses close in before the glorious day of reward arrives.

The wise climber gives himself rewards at every step of the way. He doesn't set his sights on a high, high peak and try to get there in one long, unbroken climb. He has daily plateaus: coffee breaks, sessions of play and exercise, leisurely meals that can be looked forward to with pleasure. There should also be weekly plateaus: family outings, parties, movies. And there should be other, bigger rewards. Everyone should take a yearly vacation, get away from home, see new places and faces. Mothers and fathers—particularly mothers—should park the kids with someone trustworthy and go away without them for an occasional week-end or week.

John and Gina Conning

Rewards, like stresses, are individual. It would be unprofitable to prescribe specific rewards for all people. One man's reward is another man's irritation. For example, compare the window-peeping Tom Krazinkow and the young Italian-American mother, Gina Conning. For Tom, education was a difficult, stressful process. For Gina, it could be used as a reward. One of the reasons why she had become upset was that she was deprived of her artistic and literary satisfactions during maternity. As part of her rehabilitation, she enrolled in a local college. She attended college one night a week, studying art and literary composition while her husband and mother-in-law baby-sat.

Fred and Eve Bright

It is important to remember that not all people are rewarded by the same things. Much has been made in recent years of a thing called "togetherness" as a cure for many of the mobile family's ills. The idea is that husband, wife and children should "do things" together. Basically this is a fine thought. Members of the mobile family must consciously make an effort to help each other more. But it is important that no one family member's enjoyment be sacrificed on the altar of togetherness.

Conscientious parents often put themselves out for their children in the worship of togetherness. A father like Fred Bright, who has no interest in baseball, will spend hours grimly being a pal to his sons at the Little League games. A mother who is bored stiff with science will spend a harrowing day at a technical museum with her youngsters. Husbands and wives often put themselves out in the same way for each other. A man who would much rather be doing something else will accompany his wife on a shopping trip for draperies or slipcovers, because the togetherness dogma says he should. His wife, in turn, who gets a headache from exhaust fumes, will go with him to watch the stock car races.

Togetherness must be tempered with enlightened self-interest. Family members must have a central core of common interests, but it is wiser for them to go their separate ways on projects that irritate one or the other.

It would be silly to prescribe that Fred Bright spend time trying to teach his boy about baseball. Better, in this case, to turn the boy's athletic training over to a man like the middle-aged George Kohler, who has more time on his hands and a real capacity to enjoy the game. Fred, however, was interested in nature study, and could spend many enjoyable hours hiking in the woods with a group of Boy Scouts. In this way both he and his son got rewarded, instead of one being rewarded while the other was under stress.

Carl and Alice Hager

Similarly, the intellectual Carl Hager was never able to work up any real liking for the game of bridge, which his wife Alice enjoyed. To expect him to sit morosely through evenings of the game, simply to accommodate Alice, would have been foolish.

They found activities they both liked. Through the PTA and the company transferees' club they met many new friends, broadened their social life. With a group of other young couples, they had a lot of fun attending dancing classes in the adult education program at the high school. After class each Tuesday night, the couples stopped by each others' homes for a snack. Among these new friends, Alice found a group of girls who liked bridge.

Similarly, Alice and Carl searched for activities that rewarded children without straining parents. Many mobile parents don't realize the advantage of turning their youngsters over to the George Kohlers to learn sports and hobbies. A typically pseudo-independent father may feel that he must teach his children everything they need to know. This is not necessary.

The wise parent sees to it that his children don't depend only on him for their rewards. He teaches them, or sees that they are taught, skills and knowledge that will help them win praise and recognition from their friends and teachers, that will help them have fun in many activities away from home as well as in it. Children who depend too much on their parents for rewards are likely to be burdensome. No member of a family should expect another to prop him up eternally.

Sexual intercourse is one rewarding activity that all married couples can learn to enjoy together. Unfortunately the difference in attitude between men and women in American mobile society often prevents mutual enjoyment in this realm. Link and Diane Weber are examples: he was capable of enjoying sex as a pleasure in and of itself, while Diane had been trained to regard sex as valueless except when used as an ultimate expression of fondness. In him, sexual stimulation could be turned on instantly. Like most men he had his arousal mechanism under more ready control. Diane became aroused only after a period of kissing and petting. She couldn't arouse herself at will. This is the most common situation in American marriages.

These diverse attitudes are the result of training and conditioning. To achieve enjoyment with each other, a man and woman must recognize the differences in each other's arousal-control mechanisms, cater to the differences and at the same time help recondition each other so as to bring the two attitudes closer together. Man and wife must discuss their sexual relationship, constantly look for ways of increasing and varying their mutual enjoyment. The man must take time to arouse his wife. As the experience becomes more enjoyable to her she will begin to think of sex as a pleasure in itself, thus moving toward his attitude and becoming more quickly stimulated. Each must seek the things that will arouse the other. Like all forms of togetherness, sex loses much of its value if only one partner is rewarded by it.

Couples often make the mistake of feigning enjoyment while actually merely tolerating. They may be too shy, too embarrassed to discuss each other's problems and look for solutions. But in this as in other areas of the mobile life, it is important to confer and consult. Only by talking things over can people of diverse backgrounds communicate their needs and find out how to serve each other.

A marriage in which both partners enjoy the reward of sex can withstand other stresses well. Sex becomes part of the common core of shared interests that hold the family together. Many arguments seem smaller the morning after a mutually satisfying sex experience. Many tense people are able to relax and sleep after sexual intercourse. It remains one of the best cures for insomnia.

John and Gina Conning

In some cases, women may need to assert themselves with their husbands to make the reward mutual rather than one-sided. In some cases, too, a re-thinking of old values may be required.

John Conning, for example, had to think more objectively about the sex experimentation Gina wanted. Each had to make adjustments until both were better satisfied. Gina also gradually lost her guilty feelings over birth-control practices. She saw that it could be disastrous emotionally if she rushed to have another baby before she had fully adjusted her life to her first child, her new home, community, neighbors and schedule.

Harley and Audrey Tragg

A sexual relationship that has fallen as far into disrepair as that of businessman Harley Tragg and his wife, Audrey, may look hopeless at first glance. It may look especially hopeless to one who isn't willing to go after his rewards slowly, to move step by step toward solutions of his problems. But both Harley and his wife were finding solutions to other problems that may have looked just as tough. Harley had now completely lost his obsession with suicide, and he was finding new sparkle in a life that had once seemed doomed to desolation. Audrey, too, was gaining praise and recognition as she moved about the community on her library projects and other developing activities. For the first time in many dreary years, she had the feeling that people genuinely liked her. These successes gave Audrey and Harley confidence in their own ability to change their lives.

They were already beginning to find pleasure in each other's companionship. Slowly, there was a dawn of new sexual interest. It increased as Audrey started to lose weight.

When an individual is beginning to be rewarded in diverse, important realms, he can start to give up less essential rewards elsewhere. Audrey had never been successful in losing excess weight until her life with Harley grew more pleasant and she began to get recognition for her work with the library. As she felt the growing appreciation of her husband and other people in the community, she took more pride in her personal appearance. She was surprised at how much easier it was now to stick to a diet. The frustration and resentments that had driven her to seek solace in nibbling between meals were diminishing. Her over-all total of rewards had increased. It was less and less of a struggle to control her appetite. As her figure slimmed she became steadily more attractive. Harley's sexual interest in her mounted, and her growing rewards in this realm made dieting still easier.

Alec Green

The juvenile delinquent, Alec Green, found more and more rewards in his new productiveness as the years went by. His school grades were much improved, to the extent that he could now consider college. He had earned a summer job as a lifeguard at a local swimming pool. He had diversified his circle of friends and was becoming well liked by people of both sexes, his age and older. He had taken a driver-education course, had passed his tests and earned a driver's license. The family car was his when he reserved it in advance and when his use of it didn't conflict with his parents' plans. He understood that the car was a privilege and reward for continually improving behavior.

Alec had stopped prowling for sexual experience. Sex no longer dominated his thoughts, for he had other things to occupy and reward him. As any eighteen-year-old lad will, however—especially one who has already tasted adult sexual pleasures—he kept his eyes and ears open. One day at the swimming pool he met a twenty-one-year-old girl who worked in a local restaurant. He was surprised when she agreed to go out with him that night, for in his past life the older girls he'd met had always firmly rebuffed him. He was still more surprised when, that night, she responded passionately to his sexual advances as they sat by the shore of a lake. When his hand touched her thigh, however, he stopped. He remembered his year on probation from the juvenile court, and his father's earnest warning never to risk making a girl pregnant. Also he was not exactly sure how best to proceed from there. He needed advice. Accordingly he ended the night's adventure at that point.

The next day he took his questions to his father. Burt was pleased that his son had come to him so frankly and openly. He congratulated Alec on his good sense and self-control. Then he gave the boy a few pointers.

He explained that it is a man's responsibility in intercourse to make sure his partner enjoys the experience fully as much as he. A man who considers his partner's as well as his own gratification will be welcome again in the future, and will make a better husband than one who proceeds from a selfish viewpoint. Furthermore, the sexual experience is more enjoyable to the man when his partner enters into it with pleasure and enthusiasm.

Burt recommended a reliable brand of contraceptive, told Alec to make sure he used the device. He went on to remark that a gentleman does not boast in public of his sexual exploits. A girl has a right to expect privacy after as well as during the act. Adults' sexual lives, Burt said, are absolutely and exclusively their own business as long as nobody gets hurt.

Finally, Burt remarked that he wouldn't have talked this way to Alec a few years ago. Alec had now earned the right to enjoy adult sexual pleasure because he had achieved maturity. Burt was sure his son would use his growing knowledge and sexual experience in a mature way. He counseled the boy not to let sex become the one big thing in his life, but to continue widening his interests in other productive fields.

Diane Weber

Diane Weber, meanwhile, was also finding new rewards in life after her separation from Link. Her job and her membership in Parents Without Partners were giving her abundant fun and stimulation. Her mother helped take care of her two growing children. She had a full social life and many beaus—chief among whom was the divorced young executive, Jack.

Diane had not really expected Jack to stick around when she insisted that their relationship start on an elevated level, rather than the horizontal one he originally had in mind. But Jack, too, was now learning from experience. His wife had divorced him largely because of his shallowness. He had laughed it off; he was attractive and need never be without female companionship. But now the succession of one-night affairs was beginning to pall. He was discovering that life has vastly greater riches to offer, that an intelligent woman could open for him a much more varied and stimulating world than can be found merely in a bedroom. He was also growing more and more fond of his daughter as she grew; and he wondered whether his mother, willing though she was, could really give the little girl all the motherly guidance, companionship and help that a younger woman might give. A day would come, Jack knew, when his mother's advancing years would make her physically incapable of being a full-time surrogate mother.

Jack and Diane had a few dates together, then began going out with the children on weekends—picnics, trips to museums and zoos. The children played together happily. The two adults contributed to these outings in ways that neither could have done alone. Jack had never been quite sure how to play with his little girl, and he was delighted when Diane took over. He, in turn, began teaching Diane's little boy how to throw and catch a ball. Adults and children alike had days of glorious fun together. The two half-families were beginning to blend. Each half was finding rewards in the other's company.

Life without frequent rewards is stressful and painful, no matter how brightly the distant goal may shine. Something many mobile people fail to realize is that the climb itself can be just as pleasant as the imagined joys of the golden plateau.

CHAPTER 17

The Seventh Technique: Tactful Self-Assertion

People from rural communities who visit our cities and suburbs often go home grumping about an air of brusque unfriendliness and a general impression that everybody is out to get everybody else. Though the observation is often exaggerated there is some truth in it. This is a rough, competitive world. It is a world of strangers. It is a world in which ample opportunity exists for the con man, the dishonest salesman, the non-producer who has the knack of inspiring trust in new acquaintances. People in this world must look out for themselves, see that they are rewarded, see that they are not trampled underfoot. They must strive for power, for control of their own lives.

In the more stable community, the weak and the timid were more likely to be protected by a wall of friendship. Everyone was known by many others about town. If somebody started taking advantage of a housewife, her husband, brothers and neighbors were there to help. If a husband began stepping out on his wife, her family and his—backed by the community at large—landed on him. This was an integrated town; people were not strangers, and mutual help was their support. Not only did they have more protection; they needed it less. Theirs was not a changing world. They did not deal so often with strangers, but with people they knew well and had reason to trust. The non-producer in this society had a hard time. He could perpetrate dishonest acts only a few times before news of him spread through the community, and then he was out of business.

Mobile people can replace much of the lost protection through mutual help, diversity and other techniques. But they must also learn to be self-assertive enough to increase their pleasures, protect themselves and reduce unnecessary stresses. Alice Hager, the shy Southerner, had to learn how to bargain with tradesmen and be firm with her sons when Carl could not be there to help her. The young mother, Gina, tactfully but firmly induced her husband to baby-sit for her when she pursued her outside interests and her mother-in-law was not available. Tom Krazinkow learned not to back down when people tried to push him; he found that they usually stopped pushing when they met even moderate resistance. (Little boys and girls who defend their toys find that they are bullied less.)

On the other hand, it is important not to swing the other way and become pushily assertive. Audrey Tragg, for example, had tried to make her way by bullying tradesmen and others, and had succeeded only in antagonizing them. The same was true of Alice Hager's two boys. Their overaggressive ways kept them in constant conflict with other people; their lives didn't run smoothly.

It is a self-protective, not aggressive, assertiveness that most often proves useful to mobile people. Even the self-protective kind is most profitable when coupled with tact and courtesy—when it is *firmness* rather than anger. In a world of rapid change, it is seldom profitable to give free rein to the emotion of anger. The soda-fountain clerk you dress down today may be in a position to help or hurt you tomorrow; today's subordinate may be tomorrow's boss. Anger is not useful when it comes out in a temper tantrum. It can be made useful, however, when it is controlled. It can be turned into a driving force behind creative thinking and determined effort.

John and Gina Conning

John Conning, for example, tried for years to make his father accept modern business ideas. But he never accomplished anything when he indulged in angry scenes with the older man. Their two views about the way Conning Sheet Metal should be run were too far apart to be yelled together. Once John recognized this fact he began to think.

He discussed the problem with his wife, Gina. They decided to collaborate on a booklet comparing Conning Sheet Metal with its competitors. They would show with facts and figures how automatic machinery could improve the company's profits and general competitive position. John's courses in business administration and accounting qualified him to do the research and statistical comparisons; Gina's literary skill and artistic ability would be used in the text, charts and graphs. John and Gina then invited the older couple to a veal scallopini dinner—one of John's father's favorite meals—expertly cooked by Gina. Afterward, in a rosy glow of wine, John started to talk casually about the company. The atmosphere was that of a companionable after-dinner chat, not a high-pressure office argument. Soon Gina brought out the booklet.

The older man was impressed. A month later he agreed to try things John's way. But he didn't want to make the needed changes quite as fast as John recommended. He had been through economic decline, had seen businesses fail, was wary of unnecessary risks. He wanted to keep some money in the bank in case of a recession or other unforeseen problems. Thus the older and younger generation took the best of each other's thinking and moved forward. John and Gina supplied the initiative to change; his father supplied the necessary caution. The result was that Conning Sheet Metal began to climb slowly, carefully.

With John and his mother helping her, Gina's own anger had long since abated, and with it her fearful thoughts of stabbing. As John grew less upset and less tired, felt he was getting ahead, had more free time to talk with her of their plans and problems, their sexual relationship improved steadily. Gina's desire to perform unusual sex acts waned, and John's tendency to think of them as perversions waned at the same time. He now felt that their methods of marital sexual relations were their own affair. Like most other human endeavors, sexual intercourse is accomplished best when it is approached with care, with creative thought and without hurry. John's more secure economic and family position allowed him to begin doing exactly that.

Those who are tactfully self-assertive stand a better chance of avoiding stress in the mobile world than either the aggressive or the timid. The successful mobile man looks out for himself without hurting or angering anyone. Knowing that this is not a gentle world, he is a little suspicious in advance. His suspicions stir a more cautious approach; he tries to foresee potential trouble and acts to prevent it, avoiding unpleasant situations later on. He sees to it that agreements with him are in writing, whether he is dealing with strangers or with members of his own family. He recognizes the possibility of change in people and circumstances.

He seeks to make himself the master of his own destiny. He knows that those who climb too fast and recklessly endanger their health. Yet he also knows that those who are economically secure stand the best chance of avoiding stress—and that they get better faster when they do get sick. They are the heart-attack survivors, the successful therapy patients. Those who are in a position of power can be self-assertive far more easily than those who are not.

Fred Bright discovered this. He found that, as his value to his company increased, he was in a better position to prevent his boss from overloading him with work. He could tactfully say no to his boss, once in a while, without fearing punishment. Alice Hager, too—as she diversified her activities and friendships throughout the community, she was less dependent for recognition and companionship on any one person.

Diane Weber

Diane Weber would have been better able to assert herself with Link if, during their marriage, she had made herself indispensable to him, if she had seen to it that the house and bank account were in her name as well as his, and had in other ways created for herself a position of power. But like many mobile wives she had failed to do this. Her only hold on him was that of a romantic "being in love," which, as it sometimes will, dried up and disappeared.

When Link came to her a year later and asked that the separation be transmuted to divorce, however, the tables were turned. Link needed his freedom in order to marry his wealthy divorcee friend, who had indicated to him that their relationship could not continue otherwise. Diane was now in a position of greater power, and she had learned how to use it well. She carefully controlled her vindictive feelings toward Link; she saw no point in arguing about guilt or blame or sin, or in making Link repent. Those are not forward-looking concepts. They are related to the past. Diane saw that if she acted vengefully toward Link, he would answer with anger of his own; and the result might be a long, bitter battle in the courts, expensive to both sides in money and emotional wear. Instead of dwelling on the past, Diane moved forward from it. She used past unhappiness as a lesson for the present. She asserted herself with Link, firmly and fairly. Their lawyers quickly arranged a cash and alimony settlement that protected her financially and provided for the children until they had finished college. The agreement seemed reasonable to both sides.

Diane demonstrated that self-assertiveness doesn't have to be unpleasant. When it is unpleasant, it begets anger. Anger is contagious, and when anger is boiling up on all sides it is hard to think clearly or work out mutually useful solutions.

Carl and Alice Hager

Alice Hager also achieved a nice balance between too little assertiveness and too much. She had been bred as a Southern lady. It went against the grain for her to be rough, brusque or impolite, even when she did learn to fight for her rights. She began to find ways of being firm and ladylike at the same time. She didn't say "no" outright when a friend asked her to take over a Cub Scout den before she felt ready to handle the responsibility. Instead she practiced the polite runaround. She said, "I'll think about it." This had just enough of the negative in it so that the friend began looking elsewhere, just in case. By the time Alice finally said no ("I just don't see how it will be possible with all the other things I have to do"), the friend had other likely takers for the job and wasn't let down with a bump.

Similarly, Alice avoided noisy, angry arguments by appearing to back down. When a neighbor boy tried to steal a toy belonging to one of her sons, Alice's boy blacked the thief's eye. The neighbor wife came storming over to shout at Alice. Alice could have shouted back in righteous indignation, but she knew that this would only create more anger and emotional stress. Instead she smiled pleasantly and agreed to talk to her son. She talked all right, told him to try to be friendly but to hit the bully in the other eye if he still didn't behave. The neighbor lad, having learned that it was unwise to try pushing the Hager kid around, ceased, and all was serene between the two from then on.

In handling her sons, too, Alice was firm without being loud or angry. She didn't stand in the playroom and shout at them until they cleared away their toys each night. But they soon learned that to leave the playroom untidy was to go without ice cream and other treats later. She didn't reprimand them loudly in the supermarket, the back yard and other public places where they behaved badly, for she knew that a noisy scene would embarrass her and annoy others. She waited until they were home.

She and Carl had discussed and established for their sons a clear set of rules which took into account not only the parents' ideas but also the feelings of the kids. The boys knew what the rules were, and they also knew that the rules were fair and firm. The results of obeying and disobeying, trying and not trying, were always the same. It was hard at first for Alice to be firm, but once she started to learn firmness, and had more support from Carl, she reaped abundant rewards. The youngsters were trying harder in school; there were no more notes and phone calls from harassed teachers. The boys were behaving better at home. The house no longer echoed from dawn to dusk with temper tantrums, fights, loud arguments. Some of the work that had contributed to Alice's overloading was now the boys' responsibility: they cleaned up after themselves, carried out the trash, got their own breakfast on Sundays so that Alice could sleep. Life in the Hager household was quieter and happier for all.

One of the heaviest contributors to young mobile wives' emotional trouble is a lack of firmness with their sons. Women with boys in the suburbs are considerably more likely to become disturbed than those without. In one Bergen County sampling, the children of all troubled young wives were added up and found to be three-fifths boys. (By contrast, when the children of all troubled young fathers were totaled, they turned out to be three-fifths girls. Why? Partly because a man without a son lacks a rich source of fun and relaxation.)

When the factor of parental firmness was introduced with delinquent and other troubled boys in psychotherapy, the failures in therapy declined from twenty per cent to six per cent. Undoubtedly their mothers, once the habit of firmness was ingrained, also found the world a brighter place.

Carl Hager's attitude toward self-assertiveness underwent a change along with Alice's. As she learned from him how to assert herself more, he learned from her how to temper his assertiveness with more sensitivity to other people's feelings. One of his sources of stress was a complex of difficult personal frictions in his laboratory work. He was impatient when people did not immediately see things his way; he tended to be curt and irritable in his efforts to put his ideas across. As he spent more time with Alice he began to notice, at first with amusement and then with admiring interest, how her more thoughtful way of asserting herself got results with less friction. In time he began to copy from her the polite runaround, the gentle letdown, the apparent surrender, the strategic retreat, all the while relentlessly moving forward. His difficulties in his job diminished. He came home each evening a calmer, more companionable man.

Carl, like Fred Bright, had been a climber who was all push and no pull. He had had to come up the hard way, without friends in high places to open doors for him. John Conning represented the opposite pole. He had a lot of pull—a father who owned a company. But he was a little lacking in push; he didn't have the brand of tactful self-assertiveness that could have prevented his parents from ambushing him.

Carl was able to find a more fertile middle ground. As he muted his strident self-assertiveness, stopped complaining so harshly about company policies and personalities, sought more effective and pleasant ways of gaining his ends, he grew more likable to the higher brass of the company. They had always recognized his high professional qualifications, but he had irritated them. Carl had developed a reputation among them as something of a malcontent. When he began to change, he began to win friends in the executive echelons. Now Carl, too, had pull.

CHAPTER 18

The Eighth Technique: A Reassessment of Values

One of the things that made the integrated, stable community a comfortable place in which to live was the existence of a single, clear set of standards, rules and values. These helped guide the individual in almost every situation of his life. They answered all kinds of questions, from who had what authority in a family to the correct way of diapering a baby. They helped make the society tick, helped families function well, helped individuals to live, love and work happily.

Our mobile society so far has not developed for itself such a unified set of standards, rules and values. People are improvising, living by all kinds of standards, some of which conflict with present reality and with each other. From this fact has sprung much stress and emotional trouble.

There are some people, such as Alice Hager and Gina Conning, who try to live by rote, clinging blindly to old idols, taboos, "musts" and "mustn'ts" that were fashioned for another era and are no longer useful. There are others, such as Link Weber, who have discarded older values categorically because they are old. There are still others, the non-producers, who make small attempt to attach themselves to any value at all beyond that of enjoying themselves.

A more unified system of values and a stronger national sense of direction is developing as the mobile society continues to assess its own workings, latching onto what works well and throwing out what doesn't. This process of observing and testing is being done by the people—by millions of individuals, each wondering about his own life and the lives of others, learning from successes and mistakes. This is how values develop in a democratic society. They can't be legislated into existence or promulgated as pet theories of a few powerful individuals or institutions. They are grass-roots developments.

Some of the values developed for the stable society are no longer useful. On the other hand, some of them still are. The rulebook that the mobile society is writing for itself will be made up partly of the old, partly of the new. As in all societies in the past, anything that goes into the rulebook first has to pass the test of usefulness to the majority.

Mobile people bear many stressful responsibilities. They can lighten their load by disregarding nonessentials.

John and Gina Conning

One old standard that seems destined for the scrap heap is that which describes the roles of man and woman. Back at the dawn of history, man became the provider because he was physically stronger than his mate; he was the hunter, the fisherman, the laborer in fields and later in factories. His mate, the bearer of children, fell naturally into the role of home manager. The arrangement worked well in stable societies. Neither partner became overloaded with work; both had rewards.

In the modern mobile society this ancient rule no longer has so much value. Machines now handle a large part of man's heavy labor and seem destined to take over virtually all of it in years to come. There no longer is a physical reason why woman cannot do "man's" work, for the jobs are diminishing in which strong muscle is required.

It is lucky that career opportunities are thus opening up for women, for the mobile society has created a need for diversity. A certain amount of role-swapping is necessary, particularly by husband and wife, to provide the help and rewards that were available through other means in the stable society. A woman who is prepared to step out of the home into a career not only increases her chances of happiness in case her marriage should fail, but also increases the likelihood that the marriage will succeed.

Unfortunately the old standard is still strong; it discourages such role-swapping. Gina, for example, didn't dream of asking John to help her with the dishes or diaper the baby, no matter how she ached with fatigue. There are many men who feel that to put on a housewife's apron occasionally is to surrender masculinity. These same men typically would blanch at the thought of their wives' going out to work. The working wife is seen somehow as a sign of inadequacy in the husband, an indication that he is not a good provider. He is committing a grievous sin of the mobile: he is not standing on his own feet, ruggedly pseudo-independent.

Then there is the compulsion in many women to keep a spotlessly clean house. Martha Kohler and Gina Conning were such women. They felt that nothing must ever be out of place, that no books or magazines should clutter the living room, no toys the nursery, no dishes the kitchen. No engagement was too pressing, no slough of fatigue too deep, to override the importance of a spotless house.

This, again, is a rule whose once excellent reasons have been stripped from it by social change. There was a time when household cleanliness was the only prevention against typhoid, cholera and other diseases. A woman could justly take pride in cleanliness and tidiness, for she was performing an essential service to her family and the community at large. Today antiseptic tidiness is not as vital. We have more efficient sewage systems, vaccinations, a better-informed public health service, more advanced medical care, chlorinated water, refrigerators and freezers. Yet the rule remains on the books. Many women, like Gina, still feel that it is a social error to permit untidiness in the home, even for a moment. Thus they contribute to their overloading, and to their tensions.

It would be wrong to infer from all this that the old standards should be tossed out the window wholesale. Many of them are still useful. The important thing is to think about them reasonably rather than following them by rote, to extract from them what is still valuable and discard or temporarily put aside the remainder. When Gina recognized her physical limitations, saw that she needed help from John and that there was really no pressing need to keep the house looking like a magazine illustration, she lifted another load of stress from her shoulders. A woman whose children are grown up can pay more attention to "gracious living" than one with infants or toddlers.

Another area in which some reassessment of old values and development of new ones seems called for is that of sexual conduct. In this as in other areas, only those standards can survive which are useful to modern mobile society. Those that are useless or worse—those that cause unnecessary hardship—will sooner or later be discarded.

The area of sex is developing multiple standards. In marriage, taboos are gradually being cast aside. People such as John Conning, who was shocked by his wife's sexual wishes, are slowly thawing out. Society will have to stop poking its nose into the privacy of a married couple's bedroom. The only really important thing is that both partners derive full satisfaction from their sexual relationship and that others in society aren't hurt.

The emphasis on sex in the lives of teen-agers and young adults is gradually being toned down. Early dating and going steady breed early excitement, which may result in illegitimate children or too-early marriage. Boys can prove themselves in other areas than sex—in their studies, in sports, in producing. Girls don't have to start learning at the age of twelve how to be popular with boys. Popularity is something that happens almost automatically to a girl who has made herself into an intelligent, likable, producing citizen. In doing so she has made herself valuable as a wife and has increased the chances of a successful marriage.

The woman who is still single in her late twenties is learning to relax the stricter standards that were useful to her as a teen-ager. In her hunt for a husband she is competing with widows and divorcees. Statistically, divorcees over twenty-five have a better chance of catching new husbands than do single women of the same age. Part of the reason is that many single women still are too rigidly frigid in their attitudes toward sex. They represent the old-fashioned extreme.

The pendulum has swung too far the other way in the case of teen-agers, and the result has been teen-age libertines. The best course would seem to be a moderate one: stricter standards for teen-agers, gradually relaxing as adulthood brings its greater knowledge and sense of responsibility.

Widowed, divorced, and older single people are being allowed more leeway. Those who have lost their spouses and been deprived of sexual rewards cannot reasonably be expected to enter cloisters. Their lives are likely to be stressful enough without the additional stress of self-denial. The old rule requiring abstinence of the widowed and divorced was developed before cheap, effective contraceptives and excellent treatment of venereal disease.

Diane Weber

Thinking of these things, the divorced Diane Weber entered into a new phase of her relationship with her friend, Jack. The two, with their children, were finding more and more profit in each other's company. Increasingly they shared their thoughts, plans, feelings. Diane's mother liked Jack far more than she had like Diane's former husband, Link. She knew about Jack's earlier lupine reputation, but she saw in him a steady shift toward more useful attitudes. She and Diane were both delighted when Jack won a promotion to a more responsible, higher-paying job—an indication of his growing willingness to work hard, think of the future, plan for the happiness of his little girl. Diane's mother was also pleased by Jack's growing thoughtfulness, his consideration of others' wants and feelings—something that had always been lacking in Link Weber. She saw now that it had been a mistake for teen-aged Diane to marry Link, whether or not she was having an affair with him. Marriage isn't always the best answer nowadays to the problem of promiscuity—especially marriage to a poor risk like Link Weber. Even if a girl has become pregnant, she may only compound her errors by marrying her partner-in-recklessness. How much better things would have been, Diane's mother thought, if Diane had tested and tasted for a few years before picking a mate. Diane surely would have learned, during such a period, that a man like the new Jack was a far better bet than one like Link.

Jack's mother, in turn, was charmed by Diane. The older woman appreciated Diane's sweet ways, her thoughtfulness in little things such as sending a Mother's Day card and phoning occasionally to chat. She liked Diane's affectionate but firm handling of Jack's daughter. The two grandmothers, in fact, agreed early that Jack and Diane were more than adequate replacements for the spouses both had lost.

During all this period, Jack had honored Diane's wish to keep the relationship more or less platonic. Except for an occasional good-night kiss he made no sexual advances. But there came an evening, after a day of swimming with the kids, when the memory of Diane in a bathing suit was too much for him. He made it plain to Diane that he couldn't wait any longer.

Diane by this time was certain that she and Jack could build happy, productive lives together with their children. She knew she wasn't repeating her former mistake of rushing into things. She was not letting sexual desire and romantic infatuation blind her to the other important facets of a man's and woman's relationship. She and Jack had explored these facets thoroughly and found everything there satisfactory. Now, Diane felt, she could safely give her emotions more rein. That night she gave in to her long-suppressed physical desire for Jack.

A few weeks later, they went to get their marriage license.

Tom Krazinkow

The handling of sex offenders such as Tom Krazinkow is also requiring a rearrangement of values. One of Tom's major problems was that he had no safe outlet for his sexual urges. The only outlet he had found was one that would continually expose him to trouble with society. Even when he was tasting success in college and in his uncle's drugstore, it was hard for him abruptly to stop window-peeping, which had been the one major reward in his unhappy life. He couldn't easily give up this outlet until he found another one. He did find another temporary one: when the urge to look for unshaded windows became strong, he relieved himself in the privacy of his room. In this way the urge was controlled, society's rules were respected, and no one was the loser.

This involved a considerable rearrangement of values for Tom. He had previously masturbated only with great guilt, for he had been taught that this was a wrong use of the sexual urge. Certainly it is not an ideal use, but it is far less risky than window-peeping. In order to be weaned from something bad, Tom had to make use of something which, while not perfect, was less bad. It was necessary to put up with the less-than-perfect for a while in the effort at improvement. Society can expect people to improve, but it must temporarily tolerate harmless human weaknesses. In time, as Tom became more sure of himself socially and met young people in the drugstore and at college, he began dating girls. He was moving toward the more perfect sexual expression of marriage.

Tom's attitudes and feelings about himself had changed greatly in the past few years. He had developed new skills, new confidence—in fact, a whole new personality. He was an entirely different young man from the furtive, bewildered window-peeper who had been arrested that night long ago in Pennsylvania. There were, however, two facts of his past life that still plagued him sometimes. These were his big ears and his long, difficult, alien-sounding name, Krazinkow. Both had been sources of torment in his youth. Kids had poked fun at his ears and made his name into the poor pun, Krazy Kow. Though he now had many good friends and had lost the feeling that people were laughing at him, he still felt handicapped by the two facts.

He talked over the problem with Uncle Harry. Tom had heard that the shape of ears can be changed by a relatively easy surgical operation. Harry agreed with him that having his ears bobbed would be a good idea if he was embarrassed about them. Harry agreed, too, that it might be useful to adopt a shorter, easier-to-spell name. He assured Tom that he need feel no shame in wanting to abandon the name his father had given him. A name is, after all, only a label.

Tom thought about this for a while, then made up his mind. He said he would like to adopt Harry's own last name, Kerley.

To Tom, the idea made sense. His uncle had done more to help him find a successful life than either of his parents had. He felt he was Harry's son in all but origin. Nothing would make him happier, Tom said, than to take Harry's name as a symbol of their relationship. Deeply touched, Harry replied that he, too, would be proud and happy to create such a symbol.

Thus Tom Kerley, in the space of a few years, had become an almost totally different individual—different in name, appearance and, most important, in personality. It had involved a major reassessment of old values for him. The reassessment hadn't been easy, but it had paid off handsomely.

Many of the tentative new values that the mobile society has so far developed will also have to be re-examined. Some have already shown themselves to be less than useful. Eve Bright's façade of affluence, Alice Hager's pseudo independence, Fred Bright's speculative living. Harley Tragg's dollar success, the intellectual façade of Tom Krazinkow's mother—these and others must eventually fall by the wayside as the mobile society discovers that they do not serve.

As we continue to work toward a more useful value system, the important factor will be a willingness to think objectively, to stand back from venerated traditions, doctrines and rituals, and to consider which are still useful in the new realities of today. Neither a rigid clinging to the old nor a wholesale rejection of it will serve us well. People of different cultural and religious backgrounds, perhaps with scientific assistance, will have to study what each has to offer in serviceable attitudes and ideas.

CHAPTER 19

The Ninth Technique: Emotional Control

It sometimes seems, in our complex world, that certain emotions are nothing but a nuisance—that life would be easier if we had none at all. In truth, however, the emotions are as essential to us as limbs and senses.

In a simpler world the useful role of emotions was more apparent. Early man's anger helped him overcome his natural enemies; his fear helped him escape those that he couldn't overcome immediately and goaded him to think of ways to overcome them in the future. His was largely a world of quick physical responses to emotional states. When a wild dog tried to steal his meat, the anger he felt helped him throw a spear hard at it. When he met a larger and more ferocious beast, his fear sped him rapidly up a tree. Cogitation came later, after the immediate physical response. Need inspired creativity. Having climbed the tree, he invented the bow and arrow.

The world of human affairs has become vastly more complex since then. It is no longer useful to throw something at a man because he angers you. It does not solve the problem to run away from a fear-inspiring thing such as an aggressive salesman or a suburban town. Immediate emotional responses no longer serve us as they served our early ancestors.

Thus it has been necessary to find other ways of responding to emotional states—to control the emotions so that they continue to serve in an increasingly complex environment. Of course, some people bear enormous burdens of stresses. These strain their bodies' reactions, keep their emotions almost continually aggravated. Such people have great difficulty trying to control their feelings. Usually they must first use other methods—the other eight techniques, perhaps—to diminish the load of stresses to more manageable proportions. Then they can learn to become inured to carry the remainder, and also develop other skills necessary for emotional control.

A feeling has grown up among some mobile people that it is necessary and healthy to emote all over the place. They are uncontrolled. They respond to the stimulation of the moment, follow their whims and impulses without thought of consequences, consideration of the future or concern over who gets hurt. They shout at each other and at their children in public. They make passionate love in other people's living rooms. When a responsibility annoys them they abandon it, as Link Weber abandoned his marriage. When something hurts they complain bitterly, making everyone else uncomfortable. They have temper tantrums. They are snarlers and screamers, moaners and groaners.

On the other hand, there are people who practice too much control. Fred Bright was one. He correctly saw that to complain of your troubles to everyone you meet is a poor way to win praise and respect. It is far better to grin and bear what you have to bear, put your best foot forward, meet life with a cheerful face and good humor. But Fred carried his stoicism too far. He failed to consult a doctor early about his stomach pains or to stop and think of ways in which he might ease his tensions. He tried to ignore his emotions and their physical manifestations.

Neither extreme produces useful results. Properly controlled, the emotions help us get ahead safely and happily. The achievement of emotional control is maturity.

Patience is one form of emotional control, and an invaluable one in the mobile world. A baby begins to learn it when his mother lets him cry for a few minutes before serving him his bottle. In time he learns that he needn't cry; the bottle will be forthcoming in any case. Thus he has learned a measure of patience. He has learned to control the impulse to cry when hungry. As he grows, his parents can train him to develop a longer and longer span of patience. He learns to wait for rewards until tomorrow, next week, next month. He learns not to jump up and down howling when he can't have something the minute he wants it.

Mobile adults who have been trained to be patient will not be so quick to get divorced. They will be able to live through longer periods of scarce rewards without getting upset as Alice Hager and Gina Conning did. They will not be so eager to reach for high-salary jobs, as Fred Bright did, without adequate preparation.

Perseverance is allied with patience. It is the ability to keep trying, to keep working at tasks that may not be pleasant, in order to earn rewards. "I'm too tired to put away my things," a child complains. He should be made to put them away though his immediate emotional impulse tells him not to. By putting his things away he earns his parents' praise and occasionally other, more tangible or edible treats. As the habit of persevering is gradually trained into him, he can do longer and harder jobs in seeking his rewards. Unlike Tom Krazinkow he becomes confident that, by sticking with it, he will eventually get what he wants. Confidence, the expectation of success, keeps him working. He learns that success doesn't come overnight. He keeps practicing with his basketball or on his piano until he becomes proficient, knowing that in this way he will eventually win recognition to pay him back for all the long, hard hours.

The mobile adult who has learned perseverance is likely to be a producer. He has the habit of working for what he wants. Instead of abandoning his marriage when it doesn't go exactly right he sticks with it, working for improvement. His habit of expecting success keeps him going when times are tough.

Courage is another form of control. It is an ingrained habit of blocking the emotional impulse to run and hide, facing fears and working to remove their causes. Like other kinds of control it must be learned. A very young child needs abundant help in facing what scares him. Holding his mother's hand he can walk up to a large, shaggy dog. He sees that the dog isn't going to eat him. After a few more tries he tentatively reaches out his hand and touches the dog. Nothing harmful happens. Later still, as he continues to see that the dog won't hurt him, he can walk up to it without his mother. In this way his fear is extinguished. He has had an experience in overcoming fear; he has built a little foundation of confidence in his ability to do so. He has won the reward of his mother's praise and the dog's friendly tail-wagging. His confidence grows with further successes as he grows up. Experience teaches him that he can expect success in his efforts to overcome unrealistic fear. Experience teaches him, too, that running from fears seldom eliminates them satisfactorily. He has learned to control the emotion of fear. By the time he is an adult he can face and eliminate most of his unnecessary fears alone—unless the fears, associated with too many real dangers and stresses, become overwhelming and he becomes upset. Then, like Alice Hager and George Kohler, he may once again need a helping hand.

In the older, more stable society, women had less need than men to control fear. Men in those days protected women from dangers. Today many women still show less control of the emotion than do men. Women generally are more likely to shriek at sudden frights, bite their nails as they watch suspense movies. But this is a rougher, more competitive world. Women and girls must become tougher and braver than their mothers and grandmothers had to be.

Patience, perseverance and courage are only a few examples of emotional control. All require step-by-step training. The man or woman who didn't learn control as a child cannot now be expected to learn it by tomorrow afternoon. Many will need help. Alice needed her husband to help her overcome a fear that had paralyzed her. Tom needed his uncle to help him learn perseverance. With practice, emotional control grew steadily easier for both of them. Practice makes skills such as patience more habitual, so that progressively less reward is needed for greater actual performance.

With experience in emotional control, with continued practice and continued success, comes the important element of detachment: the ability to stand back and watch one's own emotions at work. This leads to a clearer understanding of the emotions and a stronger ability to make them serve.

Take fear. A man, say, feels fear when his boss barks at him. If this man has had experience in controlling his emotions, if he has consciously and detachedly filed facts about them in his mind, he can reason something like this: "I am afraid when the boss barks. Now, I know from my own experience that some fears are realistic—that there is really something to be afraid of—and others are just spooks in the dark, like my childhood fear of the neighbor's big friendly dog. I must find out which kind of fear this is. If my boss represents a real threat to my security, I must take steps to change the situation—by making myself more valuable in my job, diversifying with my wife's help, cutting down my debts. If my boss really has little intention to hurt me, then I must extinguish my fear by consciously noting that he is inclined to bark when he has been out late the night before."

Fred and Eve Bright

This kind of emotional control is further aided by a conscious effort to direct and control thinking—a technique that might be called thought-shunting. Fred Bright used it to calm his tensions during aggravating office situations. He had reorganized his life so that he had little to fear from his boss or anyone else. Yet he continued to feel tense and fearful when his boss spoke irritably to him. The fear reaction was conditioned in him and was going to take some time to extinguish. To speed up the extinguishing process he learned to shunt his thoughts to another track when his boss was in a snarling mood. He deliberately thought of all the reasons why his boss couldn't hurt him and all the pleasant things there were in his life.

"This snarling is just noise," he told himself. "I can't be hurt. I'm doing a good job. If I get fired there's that job over at the ABC Corporation, and Eve can earn money with her interior decorating. And anyway, this weekend I can forget the whole thing when the Scouts and I go up to the woods."

It was now easy for Fred to shunt in this fashion, for the real dangers in his life were few, and the securities and rewards to which he could turn his thoughts were many. When things were different, when the dangers were great and the rewards almost non-existent, he would have had much less success in calming his tensions by shunting.

Harley and Audrey Tragg

Harley Tragg also used shunting. He was a man who had not had enough experience with his emotions or learned about them. His mistress, Joni, had overwhelmed him because he hadn't been able to sort out his various needs. He hadn't recognized that Joni, while perhaps satisfying his sexual desires, would contribute hardly at all to his need for recognition. As this became clear to him, and as his relationship with his wife improved, he was able to use shunting as effectively as Fred.

Among his growing circle of business and community acquaintances he sometimes met women who aroused quick bursts of desire in him as Joni had. But instead of wishing for the woman herself, he shunted. He calmed his rising emotions as Fred did. He thought: "There's no future in getting worked up over this woman. I'll only get myself in trouble, the way I did with Joni. I don't need this woman. I've got Audrey. She'll be waiting for me at home tonight." Later, with Audrey, he shunted in the opposite direction to re-arouse himself. He reminded himself of the woman who had aroused him earlier. Audrey took over from there.

As Harley grew more skillful in using the technique, he learned deliberately to plant shunts in his mind. Meeting a desirable woman, he made a mental note to drop a provocative hint, combined with a well-placed pat, when he got home to Audrey. As their early attempts to establish a satisfactory sexual relationship met with increasing success, these little reminders served to arouse both Audrey and himself and set the stage for better enjoyment later in the evening. It wasn't always easy for Harley, and he occasionally backslid, spent evenings with other women. But in time, as their efforts were more and more satisfying, as memories of Audrey's excited responses flooded Harley's thoughts, he became highly conditioned to the association of sexual pleasures with Audrey. Then the sight or just the thought of Audrey herself aroused him more quickly, and he had little need of shunting.

In thus improving his sex life, Harley—like many husbands—had to fight a social fact. Though it has become more acceptable socially in recent years for women to be interested in sex, men still have more of the mental stimulation that contributes to sexual performance. Thus they are more easily able to become aroused. Women don't often have the almost daily comparing of experiences that gives sexual prowess such a high value in a man's self-esteem from boyhood on. On the contrary, women are usually taught to underplay the importance of sex except in association with marriage. Because they have less of this mental component to sexual arousal, most women need a good deal more physical foreplay than do men. In marriage, women can learn to appreciate sex better mentally as they receive the training in thinking about it, discussing it and valuing it that their husbands received. Then they can become more quickly aroused mentally, and less physical stimulation is needed.

There is another important difference in men's and women's sexual behavior. What's good for the man is not always good for the woman. A man's main physically excitable area is on the penis. Thus, for him, movement after insertion is highly exciting. A woman's main nerve endings are not inside the vagina, but on the clitoris. Only a minority of women are very much stimulated by a man's inserted penis. Therefore most women require considerable preliminary foreplay, including clitoral stimulation, before they can reach a high enough level of excitement to be brought to a full climax by genital contact.

A husband and wife almost always, with patient practice and discussion, can achieve simultaneous orgasm. The husband must first stimulate his wife manually, meanwhile controlling both his physical and mental arousal. He can control them by limiting the stimulation of his penis—not exerting himself trying to arouse his wife by it alone. If he becomes too excited, he can calm himself mentally by deliberately shunting his thoughts to matters other than sex—particularly those that give him some concern or worry. When he senses or she tells him she is sufficiently aroused, he can readily redirect his attention to her and re-arouse himself.

A married couple are far more likely to achieve such success than unmarried partners. They have the social approval that diminishes interfering emotions—worry, fear, guilt. And they have the time and opportunity for practice, discussion and developing skill in satisfying each other.

As Harley and Audrey discovered these psychological and

physiological facts, and improved their personal and social lives together, they progressed toward a state of true married love. Audrey ceased to worry about Harley's waywardness with other women. When two people build together, constantly finding ways to be more useful to each other on diversified fronts—economic security, fun, community recognition, sex—they become more and more valuable to each other. Their love for each other grows correspondingly.

Anger and all other strong, potentially troublesome emotions can also be controlled. The immediate response to them can be blocked; they can be shunted aside until a more appropriate time comes for expressing them, or until calm thought can develop a more useful means of expression. When George Kohler's Little League baseball team wanted to fight some boys of a rival team who were taunting them, he called a halt. "Slugging each other won't help," he told his team. "If you're mad at them, just practice harder and try to beat them in the game this weekend." The boys couldn't just forget the taunts, but they could control and use their angry urges, express them in a more determined effort during practice sessions. Their serious attitude paid off in games that were fine displays of baseball and good sportsmanship. Thus their anger helped them win admiration, praise and respect instead of provoking bitterness and getting them in trouble.

Adult anger is controlled in the same way. A man and wife can't easily arrive at creative solutions to their difficulties by nagging, taunting, grumbling and snapping. It does no good to try arguing with a man who is angry. Emotion clouds his thinking; he is in no condition to absorb your point of view, no matter how logical it is. Nor is it always possible or even useful to heed the classic advice, "Forget it." Best to wait until the emotional boil-up has simmered down and cooled. Go on with the job at hand; temporarily put up with the irritations. Meanwhile, think of more tactful, more pleasant ways of gaining your ends—ways that will not again stir anger. When rational thinking is once again in control, talk can probe for means of preventing future situations that provoke anger.

There is a lot of anger thundering around the mobile society. People are beset with problems, many of which they have never faced before. There is a vast amount of noisy pushing, jostling, needling, competition of all kinds. Mobile people have far more need to control and direct their anger than did people of a less competitive age. Those who don't control anger are likely to find themselves embroiled in endless fights and arguments.

Those in positions of power—bosses over employees, husbands over wives, parents over children—have a particularly great responsibility to use this power wisely. Unwisely used, this power may devastate the underdog. The employee, child or wife who is not well prepared for the mobile life may be helpless against continual angry criticisms, taunts and nagging, may simmer helplessly in bitterness that has no outlet. These people in subordinate positions, in turn, can escape only by working to make themselves less dependent. Only the wife who is well diversified can shunt her thoughts to pleasant things when her husband comes home snarling.

Emotions can be brought under control in ways such as these. They can be made to serve in our complicated, emotion-charged society as effectively as they helped our early ancestor solve his relatively simple problem of what to do about a tiger.

Part Three

NEW RULES FOR A NEW LIFE

CHAPTER 20

Training Successful Children

By the time life began to look promising for Alec Green, the middle-class juvenile delinquent, he was already in his middle teens. He had lost many precious years and had much catching-up to do. In his last years of high school he had to work harder than other boys who had spent their boyhoods more productively, and he realized he would have to carry this extra burden for many years to come. He wished somebody had begun guiding him more firmly when he was younger.

Alec's problems as a boy represent some of the most common problems in Disturbia. Relatively few youngsters have as severe a combination of flaws and lacks as he. But many have his problems in milder forms. These are the gimme kids. They are not like Tom Krazinkow-Kerley, who was basically motivated to earn success. Tom kept trying, but because he lacked the right guidance and was overwhelmed by fear, he continually failed. Knocked down again and again, he finally gave up. The gimme kids—Alec, Harley Tragg's son and daughter, the sons of Alice and Carl Hager—were not motivated to try.

How can children be kept from becoming that way?

Exactly the same nine emotional techniques that serve adults can be made to serve children and teen-agers.

The first need of a youngster like Alice and Carl Hager's boys is help. He needs someone to help him develop constructive interests in diverse fields—sports, useful group activities—where he can enjoy himself and begin developing the qualities that will make him a productive, happy adult. In mobile America this guidance is primarily the responsibility of his parents. They have the most power to direct and reward.

Sports and hobbies are training grounds for adult life. Through them a boy or girl learns patience and perseverance, the willingness to keep practicing even though it isn't fun. He learns the value of effort. In the end his hard work pays off in fun, praise and recognition. As his skill grows, so does his self-confidence. He sees how his own efforts can win him what he wants. All this will eventually generalize; the same habits and attitudes help the youngster succeed in other areas of his slowly broadening life.

The trouble with the Hager boys was that they had few constructive interests and no idea how to develop more. To train anybody in productive habits, you start with existing interests and pleasures. These form a basis for the training process; the generalizing proceeds from this root. Eve Bright, for example, started building on her existing interest in beautifying her home; Audrey Tragg developed hers in library research. The Hager boys, however, had no such foundation on which to start. They had to start from scratch.

Carl and Alice Hager had previously subscribed to the popular notion that it is unwise to guide kids into interests, that they should be allowed to find themselves. This sometimes works—the youngster may happen to meet somebody who will spark an interest in something productive—but it is risky. Carl and Alice had left the matter to chance, and the gamble hadn't paid off. Now they began deliberately to corral their boys' energies.

The spring baseball season was at hand, and boys were trying out for the Little League teams. Though neither Hager boy was adept at the game, both were caught up in their classmates' enthusiasm and had a vague desire to join a team and wear a uniform. Carl knew little of the game, found it boring and wisely hesitated about involving himself in something that might prove burdensome. But he'd heard that the local adult-supervised Little League program was accomplishing a lot—teaching boys the sport, keeping them out of trouble, helping them learn sportsmanship and self-control. Carl and Alice decided to encourage their boys to try out.

Luckily, as more men like the middle-aged George Kohler were getting involved in boys' activities, there were enough teams in town so that few boys had to be turned away. The Hagers' eight- and nine-year-old sons were chosen by the team of which George Kohler was assistant manager. The manager was a construction worker, Tony, who had once played semi-pro ball and derived huge fun from coaching. Between them, George, who knew how to handle boys, and Tony, who knew the fine points of baseball, were able to spend time with their team several afternoons a week. Their players were lucky. Many other teams, though composed of more experienced players, were coached by commuters who could give time only on weekends.

Fifteen underdisciplined small boys, many of them gimme kids, can try the patience of any coach. The first few practice sessions were chaotic. The field rang with raucous shrieks: "I wanna pitch!" "Aw, do we have to catch flies again?" There were squabbles and fights. There was foul language, sometimes even directed at the coaches when some spoiled middle-class youngster was prevented from taking more than his share of turns at bat. There were all kinds of poor sportsmanship, weeping and wailing, temper tantrums. The Hager boys wanted to quit, but Carl urged them to stick with it.

Slowly, George and Tony got things straightened out. Praise encouraged effort. Firm words and discipline—bench-warming, banishment for the day—gradually cut down the bickering, cursing and pestering of managers. The boys learned to buckle down and practice when it wasn't fun, anticipating the reward of victories later in the season. They learned to encourage each other instead of throwing insults, squabbling and becoming demoralized after errors and strikeouts. They learned to be stoical, not to whimper and whine over minor scratches and bruises.

In the first practice game against another team, George saw how handicapped his boys were by their lack of previous experience. The other team routed them. But there were encouraging signs. Though George's boys weren't as skillful as their opponents in individual play, their teamwork was better. Their more frequent team practice sessions were beginning to show. George and Tony were also happy to see that their boys lost cheerfully. They didn't stamp their feet in rage after striking out or argue with the umpires, as many of the other team's boys did. They stayed relatively cool throughout the game, ended by giving the winners a somewhat forlorn but well-meant cheer.

The Hager boys and their teammates learned to profit from their mistakes. After the defeat, their managers praised their good plays, urged them on to greater effort. They practiced harder. They helped each other, coached and encouraged each other. They lost another game by a less lopsided score, then won one. They were learning that losers can come back to be winners, in baseball and in the world. Thus rewarded, they now became self-propelling. Ambitious to do still better, they practiced on their own—not just playing games but taking turns batting and fielding.

By this time, the habits they were learning on the ball field were beginning to show up elsewhere. They were developing a willingness to work, which carried over into the school classroom. Their behavior with friends was more controlled. They were more considerate toward classmates, teachers, parents.

The fifth game of the season was against a team that was so far undefeated. This team hadn't had nearly as much coaching as George's boys, but its players were all stars. As the game started, it looked as though the champions would run roughshod over George's boys. But eventually the underdog team's more frequent practicing, perseverance and emotional control began to tell. George's boys worked better as a team. They stayed calm while the other team's prima donnas, who had not been taught to control themselves, began losing their heads as the tide of the game turned against them. The champions made wild throws and wrong decisions, got mad at each other and the umpires, played progressively less intelligent baseball. George's team won.

The boys were heroes. The applause, added to the sheer fun of playing a good game, rewarded them for their weeks of sweat. They had learned the value of applying themselves, being considerate and cooperative, holding their emotions in check.

Carl and Alice supported their sons in the effort to become better baseball players. The boys' enthusiasm drew Carl out into the back yard sometimes in the evening for a catch. He attended the games and found he enjoyed watching when his sons were playing. He encouraged them, patted them on the back when they did well, bought them ice cream after a well-played game, win or lose.

Meanwhile, at home, Carl corralled their interests in another area. One of his own keen interests was music, and he began showing his sons how much fun music can be. They began to see that music represents a world of good times and recognition. In family singing and record-playing sessions they picked up rudiments of harmonic principles. In time they expressed interest in learning to play instruments, and Alice got them enrolled in the school's beginner program for future band members.

Carl had to spend a fair amount of time with the boys when he was first trying to awaken their interest in music, but later he could spend less. The boys soon needed only an occasional push from Carl and Alice to keep them practicing. They had great fun in the beginner program, and both were determined one day to become full-fledged band members. The school and the boys themselves were supplying most of the momentum. Carl thus wasn't burdened by his new sense of responsibility toward his kids; he had supplied the original thinking and initiative, but now he was able to step back to the role of a more or less casual administrator, occasional prodder and rewarder.

In this way, through baseball and music, the boys' interests were corralled. Carl made music fun for them; and they soon discovered that—as on the ball field—the more they practiced, the better they were able to play and the more fun they had. Carl fed their enthusiasm with propaganda, urging them to excel. He encouraged them to practice hard and rewarded them for their efforts. They were learning perseverance in association with pleasure.

First things must come first. Once children's interests are aroused and they are motivated to succeed, their efforts can be directed into other important areas of their lives. But parents shouldn't expect too much too fast. Learning self-control and diligence is slow in the initial stages. Too many demands beyond a youngster's (or an adult's) present-day level of performance may mean a fast build-up of inhibition, poor accomplishments, and frustration. Carl and Alice didn't crack down too hard on their boys' schoolwork until the youngsters had begun learning how to apply themselves in sports and music. Their children were so underdisciplined, had so little respect for teachers and adult authority in general, that they would have rebelled and accomplished neither in school nor out.

Other children who are not quite so unruly, who have already had greater previous training in self-control than the Hager boys, might be able to concentrate from the beginning on their studies as well as music or other interests. With such children, an immediate establishment of schoolwork rules, goals and rewards can bring results. But with Carl's children this was not possible.

The area of schoolwork is a harder one for most children than sports and hobbies, for greater effort is required for less obvious, less direct rewards. When a child has begun learning techniques of success in his out-of-school activities, he can apply them more easily in school. (Ideally he should have started learning the techniques by the time he enters first grade.) What the Hager boys were learning through baseball and music—the value of persistent effort, the usefulness of planning and preparing for the future—could now be generalized to studies.

While you can't expect too much of a boy or girl, it is equally unwise to expect too little. Youngsters should be pushed. A little anxiety is a good thing. A small fear of punishment helps motivate effort, sharpens the desire to succeed, increases alertness and makes learning quicker. A little grief makes a youngster learn foresight—planning to avoid future grief. The youngster will have to push himself when he grows up, so he must begin learning to do it now. Carl and Alice began insisting on slow, step-by-step improvement in school. They tempered their firmness with understanding and fairness. There were plenty of rewards for success, but privileges such as ice cream were denied for failure to try.

Alice and Carl trained their boys to do chores around the house. Carl showed them how to use simple tools, let them help when he did maintenance jobs or tinkered with his hi-fi set. The jobs took longer this way, but Carl saw that he could make his sons into real helpers if he took time with them in the beginning. He knew, too, perhaps as well as anybody, that a man whose only learning is from books may not be diverse enough to live happily in the mobile world. His own ineptness with tools had once been a source of stress to him and had contributed to Alice's breakdown. He wanted his sons to avoid that pitfall.

Boys and girls who are trained to help around the home can lift a major burden off their parents' backs. There was a time when middle-income people could have maids to handle household chores. Today the number of people who are willing to do domestic work has fallen and is still falling far behind the number who might want them. With diminished supply and increased demand, hourly wages for maids continue to rise. (In 1940, in Bergen County, there was one female domestic worker to every five professional and managerial families. Only ten years later the ratio was one to fourteen.) But in their children, overworked mobile parents have an excellent substitute. Girls can help dust, iron, wash dishes. Boys can help maintain the lawn and shrubbery, handle repair jobs. Both can make their beds, set the table, keep their rooms tidy, put their own belongings away. The benefits are manifold. Not only does the work get done, but the children get valuable training.

If allowed to puddle along with their parents when they are little, slopping paint and splashing dish water like Daddy and Mommy, children not only become adept earlier, but usually keep their childish enthusiasm. But if they are pushed aside because they lack skill, as the delinquent Alec Green was blocked by his father, they lose interest in household tasks and may not be willing or skillful helpers later on. However, parents must put their minds to achieving a good balance between physical chores, play and intellectual activities. Expecting children to do so many chores that they have little time or energy left for homework—their primary responsibility—is a poor solution.

Carl and Alice also began to insist more and more firmly that the boys cooperate with each other. Toys, candy, and other treats were shared. The children soon learned that their parents were little concerned with who was to blame for the spilled bag of peanuts on the kitchen floor. If both cooperated in cleaning up and promised to try to be more careful in the future, they both had not only the nuts to eat, but some grape juice too. If they complained, bickered and blamed, they got neither the nuts nor the juice, but still had to pick up.

Siblings will squabble with each other in our society for their parents' favors. There will also be occasions when they will play cooperatively. If their cooperative behavior is rewarded and their arguments and sulking punished, they will learn to be increasingly helpful to each other. This consideration will generalize to other children and win them friends. It will be respected and rewarded by their teachers and other elders.

Cooperative and considerate children are welcomed in the homes of friends and family. Overnight, weekend and week-long visits help a youngster learn he can feel secure with other adults than his parents. A well-disciplined child can visit, travel, enrich his own life. His parents can confidently leave him in the care of others when they take a needed vacation. In a new group of children he quickly makes friends. These allies help keep him from being bullied.

Children learn a great deal from their early environment simply by osmosis. The culturally enriched atmosphere of the Hagers' home offered not only a better appreciation of music, the arts and learning than did that of Tom Krazinkow-Kerley's childhood, but also provided a better use of the English language and a larger vocabulary. Thus the boys quickly learned skills and concepts that Tom had to sweat over in college. Understanding this, parents do wisely who encourage reading and family conferences, not only about family issues—rules, privileges and pleasures—but also about larger problems in the world of people, science, literature, the arts. Children's curiosity can be sparked by encouraging a questioning attitude and by answering questions appropriately, respecting the age and knowledge of the asker.

Filling a child with knowledge is not, of course, as smooth and simple as filling a bowl with sugar. There will be setbacks, times when the youngster will balk. Occasionally, even with a well-motivated child, a parent will have to resort to punishment.

The role of punishment in learning is a subject that has probably caused more argument and confusion than any other area of child management. A well-guided youngster who is learning and playing happily, and who respects his parents and teachers, can stand considerable punishment without damage to his personality. Sensible punishment is not the kind meted out by Tom Krazinkow-Kerley's father. The senior Krazinkow punished Tom for being cowardly, but gave him no help in becoming otherwise. Other parents are so severely punishing that they either push their children to rebellion or crush them to passivity. Punishment should come only after patient teaching, with plenty of reward offered for success, and only after ample warning.

An occasional whack on the bottom, denial of cake and candy, early curfews—these and other negative reinforcements help a youngster accept the stresses of life with fortitude. Punishment is best administered on the spot, quickly. It is easier for a loving parent to get a spanking out of his system while provoked than to wait until later. It is very hard for a father, coming home in the evening, to be met at the door by his wife and asked to punish a child for something that happened earlier in the day. After an on-the-spot punishment, the air can be cleared quickly. The parent calms down, explains to the youngster how he must behave in the future so that both will be spared such unhappiness. Parent and child kiss and go on about their productive lives.

Words alone aren't enough to teach children techniques of successful living. A youngster won't necessarily study simply because he is told to. Parents must arrange a youngster's life so that it pays him to study.

Many parents talk of trying to reason with their children. This is not always useful. Words are used to guide and explain, but tangible rewards and punishments give the training its backbone. A small child won't stay out of a back yard swimming pool just because he is told not to. He will stay out, however, if his mother gives him a scheduled hour each day for supervised splashing in the pool, warns him the first time and whacks him the second time he disobeys.

Both the reward and punishment are necessary parts of the training. If the youngster finds he can enter the pool in non-scheduled hours with impunity, he probably will. If he is flatly forbidden to enter the pool, he may find some other way of satisfying his yen for water—perhaps under hazardous conditions. It is the same with crossing streets, fire, alcohol, sex, cars. Youngsters' interest in these things can't be stifled by a flat "no." On the other hand, a total "yes" may also lead to trouble. Parents must show youngsters how to go about these things, laying down firm rules and insisting that the rules be obeyed.

One of the mobile society's major problems is that there are as yet too few clear, community-wide rules and values for people to follow. This applies as well to kids as to adults. A family that tries to give its children firm rules about such matters as sex and alcohol may see its effort undermined by a more permissive attitude in the family next door. The mobile community discourages firmness in parents. "Why do I have to be home by eleven?" a teen-age girl bitterly complains. "All my friends are allowed to stay out as late as they like."

Clearer, more consistent rules are slowly developing as the mobile society continues its process of observing and testing. Parents can speed up the process by conferring with one another, trying to set up a more unified system of values that will apply to all youngsters. Of course, any such value system must be flexible. It must be set up so that it can change to accommodate overlooked details or further changes in society itself. And though the laying-down of rules for kids is primarily a parental responsibility, wise parents recognize that kids have a right of appeal. A parental rule may be unworkable from the youngster's point of view, and if their point of view is reasonable it should be taken into account. Denied such a right of appeal, the kids may rebel.

The gimme kids today are operating on a mixed-up value system that is not serving them, their parents or society as a whole. Many of their values derive from those of their parents. There is a feeling among some boys and girls, for example, that schoolteachers can't really have anything worthwhile to say because they don't make much money. It's obvious that adult values will have to become more useful before mobile youngsters can view the world more realistically.

Since the community at large cannot yet be trusted to guide a youngster in the right direction, as the old stable communities could, his parents have the responsibility of encouraging him to find friends who will help him learn the right things. The notion of letting kids find themselves has a corollary: let them find their own friends. Many mobile parents hesitate to interfere with their kids' social lives; this is seen as unwarranted meddling. It isn't. Parents must make sure that their children are surrounded by an atmosphere that will encourage productiveness and good sense. A boy or girl whose friends are all gimme kids will have a hard time learning to work, no matter how carefully his parents train him.

Orderliness is another important part of a child's training. A boy or girl will profit from learning to file toys and clothes in their proper places. This will lead to proper filing of facts in his mind. If he loses a toy; he should be encouraged to remember where he put it last; his parents shouldn't rush to find it for him or buy him a new one. Eventually he will learn that it is easier to put things away properly than to waste time searching. By figuring out with his parents the most convenient storage places, he learns methods of orderliness, not only with belongings, but with thoughts.

Children may resent being trained. Naturally they would rather be given rewards than made to work for them. Like Alice Hager they resist becoming more independent. They balk at picking up their own toys, dressing and caring for themselves. They would much rather have someone else do it all for them.

fer and consult with husband, family, experienced friends. Discuss your plans and worries. (*Planning and Preparation*)

ep up your outside interests. Of course, with a baby in the home, you may have to cut down your outside responsibilities or rearrange your schedule. But don't give up interests and pleasures entirely. (*Diversity, Rest and Reward, Planning and Preparation*)

range for babysitters in advance. (*Planning and Preparation, Rest and Reward*)

et a family doctor now. Knowing he stands ready in case of need will help relieve any worries you may have about your own or family members' health. (*Emotional Control, Planning and Preparation*)

guidance talks outlining these points were delivered to ex-
t mothers who were attending regular baby-care (diaper-
eding, bathing) classes in a Bergen County hospital. Some
ese mothers were attending the classes alone; some with
husbands, the expectant fathers. Certain other mothers
ding the baby-care classes were not given the two special
nce talks. These women were the controls; they provided
is for comparison with the mothers who did hear the talks.
purposes of comparison the mothers were divided into four
os:

1. Control mothers: expectant mothers who attended the regular baby-care classes alone and *did not* hear the special emotional guidance talks.
2. Control mothers with husbands: those who attended the classes with their husbands and *did not* hear the guidance talks.
3. Instructed mothers: those who attended alone and heard the guidance talks.

But parents must require all these things. Children must get used to doing things that aren't enjoyable. Only thus can they prepare themselves to live happily in a rough, competitive world.

Children become smart when they are trained to be smart—when their parents so arrange their lives that they *want* to be smart. The key is firm parental guidance and expectation. When such guidance was added to the lives of a group of delinquent and troubled boys in Bergen County, their IQ's rose on the average nine points, one point per month of such guidance. By contrast, a group of disturbed boys who received only deep-probing, uncovering therapy showed no improvement in IQ tests. Their IQ's dropped by a mean of 0.8 points.

CHAPTER 21

How Emotional Difficulties Can Be Prevented

The stresses and strains of getting ahead are real and often acute. People undergoing them can easily become blue, tense, irritable and disgusted with life. Sometimes, like the people in the case histories, they may have severe emotional disorders. But even when these disorders seem morbid, they can usually be readily managed through the nine simple techniques of emotional adjustment.

All this has been shown. But an important question remains. Can the nine techniques also be used to *prevent* emotional difficulties? Are they as useful in preserving serenity as in recapturing it after it is lost?

To find out, a three-year study was conducted in Bergen County. Once again, for the sake of scientific convenience, the subjects were expectant mothers. The basic idea was, in effect, to compare the emotional reactions to childbirth and new motherhood of two groups of women: a group that had been instructed in the nine techniques of emotional adjustment, and a group that hadn't.

The instructions given to the fir
forty-minute guidance talks, delive
pregnancy. These talks outlined the n
emphasis on the problems faced by
mobile world. The main points cove
below. The points apply specifically
each point is drawn from one or mor
niques. Along with each point, the tec
which it is drawn is listed in parenthes

Get help and advice from family
husband balks, find ways of s
stirring up anger, how badly
(*Mutual Help, Tactful Self-*
Control)

Make friends with other young co
dren; talk with them and get
advice. (*Planning and Prepar*
ward)

Don't be greatly concerned with ap
lously tidy house, a crabgrass-f
will mean a lot of work. Don
with other, less important task
Values, Rest and Reward, Prod
tion)

Don't move soon after the baby arriv
Care)

Get plenty of rest and plenty of slee
physical limitations. (*Rest and*
Help, Climbing with Care)

Avoid being a nurse to elderly relat
(*Self-Assertion, Rest and Reward*)

4. Instructed mothers with husbands: those who attended and heard the guidance talks with their husbands.

The instructed and control groups were matched so that there was no significant difference among them in factors such as age, number of children, socioeconomic status, education, religion and other social factors. They were also matched according to the amount of stress the women were carrying as they approached childbirth. The stress factors in the lives of all the women were counted (as explained in Chapter Three). There turned out to be no significant difference among the four groups in their stress-factor scores.

Previous studies had shown that a count of stress-factors gives a fairly reliable prediction of emotional upset. Thus, left to themselves, the four groups could be expected to go through the childbearing and new motherhood experience with roughly equal numbers of upsets.

But the groups were not left to themselves. The guidance talks intervened. The two groups of mothers labeled "instructed" listened for a total of eighty minutes to explanations of the techniques for successful living in a mobile world. These explanations, in effect, suggested ways of unloading stresses—reducing stress-factor scores.

Those eighty minutes made a startling difference in the emotional outcome of the instructed mothers' maternity experience. The table below shows what percentage of mothers in each group became emotionally upset during the six months after childbirth:

	Per cent Upset
Control mothers	40%
Control mothers with husbands	34
Instructed mothers	23
Instructed mothers with husbands	11

Obviously the techniques work well as preventive measures. Obviously, too, they are simple enough to be understood and used by the layman with only brief instruction.

The husband-accompanied instructed mothers fared best of all. Having listened to the talks with their husbands, they apparently went home and worked seriously with their husbands to prepare for life with a baby in a mobile society. The result was that they unloaded stresses more than any of the other groups and had the fewest emotional disturbances—only a fourth as many upsets as the control mothers.

The instructed mothers who came to the classes without their husbands were not quite so lucky. Having heard the talks alone, they then had to go home and convey the talks' warnings and suggestions to their husbands. They needed their husbands' co-operation, for successful living in a mobile society requires thought, effort and mutual help among all members of a family. Apparently not all of the husbands in this group understood what their wives were driving at, or were willing to cooperate in any case. One can imagine a husband grumbling: "Slow down? Who do those doctors think they are, telling me my business?" Or you can hear another's anguished cry: "Bring your mother here to live with us?" The wife tries to explain the reasons, forgets some of them, states the case inadequately. Result: baby blues or worse.

Still, these unaccompanied instructed mothers had far fewer emotional upsets than either group of control mothers. The case was proven. The experiment had shown that emotional problems in mobile people can be handled very quickly and simply. Two brief talks had pointed out some emotional pitfalls of mobile living that may not have been apparent, suggested some common-sense precautions. The mothers and their husbands had done the rest themselves. They'd become, in effect, their own therapists. By making a few uncomplicated changes in their lives, many of them had saved themselves and their families from grief—and in some cases, perhaps, from tragedy.

Not only did the instructed mothers have fewer upsets, but the upsets they did have were generally mild. Many of them had only brief attacks of the baby blues, which went away after a day or two. None of the instructed mothers needed psychiatric treatment. But among the control mothers who attended the baby-care classes without their husbands, eight per cent had difficulties so severe that they required psychiatric help.

Moreover, the instructed mothers as a whole had greater success with their babies. In a follow-up study about six months after each mother's delivery, it was found that only eight and one-half per cent of the instructed mothers' babies had feeding or sleep disturbances or irritability. Among the control mothers, twenty-one per cent of the babies had these problems. Probably two basic factors contributed to the instructed mothers' greater success. First, they prepared themselves better to care for their infants, gathered knowledge and advice, generally went about the job more surely and efficiently. Second, they arranged their lives so that they themselves were calmer and happier. Even an infant recognizes when he is being handled roughly and short-temperedly, and this may make him less content with the world than he might be.

This was the broad, general conclusion of the experiment: that the instructed mothers had less emotional trouble than the controls. But there were also some more detailed findings. The experiment was engineered in advance to find out specifically what steps the more successful mothers took and what other features there were in their lives that had helped them avoid upsets.

Before the special guidance talks were given, all the mothers were asked to fill out a detailed questionnaire. They answered questions on such subjects as the amount of help they expected to have with the baby, their husbands' availability to help, their intentions in regard to social activities after the baby was born. Shortly after her baby was delivered, each mother filled out a second questionnaire to see whether she had changed her mind or behavior in any of these areas. (This second questionnaire was given to all the mothers, instructed and controls alike. The instructed mothers, as was to be expected, showed considerably more changes of mind and behavior in accord with the guidance talks' suggestions than did the control mothers.) In the end, the mothers' emotional reactions and the information on these questionnaires were compared and interrelated by an IBM machine.

All this produced detailed findings about the various ways in which mothers arranged their lives. These findings give further indications that the nine techniques of emotional adjustment are useful in preventing disturbance. Each of the techniques seems to have value:

Mutual Help: Among mothers who changed and got more help with their babies than they'd previously planned (not including help from their husbands), fourteen per cent had emotional upsets in the six months after delivery. Of those who made no change in their plans or behavior, twenty-five per cent had trouble. Of those who tried to get along on less help, forty-four per cent became upset.

The value of help shows up, too, in the fact that mothers who attended the baby-care classes with their husbands had fewer upsets than those who attended alone. The simple fact that a husband was willing to come along to such a class showed he was probably aware, at least to some extent, that his responsibilities with a new baby went further than merely passing out cigars. And, of course, in the instructed groups, the husbands heard the special guidance talks and thus were more likely to help their wives apply the talks' suggestions.

Producing: In general and with admitted exceptions, society pays for value received. If a man's income is high, you can usually assume that he, with his wife's help, is producing something of great usefulness to society. Thus, broadly, income can be related to productiveness.

Instructed mothers of the higher income classes were more successful in avoiding upsets than those of lower income groups. Those of the higher classes could better afford to hire help and baby-sitters, had fewer financial worries, in general were more in control of their lives and hence (like upper-income heart-disease patients) in a better position to unload stresses. This table shows what percentage of instructed mothers from each income group became upset:

Income Group	*Percentage Upset*
Middle	6%
Lower middle	17
Upper laboring	20

Planning and Preparation: Instructed mothers with college educations were more successful in avoiding trouble than those with only high school diplomas. Among college graduates who heard the special guidance talks, ten per cent had upsets. Among high school graduates, exactly twice as many: twenty per cent. The more educated mothers were likely to be more diverse in their interests, more practiced in planning and organizing, more confident of their ability to solve problems.

Another indication of the value of preparation lies in the fact that two guidance talks turned out to be better than one. Some of the instructed mothers missed one or the other of the two talks; and among them, thirty-three per cent had trouble. Among the mothers who heard both talks, only eleven per cent had upsets. (Even those who heard only one talk, of course, fared better than the control mothers who heard none.)

Diversity: Mothers who continued their social activities on a moderate scale fared better than those who stayed cooped up at home. One indication of this can be seen in the mothers' arrangements for baby-sitters. Among those who changed their minds and lined up sitters earlier than they had previously planned, twenty per cent had upsets. Among those who made no change of plans: thirty per cent. The value of diversity also shows up in the fact that better-educated mothers were more successful in avoiding upsets.

Climbing with Care: Some of the mothers had been planning to move to a new home while pregnant or shortly after their babies were born. Among those who were able to delay the move until after the baby was six months old, none had upsets. Others decided to risk it and move earlier than they'd planned, before the baby was six months old. Of these mothers, forty-three per cent had emotional disturbances. This less successful group of mothers ran into many of the problems that tormented Alice Hager and Gina Conning.

Rest and Reward: Among women who changed and made more friends with parents of young children, fourteen per cent had upsets. Among those who tried to get along with fewer young-adult friends: fifty-nine per cent. Congenial company, friends in situations similar to one's own—these are obviously rich sources of reward after a hard day's work. To enjoy such a reward, of course, baby-sitters are often necessary. The fact that mothers who lined up sitters early had fewer upsets is another indication that rewards are good preventive medicine.

That rest also has great value is shown by the success of mothers who arranged to get plenty of help, and by the relative success of higher-income mothers, who presumably could hire help and baby-sitters more easily.

Tactful Self-Assertion: Some mothers were able to persuade their husbands to provide more help and companionship—a result, in many cases, of tactful self-assertion. Among these women, only twelve per cent had upsets. Among those who managed no such change, thirty per cent had trouble.

Reassessment of Values: Among mothers who put less emphasis on household tidiness than they'd once felt necessary, eighteen per cent had trouble. Of those who made no change in this particular area of values, forty per cent became upset. A reassessment of values was also involved for some husbands, undoubtedly, in agreeing to make themselves more available to their wives.

Emotional Control: Many factors can be involved for a woman in a decision to cut short an education. Among them may be several factors related to emotional control: lack of the perseverance needed for studying, lack of patience, a lack of sexual control and a resulting premature marriage. Such emotional-control factors undoubtedly contribute to the fact that control mothers who had quit college were twice as likely to become upset as those who had graduated. They were also more frequently upset than high school graduates who never began college.

Controls	*Percentage Upset*
College graduates	23%
College quitters	45
High school graduates	30

But among the instructed mothers, who were taught the technique of emotional control by the guidance talks, those who hadn't finished college became disturbed only slightly more often than college graduates and less often than high school graduates:

Instructed Mothers	*Percentage Upset*
College graduates	10%
College quitters	13
High school graduates	20

Thus it is apparent that the nine techniques of adjustment are useful in prevention, as in treatment. And if an old bromide may be repeated, an ounce of prevention is worth a pound of cure. It is far easier to use the techniques preventively, before you are overloaded, while you are thinking rationally. It is far harder after the body's emergency mechanisms have come into play and you are less able to help yourself—after you have become preoccupied, fearful, angry, tense, depressed.

One important question remains to be answered: how permanent is the effect of learning the nine techniques?

An indication came from a follow-up study of half the mothers when their babies were about six months old. Among control mothers, twenty-eight per cent were having problems at the half-year mark. Among the instructed mothers: two per cent.

It may be, indeed, that learning and successfully applying the nine techniques creates permanent changes in the personality. To weather a potentially trying experience such as maternity, to know that dangers are lurking about but to avoid or defeat them through one's own efforts, might easily boost self-respect. Traversing the difficult period safely, a young mother might learn much about her own emotions. Confidence in herself, and in others on whom she found she could depend, might easily increase. As she practiced using techniques of adjustment they might become more and more habitual; she might weave them into her general approach to all life situations.

People who haven't succeeded in some important step during their lives—educational quitters and divorcees, for instance—are more than normally likely to have emotional trouble. Conversely, those who succeed in a difficult period may come out of it better equipped for life and its problems than they were before.

Much more study is needed in this field of preventing emotional problems. The Bergen County prevention study dealt only with child-bearing women; and while the findings on them can presumably be generalized to other groups, it would be useful to have more detailed knowledge of the workings of prevention in these other groups. What are the most useful specific ways in which young husbands, for example, can apply the nine techniques to preserve peace and happiness? What are the special pitfalls facing young people about to enter college? Men about to retire? Children going into hospitals?

Many answers to these questions can be gathered by observing people in Disturbia, finding out what successful people did that unsuccessful people didn't do, and vice versa. But other kinds of study—from controlled scientific experiments to the everyday observations and experiments of the men and women themselves—can also contribute.

One thing seems clear. Life in Disturbia need not be nearly so stressful as it has been.

CHAPTER 22

A New Integration

If mobile people are to get the most fun and the least pain from life, their communities must be integrated. How can this be done?

Some of the answers may lie in the nine techniques that have proven successful in Bergen County. In attending to their own happiness, mobile people automatically add a brick or two to the community structure. The alcoholic George Kohler, for instance, found contentment partly by becoming a Little League manager. Thus he helped the community provide constructive activities for boys. George's suicidal wife, Martha, found some of her own answers by working in her church's social programs. This, too, contributed to the town's integration. This is how the disturbed suburban community can become a better place to live: through the work of thousands of individuals, each considerately seeking the best route to his own happiness.

Suburban towns today are groping, testing, improvising. As the process continues, far-ranging changes may take place. Already, there are signs that these changes are starting. In Bergen County, for instance, a group of women in the Junior League of Englewood, New Jersey, banded together with the women of the Northern Valley Chapter of the National Council of Jewish Women to establish the Homemakers' Service. Their efforts alone in the early years got the program started and kept it going. The Homemakers are now of service to the hundreds of Alice Hagers and other wives who lack family and other help in keeping their homes together when they become ill.

Fifteen or twenty years from now, the restless, disintegrated, pioneer Suburbia we know today may exist only in isolated patches. Ideas and tools for integration are being forged, in towns throughout the nation and the world. Mobile people will have to look over these ideas and tools, pick those that seem useful, forge new ones when necessary, and go to work.

The integrated mobile community would be one in which social mechanisms existed by which people could help each other. It would be a community that supported the individual.

One important ingredient of such a community would be an abundance of social organizations—gathering places where people could meet for enjoyment and exchange of information and ideas. These gathering places would welcome newcomers and, in fact, might provide special orientation for them. Many suburban towns have already seen the need for such gathering points. Community recreation and adult education centers have been established. Churches are becoming social organizations rather than merely centers of religious worship.

In its building of organizations, the integrated mobile town could be helped by business, which has done so much to create the mobility of Disturbia. There is a need for social organizations that are nationwide in scope, with chapters in many communities. Belonging to such an organization, a family can move from one town to another, rejoining a new chapter and thus suffering a minimum of disruption. Such organizations do exist—women's clubs, Scouts, university societies—but they have not been made fully available to all who have needed them. Business could help by sponsoring social clubs for the families of employees, with chapters in all areas to which transferees might be sent. Many companies have already set up such clubs. The cost is probably returned to the companies many times over in contentment and general performances of employees.

Business can also help by its continued move of plants and offices into suburban areas. This will cut the burden of taxes on the individual homeowner. It will also reduce the strain of commuting for many men. Some city-planning authorities even foresee a day when the ideal metropolitan area will be composed of many small industrial and commercial centers instead of one giant central city surrounded by vast distances of suburb. A more immediate hope for the commuter seems to lie, however, in continued development of more efficient public transit facilities such as many cities are considering: suburban subways, overhead monorail systems, exclusive rights-of-way for buses during rush hours. All this will reduce the need to drive a car to work and alleviate, for many commuters, the special stresses of vehicle driving.

There is a need for more study and planning in such areas as these. Most suburban towns have systematic planning for housing, roads, finance, schools. Now many communities are beginning to think about human-element planning, in which housing authorities and other municipal agencies would consider social and psychological needs. One housing developer in New Jersey, for example, provides a trained sociologist to help newcomers move into a development and become integrated into the community. As human-element planning becomes a more accepted part of community affairs, many changes might be made. Perhaps a trend will be started toward two-family houses, in which the families could baby-sit for each other, help each other in sickness and other emergencies, provide other kinds of mutual service. Perhaps towns will provide special orientation lectures and tours for newcomers, as businesses often do for new employees.

There must be an expansion of facilities for taking care of children. The integrated mobile community would have arrangements by which wives could swap baby-sitting and nursery services, as many do already. It would also have provisions by which teen-age girls and older, more experienced women such as Martha Kohler could be marshaled effectively for this purpose. The older women would be particularly useful. They would not be simply baby-sitters; they'd be home managers, grandmother-surrogates. They could take over a home for a weekend while the parents went away, or for longer periods during illnesses and other emergencies. They could also be brought in to help younger mothers with new babies.

Men such as George Kohler—older or retired men, men who are not heavily involved with climbing or are not gaining enough rewards or winning medals in it—can serve as the grandfathers and uncles of the community. These men can help train both children and adults in skills that will make the mobile suburban life easier. George Kohler might help the regular shop teacher in a home repair course in adult education, thus helping city-bred men like Carl Hager adjust to the stressful demands of home-ownership. In return, the more financially sophisticated men such as Harley Tragg or the wayward Link Weber—men who have been successful in making money—could advise men such as George or Fred Bright in ways of investing and saving, perhaps through the medium of investment clubs.

Thus each community member can help others as he helps himself. In so doing, he contributes to the community's integration. A man such as Link Weber, drawn into community activities that interest him—investment clubs, local politics—would have less reason to seek after-hours pleasures in the far-off city. Instead of drifting away from his wife, he would be working with her in the same community. Instead of finding the suburban society boring and contrasting it disparagingly with the glamorous world of the city, he would help it to become more stimulating—perhaps with financial profit to himself. Beyond this, practical considerations would stand in the way of his having affairs with other women. It would be difficult to conduct a clandestine affair in the integrated community where he was known, and he would be too busy for affairs to start easily in the city. Instead of staying in town to wine and dine a glamorous client, he would have to go home and attend an investors' club meeting. He would have good reasons for learning the technique of emotional shunting, carrying his city-bred sexual arousals home to his wife.

A man such as George Kohler who directly contributes work to the community might be paid for it. Many mobile communities have seen the need for children's and adults' organizations, but often the burden of administering such programs falls on unpaid volunteers—conscientious men and women who are already chin-deep in responsibilities. Men such as Fred Bright, for example, are often asked to take over Little League teams and often agree to do so—even though they are working hard to make a living, lack time to mow their own lawns and are little interested in baseball in any case. Overloaded young mothers like Alice Hager are asked to take charge of Cub Scout dens. Hard-working, underpaid teachers are asked to contribute time to after-hours activity groups in the schools.

Much of this necessary work can be more effectively assigned. Retired men or men such as George can handle many of the boys' activities. In return they could get a salary from the town, or perhaps some kind of tax rebate. Energies of teen-age boys such as Alec Green can also be harnessed for this work. They can serve as smaller boys' swimming coaches, hobby guides, playground supervisors. Teen-age girls, similarly, can serve as hospital aides, baby-sitters or teachers' aides. These kinds of after-school service might be meshed with the school curriculum, for they could be realistically thought of as a vital part of education for success in the mobile world. The boy or girl performing such service might be rewarded in school credits or spending money, or both. Thus the youngsters will not only provide real and needed services to the community; they will also be helped in becoming producers. They will learn that society hands out rewards for useful work.

Adults and children must learn to reweave society's fabric, ripped and torn by the mobility which has arisen from advances in the physical sciences. They can learn the principles of social science in the classroom and practice the skills in the laboratory of the community.

Education will demand much of the integrated community's energy. Undoubtedly there will be changes in our present attitude toward education and even in educational methods—changes that will help education do its job better in the mobile world. Many observers have already seen a need for more male teachers in grade and high schools. Male teachers could help guide and discipline boys, replace some of the firmness that the mobile community lacks.

Many, too, have seen a need for higher teacher salaries to attract a greater number of high-caliber men and women into the profession. During the past decade there has been a casting-about for possible sources of money with which to pay these higher salaries. It has been suggested that the federal government contribute to community education funds, and this certainly would be a reasonable investment. The money that the government spent to help ex-GI's educate themselves after the Second World War has undoubtedly been returned to the nation many times over in increased productivity—and, more specifically, to the Treasury in bigger tax collections from higher incomes. Teacher-salary money might also come, as many towns have already seen, from paying less attention to the façade of education. A school can be attractive without being lavish. Russian children go to school in buildings that often are, by our standards, bleak and dreary. But it appears that cinderblock might be as good an educational medium as marble.

Adult education would also flourish in the integrated mobile community, as it is already beginning to do. Perhaps scholarships might be provided for part-time adult education. It would be reasonable, too, to provide direct public encouragement of education by making educational expenses tax-deductible. All areas of the community must cooperate in the continual process of schooling. The link between business and education, already being forged, might be strengthened. Mental hospitals might be affiliated with vocational training, recreation and rehabilitation centers, perhaps even with colleges, so that patients could be helped in finding themselves a more secure place in the mobile world.

Changes such as these will both contribute to and spring from a gradual reorganization of values. As women such as Eve Bright and men such as Fred gain more satisfactions from service to society, the façade syndrome is likely to recede. People will find it less important to cultivate the appearance of material success, for they will have other ways of earning society's applause. In a community where people know each other, real service will be valued more highly than a show of wealth. Instead of seeking the status of appearances, people will seek the status of genuine worth to society.

Other changes in values are likely to follow. The roles of man and woman will undoubtedly become more and more interchangeable. Russia, our dynamic competitor, is ahead of us in seeing the need for this interchangeability of roles in a mobile society. Russian women work hard to serve their society. The Russian social system encourages women to be strong and self-reliant. The same can be said of another powerful new competitor: Red China. Our society must do the same if it is to remain powerful. The kind of softness that was in Alice Hager, the non-productiveness that was in Eve Bright and Audrey Tragg, the parasitism of glamorous Joni, must be discouraged in coming generations of girls. They will serve themselves, their families and society best by developing self-reliance, diversity, the ability to change roles, if need be, with men. Yet they can retain their basic roles as wife and mother. They needn't abandon their femininity as Russian and Chinese woman have to some extent had to do. (Russian women are now reviving their interest in fashions and cosmetics as their standard of living improves.)

It seems likely, indeed, that marriages in the future will be based less and less on the concept of romantic love, the ephemeral basis on which many young unions today are formed and in the collapse of which they split asunder. Our requirements in marriage partners may swing back to resemble those of men and women in a bygone agricultural era. In those days, a man chose a wife for sexual attractiveness, for her ability to help him on the farm and because she could give him children who might help him expand the farm. Since then, men's and women's roles have drifted apart. The economic value of wives and children has declined; husbands don't need them so much. On the surface there often seems little left but romance as a basis for marriage. But as the mobile society feels its way toward a new integration, usefulness—the ability of each to complement the other as a working partner—may once again grow in importance. These will be strong marriages. They will hold together because each partner will have compelling reasons for maintaining the union. Each will feel that he needs the other to accomplish his goals in life. Man, wife, and children will all have more value to each other.

Numerous other value changes are appearing on the horizon as the mobile society seeks its answers. Religions, for example, are discovering that they must allow flexibility in their teachings to accommodate the changing society's needs. Intelligent clergymen of all faiths, particularly younger men, are seeing that it is more useful to encourage service to society than to require strict, letter-for-letter adherence to dogma and ritual. It may become necessary to teach old dogma new tricks.

It is likely, for instance, that as people work for higher standards of living, as they grow better educated and seek new rewards in travel, cultural pursuits and entertainment, they will find reason for holding down the sizes of their families and thus, perhaps, will come into conflict with stipulations against birth control. Even the requirement that one go to church every weekend is causing conflict in some groups. In the communities of fifty years ago, this was an easy rule to obey, for people stayed in town over a weekend and the church was a focus of community social activity. Now the weekend is more often a time for family travel: visiting distant friends, picnicking, boating and other activities that draw the suburban family away from its home town. Possibly churches will resolve the conflict by permitting attendance on any of several days of the week—as some churches already do. Those churches that become organizations for community service, instead of simply centers of religious worship, are also likely to have less conflict.

Mobile people lead a life that requires much emotional control; they are under a great weight of requirements and obligations. As they seek to unload the stress in their lives, they will undoubtedly seek to discard some of this weight. They will think over their obligations and abandon those that seem less compelling. Thus, religions will probably find it necessary to relax some of their stricter self-control requirements in areas such as diet and marital sex.

As the mobile society grows older, the needed rules and values can be developed. Efforts are already being made to do so in many suburban communities. Responsible teen-agers have met and drawn up rules of conduct for themselves. Conferences on delinquency and other problems have been called by church and civic groups. Rules governing baby-sitters and their employers are being established.

The integration of the mobile community is happening gradually. One by one, ideas are being scrutinized and tested. Those that prove useful will be adopted; those that don't will be abandoned. These are grass-roots developments, originated and established by the mass of mobile people rather than legislated by governing bodies or proclaimed as dogma by authoritarian people or institutions. Science may speed up the process by pointing out facts and relationships. Progress will come as a result of slow advance on many fronts, with all the people in the community thinking and working toward the goals. The result will be a happier, stronger people.

Our society must remain strong. America was built by strong people, and the mobile society today is still composed largely of strong people. The huge growth of the suburbs is tangible evidence of their drive and toughness. But a softening has set in, and this could be dangerous.

Russia and China are akin to mobile newcomers who have struggled up from the lower classes to buy homes in the suburbs. They are tough, hard-working, aggressive nations, ready to push others out of the way if their climb can thus be speeded up. America is the older resident. Times have been good and life has been easy, but now the newcomer nations are bringing in their own sharp brand of competition, and life will not be easy any more. If we are not strong as a nation, we will be trampled like the middle-aged George and Martha Kohler.

The something-for-nothing syndrome must be extinguished. The gimme kids must be put to work. The speculative way of life—the urge to get ahead by shortcuts—cannot serve us well in this competitive world. The newcomer nations who are moving into our happy suburb are both speculators and producers; they are willing to work for what they want, but because they want it fast they are willing to take the ultimate speculation: they are speculating with the possibility of war. We cannot afford to speculate thus. We can see all about us the danger, anxiety and tension that speculation breeds. We must produce to make ourselves strong. We must remain protectively self-assertive against aggressors. But, at the same time, we must seek an integration of mutual help with them.

We have much to learn from the Russians, and they from us. Their toughness and persistence can be a useful model for us. In turn, we can teach them some of the lessons we have learned as more seasoned travelers on the road to wealth. Case histories in the medical literature indicate that Russian men, women, and children are starting to face emotional problems of disintegration similar to ours as their society grows steadily more mobile. We can show them some of the solutions to these problems that we have found workable. In particular we can teach them that, though their toughness is admirable, their more larcenous kind of self-assertion will probably not be useful to them in the long run and will only get them into trouble. We can urge them to climb more carefully.

All over the world today there are millions of people struggling upward from humble origins. There are nations big and small climbing toward their golden plateaus. All of them, individuals and nations alike, can learn a lesson from the suburbanite with his car, house and quarter-acre plot. The lesson is that it is dangerous to climb too far too fast too recklessly.

INDEX

Index